ENGINEERING SAFETY

Engineering Safety is a new title in the
McGraw-Hill International Series in Civil Engineering

ENGINEERING SAFETY

ENGINEERING SAFETY

Edited by

David Blockley

Professor of Civil Engineering
University of Bristol

McGRAW-HILL BOOK COMPANY

London · New York · St Louis · San Francisco · Auckland
Bogotá · Caracas · Hamburg · Lisbon · Madrid · Mexico
Milan · Montreal · New Delhi · Panama · Paris · San Juan
São Paulo · Singapore · Sydney · Tokyo · Toronto

Published by
McGRAW-HILL Book Company Europe
Shoppenhangers Road · Maidenhead · Berkshire · SL6 2QL · England
Tel. 0628 23432; Fax 0628 770224

British Library Cataloguing in Publication Data

Engineering safety.
  I. Blockley, David
  363.119620
  ISBN 0-07-707593-5

Library of Congress Cataloging-in-Publication Data

Engineering safety/edited by David Blockley.
    p.   cm. – (McGraw-Hill international series in civil engineering)
    Includes bibliographical references and index.
    ISBN 0-07-707593-5
    1. Reliability (Engineering). 2. Civil engineering–safety measures.
    3. Safety factor in engineering. 4. Risk assessment.
    I. Blockley, D. I. II. Series.
    TA192.E54   1992
  S20'.00452–dc20   91-45212
                                                                      CIP

1234CUP9432

Typeset by P & R Typesetters Ltd, Salisbury, Wiltshire
and printed and bound in Great Britain at the University Press, Cambridge

CONTENTS

NOTES ON THE CONTRIBUTORS

David E. Allen was awarded a PhD from the University of Illinois in 1966, and has been a researcher with the National Research Council of Canada ever since. He has authored about fifty papers on diverse subjects related to structural engineering. He received the Canadian Standards Association Award of Merit for his work on the development of structural codes and standards based on limit state principles.

David I. Blockley gained his PhD from the University of Sheffield in 1967. In 1969 he became a lecturer in Civil Engineering at the University of Bristol, and was promoted to a readership in 1982, and a personal Chair in 1989. In the same year be became Head of the Department of Civil Engineering, a post which he currently holds. He was awarded a DSc in 1987, and is the author of over 70 papers and a book. He has won several technical awards for his work, including the Telford Gold Medal of the Institution of Civil Engineers.

John B. Caldwell gained a PhD in Civil Engineering at Bristol University before joining the Royal Naval Scientific Service. In 1966 he was appointed to the Chair of Naval Architecture at Newcastle University where he later became Dean of Engineering. His publications mainly concern marine structural design, safety and education. He is a Fellow of Engineering and was President of the Royal Institution of Naval Architects from 1984 to 1987.

Joseph B. Comerford studied the application of artificial intelligence in civil engineering before being awarded a PhD in 1989 from the University of Bristol. He now works as a consultant for ISMES S.p.a., Italy, in the advanced technology group, developing software systems to assist in the management of the safety of dams. He also works occasionally for international organizations in disaster relief.

Bill Cranston obtained his PhD from the University of Glasgow, and subsequently served in a variety of positions with the Cement and Concrete Association within the UK, latterly as a Director responsible for the technical promotion of concrete over a wide field of applications. In 1988 he was appointed Professor and Head of the Department of Civil Engineering at Paisley College in Scotland.

Bruce R. Ellingwood was educated at the University of Illinois, where he received a PhD degree in 1972. After a career at the National Institute of Standards and Technology, he joined the Civil Engineering Department at the Johns Hopkins University in 1986, and has held the position of Professor and Chairman since 1990. He has authored over 100 papers and reports on structural load modelling, probabilistic codified design and related topics.

David G. Elms worked as a structural dynamics specialist at the De Havilland Aircraft Company before obtaining a PhD at Princeton. He then joined the University of Canterbury, New Zealand, where he is now Professor of Civil Engineering. He is the author of one book, and around 80 papers on risk, systems methodology and geotechnical engineering.

Michele A. Fanelli first worked for the Italian National Power Board (ENEL) in 1963, and he is now acting Director of the Centre for Hydraulic and Structural Research at ENEL. He is the author of more than 200 technical papers, and holds the titles of Ingénieur Hydraulicien de l'Université de Grenoble (1956) and of Free Teaching Professor of Construction Techniques (1970).

Michael P. Furmston was called to the bar by Gray's Inn in 1960. He has lectured at Birmingham, Belfast, and Oxford, and has been Professor of Law at the University of Bristol since 1978. He was Dean of the Law Faculty from 1980 to 1984, and Pro-Vice-Chancellor of the University from 1986 to 1989. He is the author of some thirty books, principally in the field of contract and construction law.

Theodore V. Galambos has taught structural engineering and conducted research on steel structural behaviour and design at Lehigh University, Washington University and at the University of Minnesota, where he is now Professor of Civil Engineering. He has been intimately involved with the development of Limit States Design codes for most of his career.

B. John Garrick holds a PhD from the University of California, Los Angeles. He is now President and Chief Executive Officer of PLG, Inc, an engineering and technology consulting firm. He is a physicist and an engineer with a background in research, engineering, analysis and technical management. His area of expertise is quantitative risk assessment, which followed considerable work in nuclear engineering.

Paul W. Jowitt is Professor of Civil Engineering Systems at Heriot-Watt University. His research interests include the use of systems and optimization methods, particularly in water resources engineering. Work undertaken for Severn–Trent Water Authority led to the publication of the paper 'Assessing the Reliability of Supply and Level of Service of Water Distribution Systems' which was awarded the 1987 Trevithick Premium by the Institution of Civil Engineers.

Trevor A. Kletz joined Imperial Chemical Industries in 1944 where he has spent the last fourteen years as safety advisor to the Petrochemicals Division. In 1978 he was appointed Visiting Industrial Professor at Loughborough University of Technology, and in 1982 he joined the University full-time, becoming a Visiting Fellow in 1986. He has written 7 books and over 100 papers on loss prevention and process safety, and is a Fellow of the Fellowship of Engineering.

Miroslav Matousek gained his doctorate in 1982 from the Technical University of Zurich, Switzerland, following research into the safety of buildings. Between 1983 and 1990 he led the Department of Safety, Quality Assurance and Environmental Impact in a consulting company in Zurich. In 1991 he founded his own engineering consultancy. He is the author of many papers and reports concerning the analysis of damage, human errors, safety and quality assurance.

Robert E. Melchers obtained his PhD from Cambridge University in 1971. He spent a number of years in consulting and eleven years with the Department of Civil Engineering at Monash University. He was appointed Professor of Civil Engineering at the University of Newcastle, Australia, in 1986. His main research areas are in structural reliability theory applied to complex structures, structural performance, monitoring, rehabilitation and the behaviour of offshore structures.

Nick F. Pidgeon was awarded a PhD in Psychology from the University of Bristol in 1986. He conducted interdisciplinary research into structural failures in the UK construction industry, and then joined Birkbeck College, University of London, as a lecturer in Psychology in 1989. He has authored a number of technical papers on risk and accidents, one of which was awarded the Oscar Faber Diploma of the Institution of Structural Engineers.

Stuart G. Reid worked as a structural engineer for several years before obtaining a PhD from McGill University in 1981. He subsequently worked as a Research Scientist with the CSIRO, Australia, and he is now Senior Lecturer in Civil Engineering at the University of Sydney. He is the author of about 70 technical papers and reports, mainly on risk and reliability analysis, reinforced concrete behaviour, and glass safety and strength.

Naruhito Shiraishi gained his doctorate from Kyoto University, Japan in 1971, where he held the position of Associate Professor. In 1975 he was made Professor in the Department of Civil Engineering. He was awarded the TANAKA Prize from the Japanese Society of Civil Engineers in 1990, and has served on several bridge and highway committees.

John R. Stone worked for ten years in industrial design before undertaking research into structural failures, after which he obtained a PhD in 1990. He is presently a Research Fellow in the Department of Civil Engineering at the University of Bristol, and his research interests include the application of artificial intelligence and machine learning to the problem of engineering safety.

Carl J. Turkstra completed his PhD in Civil Engineering at the University of Waterloo in 1962. In 1982 he became Professor and Head of the Department of Civil Engineering at the Polytechnic University in Brooklyn, New York. Within the field of structural risk analysis, he is best known for 'Turkstra's Rule' for design load combinations. In 1991, he left teaching and research to become President of the Turkstra Lumber Company in Canada.

Barry A. Turner gained his doctorate in sociology at Exeter University in 1976. He is now Research Professor of European Business at Middlesex Business School, and is Chairman of an international cultural research network. He has published two books on corporate culture, and is best known for the model developed in his book *Man-made Disasters*. Over the past decade he has directed a programme of research into decision-making and safety in structural engineering, in collaboration with David Blockley.

PREFACE

The purpose of this book is to present an overview of engineering safety for graduate engineers who are not specialists in safety but who are concerned with the planning, design, construction and maintenance of large engineered facilities such as dams, bridges, buildings, power stations, process plant and marine structures.

There are at least two interpretations of the words of the title 'Engineering Safety'. Firstly, when both words are taken as nouns, they refer to a technical topic, the safety of engineered artefacts and systems of artefacts: this is the traditional province of engineers. Secondly, when engineering is the present participle, the title refers to the way in which safety is managed, controlled or engineered: this is the traditional province of managers who may or may not be qualified engineers. These two views or paradigms have tended to be separate; engineering safety researchers have largely shied away from the prospect of becoming involved with the psychology and sociology of safety management while the social science researchers do not have the engineering knowledge to understand detailed technical matters. One of the central purposes of this book is to attempt to bring these views closer together so that engineering safety is seen as a problem at the social/technical interface.

The book is divided into four parts: (1) The Problem; (2) The Theory; (3) The Applications; (4) The Epilogue.

The nature of the problem in Part One is set in a general way in Chapter 1 and a discussion of the development and role of risk assessment is given in Chapter 2. In order to attract the general engineering reader into the topic some emphasis is given to the very practical issues concerning the new generations of codes of practice world-wide in Chapter 3. In particular the introduction of limit state design in Eurocodes and LRFD (load and resistance factor design) in the United States has caused controversy. Codes are the means by which acceptable risk criteria are set without explicitly stating what those levels are. The rapid introduction of quality assurance (QA), which is discussed in Chapter 4, into the construction industry is also not without its practical problems. QA is directly concerned with the way in which risk and safety is managed.

However, in order to appreciate the background to the developments it is necessary to address the fundamental theory on which they are partly based. The objective of Part Two of the book is to introduce these ideas while keeping the mathematics to a minimum. An elementary knowledge of probability theory is all that is assumed. The wider concepts of the social science theory of risk perception and communication within human organizations are also presented in this section.

Most engineers are primarily interested in how these ideas relate to their own discipline. In Part Three a review of safety assessment and control in some of the major engineering industries which involve large-scale construction is presented. The application areas are not exhaustive but are intended to be representative; they include dams, marine structures, water supply, bridges, nuclear and process industries.

Finally, in Part Four a critique of the state of the art and a look towards the future is presented. In particular the role of the law in the tacit setting of risk levels is reviewed and the use of modern techniques of artificial intelligence (AI) discussed. The objectives of this final section are to help the reader to better interpret some of the more specific technical books and research literature and view them in the wider context of the social/technical interface and to help identify those areas of the topic where research effort is required.

Inevitably, any attempt to bring the views of various authors together in one volume is hazardous. There is potential for repetition, inconsistency and for differences of emphasis. Some of the topics, particularly relating to the theories of probability and reliability, are examined by authors from various perspectives and some small amount of repetition has been necessary for continuity of flow. The inconsistencies have hopefully been removed. By contrast the differences of interpretation and emphasis need to be drawn out and discussed. The last chapter is an attempt to do just that and if the book contributes towards that process for the subject of engineering safety as a whole, then the objectives will have been achieved.

The topic of this book is self-evidently important. The construction industry touches the lives of everyone as buildings, bridges, highways, water supply and power stations are central to all our lives. The turnover of the construction industry alone in the United Kingdom represents something of the order of 20 per cent of the gross domestic product (GDP). Major technological failures such as Three Mile Island, the Bhopal Disaster, the loss of the Space Shuttle Challenger, Chernobyl and the Piper Alpha explosion have focused the attention of the public, the media and the regulators as never before. The critical role of human agency in the preconditions to disaster is now widely recognized. Many of the less publicized small failures have similar characteristics. There is an urgent need for more attention to be paid to the performance of all engineering systems as sociotechnical systems. The expectation that society as a whole has of the engineering professions may have to undergo fundamental revisions as it is increasingly realized that no enterprise is without risk; there is no such thing as perfect safety.

When disaster is blamed on human error, it is not sufficient to isolate a few negligent individuals, remove them from their jobs and argue that 'it will never happen again'. Similarly when an accident occurs in one country, it is not sufficient to argue that the 'safety culture' of another country is such that 'it couldn't happen here'. The discussion of risk strikes at the very roots of our society, our knowledge, our values, our emotions and indeed our very existence. It requires us to think about what scientific knowledge is, the perspectives from which we argue, the rationality of what we fear and the way we act. Its importance cannot be overemphasized.

The text is written for all graduate engineers and professionals who have contact with large constructed facilities. It is directed at civil engineers who are concerned with buildings, bridges, dams, reservoirs; mechanical and electrical engineers who are involved with plant that operates in large structures; engineers concerned with the process industries and engineers and naval architects who are involved with large marine structures.

The aim is to give the 'broad picture' and for this reason the number of references for each chapter has purposely been kept low and therefore restricted to the major contributions. It is acknowledged that a minority of readers might prefer more complete referencing; however, they will be able to trace other material through those references given. In order to operate the detailed procedures referred to in the text, the reader will need to consult appropriate references.

The text should be of interest to all practising engineers as general reading and will be of interest to engineering and social science researchers who wish to pursue their work at the social/technical interface. It may also be useful for postgraduate studies in safety and might well be used in some undergraduate course modules in engineering.

David I. Blockley

PART
ONE

THE PROBLEM

ONE

SETTING THE SCENE

D. I. BLOCKLEY

1.1 INTRODUCTION

How safe is safe enough? How do we and how should we decide on values for factors of safety? What indeed are safety factors? Just what are they intended to cover? How are the other matters important for safety dealt with? Are the 'truths' of deterministic science sufficient for the uncertainties of practical engineering? What is the nature of these uncertainties? Are engineering failures really failures of engineers? Is design to manage trouble as important as design to prevent trouble? Is engineering simply an 'applied science' or a decision process in which science is applied?

The objective of this book is to examine these and many other questions that relate to the safety of large engineered facilities such as bridges, buildings, dams, power stations and marine structures. Engineering is basically about making things, artefacts. The use of the word artefact is not intended to imply that engineers are concerned only with single objects; it refers also to complex systems of objects, such as a power station or chemical works. The successes of engineering are all around us. As the power of technology has grown, there has been an increasing tendency to depend on it for our daily needs. The growth of technology has been largely due to the successful application of the physical sciences to a wide range of practical problems. In the development of these applications it has been natural for engineers to concentrate on the physical processes involved and this has been reflected in the education and training of engineers. A report of the Council for

National Academic Awards on 'Goals of Education in the UK' has suggested that the education engineers receive is 'both technically narrow and narrowly technical'. Many people argue that engineering education overemphasizes engineering science in one field rather than attempting to deal with engineering as a process; there seem to be few attempts to teach business and management skills. Engineering is, of course, not only about deciding what is to be made, the artefact, but also involves deciding how it should be made and getting it made. The process inevitably involves people. Engineers, in their quest to discover ways of organizing nature and flushed with their successes in the physical sciences have perhaps rather neglected their reliance on human infallibility. In engineering only the hardware is a physical system; the system that designs it, produces it and uses it involves humans and is therefore complex and vulnerable. Of course what is taught reflects, on the whole, our collective understanding of 'things as they are'. It is often argued that it is not the topic of an individual's education that matters but rather his/her abilities and attitudes. It is not only knowledge and technical ability that are important but also such characteristics as openness of mind and the ability to communicate, to organize and to formulate problems.

In spite of their successes most engineers feel uncomfortable about intellectualizing what they see as an essentially practical activity. Almost all of the presently adopted answers to the questions about safety, posed earlier, have stemmed from the real and overriding practical need to 'get the job done'. Engineers understandably like to concentrate on the tangible, the measurable, the 'objective' parts of human knowledge. Why is it then that questions of safety have become of central concern to engineers and non-engineers alike?

There are at least two groups of reasons. The first derives both from inside and from outside of the engineering profession. The second derives principally from engineering itself. For the first group of reasons one has to look no further than the media. With the increasing power of technology there is inevitably an increasing potential for large-scale disruption if it fails. When major accidents happen they hit the headlines. Chernobyl, Three Mile Island, the Shuttle, the Zeebrugge ferry, Bhopal, Ronan Point and West Gate Bridge are just a few examples of recent years; there are sadly many more. Scares over food quality, intensive farming methods and the effects of chemical pollutants, such as the damage to the ozone layer by CFC gases, are parallel concerns in other industries. Earthquakes, tornadoes and hurricanes hit the news when buildings and structures are torn apart and untold damage and human misery is caused. All of these disasters hold important lessons for engineers and for non-engineers alike. A great deal of effort is put into learning from them.

The second group of reasons for concern about safety, which comes principally from within the engineering profession, concerns the delicate balance between cost and safety. As our knowledge of physical system behaviour develops it is clearly desirable to use that knowledge to reduce the cost of an artefact. This is usually done through being able to predict with greater certainty how that artefact will behave in use. The consequent need to consider the balance between the demands on an artefact and its capacity to resist those demands has led to the developments of reliability theory. The introduction of new methods to engineering design inevitably provokes controversy. The concept of 'limit state design' methodology as implemented in many codes of practice world-wide has caused much concern, debate and even resentment in some professional engineering circles.

Questions concerning engineering safety are profound and difficult because all of them, at root, involve the most fundamental problem of all, 'What is truth?' Engineers have to make decisions concerning the future using knowledge and information necessarily rooted in the past. Magee[1] summarized this problem very neatly, 'Just because past futures have resembled past pasts, it does not follow that future futures will all resemble future pasts.' In other words, the assumption that the world is regular is psychological and not a logical one. And that is not all. Our knowledge is necessarily incomplete since how can we know what we do not know? Plato wrote about this, long ago, in the Meno : 'And how will you inquire, Socrates, into that which you know not? What will you put forth as the subject of inquiry? And if you find out what you want how will you ever know that this is what you did not know?'

Handy[2] has argued that our society is entering an 'Age of Unreason' when the only prediction that will hold true is that no prediction will hold true; a time therefore for bold imaginings in private life as well as public, for thinking the unlikely; a time of constant and rapid change. Clearly there are some aspects of engineering where regularity can be assumed, but it would be naive to think that any system involving human beings is entirely predictable.

An engineer therefore has to be a philosopher by night and a 'man of action' by day. He or she must be a generalist and a specialist and must retain an overview whilst attending to detail. If a chair is designed it should be a chair of appropriate quality. That means it should be a beautiful chair, comfortable to sit in, able to support the heaviest people and sold at a price that people can afford. An engineer must be aware of the limitations of his/her knowledge but not allow those limitations to paralyse the capacity for decision and action. His or her purpose is to produce an artefact, to satisfy a human need, and that need includes safety.

The objectives of this chapter are to set the scene for the rest of the book. The discussion will begin with a brief examination of some practical issues. In order to understand and deal with these issues thoroughly we need to address some basic matters such as 'What can society expect of engineers?', 'What is the nature of engineering and engineering knowledge?', 'How is uncertainty managed and is safety a special part of quality?'.

1.2 PRACTICAL ISSUES

Decision makers today are more interested in ensuring value for money than ever before. Control is the keyword: management and control of cost and quality to meet objectives are the key issues.

Procedures and capital investment programmes are becoming more and more sophisticated each year. Quality assurance (QA) and quality control (QC) have emerged to meet the generally perceived need to improve the quality of work. Failures to meet time or cost targets on projects are often well publicized when they occur. This is bad both for the individual companies involved and for the industry as a whole. The poor performance may be due, for example, to acceptance of unrealistic estimates and ignorance or neglect of risks. Certain clients may curtail the responsibilities of their professional advisers in order to obtain what they perceive as greater certainty over the cost outcome. This, of course, may not be in the client's own best interest if the resulting quality of the work is not what the client was expecting. As traditional responsibilities change engineers are increasingly realizing that they require at least 'state of the art' management techniques. The difficulty then is that most engineers have received little stimulation in management topics from their formal education.

A study by the University of Bradford in the United Kingdom for the Engineering Management Group Board of the Institution of Civil Engineers in 1988 demonstrated the need felt by many UK engineers for better management training. Management is important for site safety because construction is a dangerous business. Between 1981 and 1985 there were two deaths every week, on average, on UK construction sites. It has been reported by the UK Health and Safety Executive[3] that 90 per cent of these could have been prevented and that in 70 per cent of the cases positive action by management could have saved lives. A recent on-site study of 60 construction case histories together with detailed information on 260 other projects and a statistical analysis of 8000 projects concluded that 'the research showed plainly that management was all too often inadequate'.

Probably the simplest possible characterization of the tasks of an engineer is that they fall into one of two groups. These groups are:

1. The set of decisions as to what is to be made
2. The set of decisions as to how it is to be made and ensuring that it is made

The first is, in essence, design; the second is, in essence, manufacture or construction. The emphasis in the first is, largely, but not totally, technical, that is on 'applying' science; the emphasis in the second is, largely, but not totally, organizational, that is managing a project. As far as any formal application of science is concerned it is not difficult to see the reasons why it has been applied more to design than to construction. If we think back to the time when an engineer like Telford faced up to these problems, it was quite natural for applied scientists to concentrate on those issues in engineering problems that could be most easily tackled. The problems were chosen so that solutions could be tested against some aspect of reality. Thus because theories could be developed as, for example, in elasticity, and tested in the laboratory using repeatable experiments, a body of knowledge was developed, most of which was eventually very useful to designers. As the success of engineering physical science developed over the years it began to colour the whole attitude of engineers; it led to a technical 'world view' of engineering. As a result engineering is still largely associated with 'applied science' in intellectual circles. Evidence for this is the large number of university engineering departments which are part of Faculties of Applied Science and which award a science degree.

The success story in the physical sciences contrasts sharply with our lack of success in coping with human and organizational problems. Indeed, very few university engineering departments count social or management scientists in their ranks. The reason for this relative lack of success is quite clear: it is extremely difficult to produce theories about human behaviour that can be highly tested; it is difficult to set up repeatable experiments; indeed, it is difficult to dependably measure many of the important characteristics in a controlled way.

These two simplified aspects of engineering, the technical and the managerial, manifest themselves in our consideration of safety. The technical 'world view' has led to the development of risk analysis and reliability theory. It is a view that sees engineering failure as, largely, a technical problem. Accounts and analyses of failure, written from this view, usually concentrate on the technical factors and make little mention of the human factors. It would be wrong to suggest, however, that human factors are totally unrecognized, but they are considered from a technical point of view. A manifestation of this is the way in which attempts are made to mathematize and formalize the treatment, usually on the basis of some sort of statistical model. As a result there has been a tendency to attribute human error to individual mistakes and lapses. Other writers, with other perspectives, have revealed that human factors in engineering failures are often much more subtle and relate to organizational matters.

Two specific examples of practical issues that have caused much controversy world wide stem from these two approaches. They are, firstly, the adoption in many countries of 'limit state' design, in one form or another, for technical design codes of practice and, secondly, the use of QA and QC for the better management of the design and construction process. Both of these practical issues will be addressed at length in this book as they are quite obviously concerned with improving engineering safety. However, it is worth noting at this stage some of the objections raised against them. For example, some of the common criticisms levelled at the implementation of limit state design, particularly with the use of partial factors, seem to be that limit state design: (1) is more complicated than earlier methods; (2) removes the need for engineering judgement; (3) depends upon an inappropriate use of statistics and probability; (4) results in long and complicated codes of practice; (5) cannot deal with the fact that uncertainty is diverse and prescribed factors are not appropriate when uncertainty varies from site to site.

In a similar manner QA and QC procedures are often criticized for (1) producing too much paperwork; (2) being used in inappropriate ways; (3) not being directed at the real issues.

These practical issues will be referred to many times in the pages that follow in the somewhat broader context of engineering safety as a whole. In the last chapter we will return to them directly for another look.

1.3 WHAT CAN SOCIETY EXPECT?

Perhaps the single most important question of all concerning the safety of modern engineered systems that engineers have to address is 'What can society expect of us?'; that is 'What does society have a right to expect and what are engineers obliged to provide?' Should society expect no failures? Is it reasonable to expect perfect reliability of an engineered artefact whether it be a washing machine, bridge, nuclear reactor, offshore oil rig or nuclear defence system?

It will be useful to note some definitions of our basic terms: safety, risk and hazard. Safety has been defined as[4] 'freedom from unacceptable risks/personal harm'. Meeting this requirement clearly poses the problem of deciding what is 'acceptable'. In the courts safety has been defined as 'the elimination of danger' where danger is the balance between the chance of an accident and the result of an accident.

A risk is the combined effect of the chances of occurrence of some undesirable event and its consequences in a given context. Risk analysis refers to the attempt to identify and if possible quantify the likelihoods of adverse consequences arising from a particular project or course of action, and to use these estimates as an aid to decision making.

A hazard has been defined as 'a set of conditions in the operation of a product or system with the potential for initiating an accident sequence'.

No one and nothing is ever perfect; there is always a risk that events will not turn out as planned. One important distinction to bear in mind, as the discussion progresses, is between the meaning associated with the way the words risk and hazard are used in everyday language and the more formal and specialized definitions used in risk and reliability theories. The distinction will hopefully become clear as the discussion progresses.

People's expectations concerning risk are extremely complex and not necessarily rational. Many people seem to have an inner psychological need for certainty. The search for certainty as 'truth' has been at the heart of Western thought, both in science and religion. Perhaps this search for certainty is at the root of some people's inner tensions concerning risk, since it is obvious to all that uncertainty is all around us in our daily lives. However, there are some things that we think we can rely on. Everyone knows the old adage 'as safe as houses'. Even in biblical times reference was made to the safety of houses built upon good foundations and those built upon poor foundations as examples of the consequences of good and bad conduct (Luke 6). Most people seem to expect engineered facilities to be as 'safe as houses'. This expectation puts the task of any engineer concerned with the built environment in an especially critical position.

There are many factors that affect people's attitude to risk. Throughout history certain people have found activities involving great risk to be stimulating, presumably because in this way they achieve an increased awareness of the richness of life: in simple terms it is exciting. Some people find it exciting to watch other people take risks; manifestations of this are the popularity of circus stunts and dangerous sports such as motor racing. Many other people avoid risk whenever possible; they are risk aversive. A major factor in determining an individual's attitude is whether the risk has been sought out and is present for a relatively short time, such as a mountaineer scaling some particularly difficult rock face, or whether the risk is ever present and unavoidable in daily life. At the root of this, perhaps, is fear. Fear is exciting—life would be dull without it. As long as an individual feels capable of controlling the risk by his/her own actions, even if it takes all of the inner resources that can be mustered, then the risk is acceptable; in fact it is stimulating and challenging. If an individual feels incapable of controlling the risk, and receives no stimulation from it, then it is threatening and will be perceived in a qualitatively different way.

Another important factor in determining public sensitivity to risk is the consequences of an event. There is a tendency to be more concerned about the possibility of one accident costing, say, 50 lives than 50 accidents costing one life each. It is a well-known effect in many situations that people's threshold of reaction to unpleasantness can be lowered by the frequency of an event.

One person's decision about risk may not seem rational to another person. A non-smoker will probably not be able to understand the judgement of the 20-cigarettes-a-day smoker. The benefits of smoking (the induced feelings of pleasure and calm) presumably outweigh, in the smoker's mind, the disbenefits of smoking (increased risk of poor health and earlier death). Almost certainly the first, habit-forming, cigarette will not have been taken through a rationally thought-out decision process.

Engineering safety is about predicting and managing the risks involved in building and operating engineered facilities. Risk prediction is based on physical science and engineering principles. Risk management is largely a question of human organization and human behaviour. It involves the psychology of individuals and the sociology of organizations. Engineering safety operates at the boundary of technology and social science; it is a sociotechnical problem.

The practical answer to the question of what society can expect of engineers is, of course, expressed in the law. People need protection from the excesses of individuals. Regulations are produced to control the actions of individuals and organizations for the good of society as a whole. Codes of Practice are used for this purpose, but they are written, as the name implies, as codes of good conduct and practice.

Thus it is clear that an answer to the question of 'What can society expect of engineers' is not trivial. It is necessary to address questions that lie at the very heart of our understanding of our knowledge of science, technology and society. In order to attempt any sort of answer we need to explore the nature of engineering and society. Inevitably this will expose an author's own 'world views'.

1.4 WORLD VIEW

The argument so far has hinted at a fundamental feature of all analysis which needs clarifying before we proceed further. Everything we think and do depends on a point of view—it depends on the way we look at the world. In philosophy this is called the 'Weltanschauung'.[5] We attribute meaning to something by interpreting it in the light of our experience and education. Thus the same issue will tend to be formulated as an economic problem by an economist, as a technical problem by an engineer and as an organizational problem by a sociologist and so on. Each 'world view' may be valid in the sense that it may be internally consistent and that propositions deduced from it correspond to the perceived facts. However, the 'world views' may lead to quite different and possibly incompatible strategies for actions required to solve the problems and resolve the basic issues.

In considering how these differing world views are formed, it is probably useful to have in mind some sort of model of the process of the brain. In the simplest of terms this can be characterized as follows. When we perceive something a set of messages is sent to our brains from our sense organs. The mind learns to organize these messages into patterns. We can think of the patterns as being some chemical or electrical phenomena in a neurone network or just as an abstract pattern. For our purpose here the exact nature of the patterns does not matter; the important idea is that the patterns are the 'software' of our brains. When sets of patterns are formed and laid down in the brain the mind no longer has to analyse or sort the information. All that is required is a strong enough message to trigger an existing pattern and the mind then follows it. This is a simple model of recognition. Unless there are competing patterns, anything remotely similar to the established pattern will be treated as if it were that pattern. The purpose of thinking is to find patterns and of course it is possible to lock into the wrong pattern. It is also necessary to learn new patterns by relating them to patterns already laid down, that is learning and understanding. Some patterns are genetically inherited and these therefore constitute part of the 'hardware', the patterns that we share with our parents. What is clear is that by having a large repertoire of patterns, that is a large richness of experience, then thinking is potentially much more powerful. A danger is that thinking can be limited to a small set of patterns and the result is intolerance and a lack of imagination.

Thus we can imagine a person's world view as a set of patterns laid down in the brain. All new experiences are interpreted in the context of this world view. Two people will tend to have similar world views if they come from similar cultural, social and educational backgrounds.

As already mentioned there seem to be, in current practice, two groups of people holding largely separate world views concerning engineering safety: the technical and the human. The differences between these views arise from the whole history of Western philosophy that has seen human beings as quite distinct entities from the rest of the world. It is exemplified by the mind–body dualism of Descartes which was based on his famous dictum 'I think therefore I am'. In other words we, as human beings, are encouraged by our culture to see ourselves as objective observers of the world, as somehow separate and not part of it. The mind and body are quite separate and distinct. This implies that we are therefore free to use our ideas to manipulate the world. We tend to believe that since we are objective disinterested observers of the world, then any manipulation of the world will not really affect us. This view leads to important definitions which express how we think. For example, Thomas Tredgold's famous definition of civil engineering is 'the art of directing the great sources of power in nature for the use and convenience of man'. This states quite clearly that the forces of nature are there to be controlled by man and that these forces are quite separate, that man is remote from nature.

However, there is another 'world view' which stems from the philosophers of language such as Wittgenstein and Heidegger. This view is that human beings are an integral part of the world—that humans are actors on a world stage. Holders of this view argue that an objective, value neutral, view is impossible. In other words to argue that nature consists of objective, non-involved, mindless physical particles is a stance that is just as value laden as any insistence on a particular form of government. This view forces us to think of any system that includes human beings and physical entities as a totality of integrated and interdependent elements. This view is one that is in tune with much modern thinking regarding the environment. People are increasingly realizing that we must look after the planet earth since we rely on it for our very existence. It is becoming obvious that we are not at all separate from the planet; we are part of the planet.

If this world view is adopted then we must reexamine the way in which we identify the systems we wish to design, build and manage. In any system identification analysis there are, at least, two basic types of questions. One set of questions is issue related and the other set is task related. Issue-related questions are, for example, 'What do we wish to achieve? and What are our goals or objectives?'. Task-related questions are, for example, 'What is the artefact or engineered facility going to have to do?' and 'What is its function?'. It is, of course, all too easy to concentrate on tasks, with inadequate attention to the underlying issues because of the need to get the job done. However, you cannot solve a problem successfully until you know what the problem is. Issue-related questions are concerned with the debate on the definition of the system requirements in the broadest sense. We will return to these matters at the end of this chapter. Task-related questions concern the forming of the system that has been defined with appropriate emphasis on technical and human world views.

It is inevitable that the authors of this book and their readers will have different, in some cases very different, world views. If this point is appreciated then the communication process will be much more effective since we will be looking for ideas that occupy the common ground rather more than the more usual search for fine differences. Our purpose is to attempt to improve knowledge and understanding, a central purpose of any intellectual endeavour.

1.5 SCIENCE

Since the turn of the century there has been a revolution in the way we view science. Before Einstein's relativity theory was accepted and prior to the development of quantum mechanics, scientists thought that scientific knowledge, and in particular Newtonian mechanics, was the absolute truth. (There are various philosophical versions of what is meant by truth; here we will adopt the common-sense interpretation which is simply that a proposition is true if it corresponds to the facts.) Kant was strongly under the influence of the success of Newtonian mechanics and thought that he had identified all of the components of the categories that underpin all knowledge. This view is now untenable. Heisenberg's uncertainty principle, which effectively asserts that there are limits to what we can measure, is an example of the new attitude of uncertainty. At the microlevel of analysis in quantum mechanics a unique correspondence between precise positions and momenta of some postulated element, like an electron, at two different times cannot

paradigm become necessary at higher and higher levels, until only a major revolution will achieve a satisfactory resolution of the problems.

Associated with this process is the human problem concerning the general acceptance of new ideas. Inherent in all human systems is an inertia that manifests itself as a reluctance to accept fundamental alterations to the current ways of doing things—the current paradigm.

Just as physics has undergone revolutionary change in this century, so has mathematics. In 1930 Gödel wrecked the then-existing notions of mathematical proof. He showed that if axiomatic set theory is consistent, there exist theorems that can neither be proved nor disproved, and that there is no constructive procedure which will prove axiomatic set theory to be consistent. In fact, later developments have shown that any axiomatic system, sufficiently extensive to allow the formulation of arithmetic, will suffer the same defect. In fact it is not the axioms that are at fault but arithmetic itself. Stewart[9] concludes his book: '... so the foundations of mathematics remain wobbly despite all efforts to consolidate them. ... For the truth is that intuition will always prevail over mere logic. ... There is always the feeling that logic can be changed; we would prefer not to change the theorems.' Thus even mathematics can be conceived of as a model of the way we think about the world.

1.6 ENGINEERING

What is engineering about? Is it about making money for the people involved in it or is it about making good quality artefacts for the society it serves? It clearly is made up of business organizations trading goods and services for money and they must make some profit to survive. On the other hand, society needs and expects food, clothing, power supplies, transport systems, shelter and accommodation and so on. All of these require an infrastructure of engineered products and facilities that must work safely. If the requirements of business and society are in harmony then all is well. If they are in conflict which one dominates?

A question such as this again strikes at the roots of the kind of society we live in. In a democracy the theory is that we aim to achieve consensus by voting for politicians who will take the actions which are required to achieve these delicate balances. The actuality is a compromise between the theory and the requirements of efficiency which is drawn slightly differently in various democratic countries. We will argue that it is in the best interests of both business and society (and in fact for everyone) to think in terms of quality. However, before we can reach that point one of the key issues which must be discussed is the status of engineering knowledge in relation to scientific knowledge. If scientific and mathematical knowledge is perceived as sets of models, then engineering knowledge cannot claim greater status and must also be so characterized. Engineering is also quite clearly a problem-solving process, as Popper describes science, but there are differences which must be explained.

We can classify engineering knowledge into three components, all of which are models of our collective experience. The first is scientific knowledge, consisting for most engineers of Newtonian mechanics, tested in precise laboratory conditions. The second is the application of those models, with necessary approximating assumptions, to the design of engineering artefacts. These applications are tested by the success or failure of actual artefacts and by some laboratory work on idealized components. The third component, 'rules of thumb' or heuristics, is also tested by these methods. We will need to consider each of these components in turn.

For nearly all engineering activity Newtonian mechanics is assumed to be the scientific description of the physical world. However, in order to solve practical problems, engineers have had to derive many different theoretical models based on this science with various sets of idealizing assumptions. One of the important skills of an engineer is to be able to make judgements about the quality of the applicability of these models. The applied scientist and engineering scientist, like the pure scientist, attempts to work in laboratory conditions but is motivated more by the need to produce theoretical models directly for use by engineers. An attempt is made to make sense out of data concerning incompletely understood phenomena in order to help make some sort of prediction. The stategy adopted may range from that of the pure scientist at one extreme to mere curve fitting and data extrapolation at the other.

Thus the engineer has quite a different set of problems than that of the scientist. In designing and building a structure, for example, the engineer comes across problems about which decisions must be made. If sufficient data or well-developed models are not available then judgement and experience must be used to overcome the difficulty. There is no choice—a decision must be made. The research scientist is not forced to make practical decisions about matters that are both central to his purpose and highly uncertain. For the engineer, experience and judgement must take over when scientific knowledge fails.

The knowledge of an engineer is often characterized as 'know-how' whereas that of the scientist is said to be 'knowing-that'. This, in the view of many, implies that scientific knowledge is superior. Superficially the difference may seem substantial, but at a deeper level it is not.

First, consider methods of solving problems in the context of the needs and objectives of the problem solver: de Bono[10] relates a particularly appropriate analogy:

> Consider a steep valley that has to be crossed. If you are on foot and in a hurry you could run across the flimsy bridge that spans the top of the valley. If you have a car you would use the shorter and stronger bridge that is set lower down in the valley wall. If you had

a truck, you would want to use an even shorter and stronger bridge set nearer to the valley floor. If you want absolute safety and reliability you would descend to the valley floor, cross it and climb up the other side. These bridges of different strengths set at different levels correspond to different levels of understanding. You use the bridge or level that is strong enough for your purpose. You do not need to descend to the valley floor every time you want to cross any more than you need to know the molecular structure of albumen in order to boil an egg. If you are in a hurry the long flimsy bridge across the top of the valley might be more practical.

Thus it is the usefulness or appropriateness of any particular method that is the main interest of the problem solver. It is quite wrong to suggest that detailed explanations of phenomena are better or worse than those which are more vague. Often a detailed explanation adds no more usefulness but does add a false appearance of validity. Vague answers need to have enough precision to be useful in solving a particular problem. The way engineers characterize their collective experience (as distinct from each individual's experience which will not concern us here) is by using 'rules of thumb' or heuristics. These derive from the craft origins of engineering and are really dependable, common-sense hypotheses, but of very restricted scope and application. They have developed by a process of trial and error which is very similar to that described earlier, but with the very important differences that are discussed later. 'Rules of thumb' suffer from the major feature of all common-sense knowledge which is that while it claims to be correct, it is not often aware of the limits within which it is valid or successful. It is most effective when the underlying factors affecting it remain virtually constant, but since these factors are often not identified or recognized then it is incomplete. Scientific knowledge provides us with models that have a greater degree of abstraction and are therefore much more general with greater scope and application.

Historically the first rules to be developed were rules of proportion, based on the geometry developed by the ancient Greeks. Vitruvius and Palladio quote many examples of them. More modern examples of rules are quoted in the engineer's handbook of 1859. For example, for the deflection of rectangular beams: 'Multiply the square of the length in feet by 0.02 and the product divided by the depth in inches equals the deflection.' For the strength of cast iron girders the rule was: 'The area of the bottom flange multiplied by the depth both in inches, and the product divided by the length in feet, equals the permanent load distributed in tons allowing the permanent load to be one fourth of the breaking weight.' Empirical formulae such as these fitted to test data obtained in the laboratory contrast sharply with the results of the French elasticians of the period.

There are many modern equivalents of such rules. At the most simple level, for example, are the rules for determining the spacing of bolt holes in a steel joint. Other rules, based on some use of mechanics and some laboratory test data, seem authoritative but if the underlying assumptions are examined they bear only a partial relationship to the actual behaviour of the structural element. For example, in order to determine the number and size of steel bolts required in a moment-carrying steel end plate connection, a common assumption made is that the joint rotates about the bottom row of bolts and that the forces in the rest of the bolts are proportional to their distances from the bottom row. In reality the problem of understanding the detailed mechanics of the joint behaviour is very difficult because of the many stress discontinuities and unknown load distributions. The method adopted in design works satisfactorily because it produces reasonably safe and economic solutions.

Clearly many approximating assumptions are found in all design calculations: joints are assumed to be fixed or pinned, loads are assumed to be uniformly distributed and wind loads are assumed to be static pressures. The approximations are justified only to the extent that they have been used in the past to produce designs that have not failed. Just as there are current paradigms in science, so there are current paradigms in engineering. In order to design a given type of artefact a current set of models is used which makes up the current calculational procedure model (CPM). For example, the design of a steel pitched roof portal frame building may involve the use of plastic theory and a number of simplifying assumptions including pinned or fixed joints, ignoring the stiffening effect of cladding and its effects on the postulated failure mechanism. Among many other assumptions are that the roof loads are taken to be uniformly distributed, and checks are made to account for such effects as finite deflections before collapse, strain hardening and buckling. Clearly, further research will modify this model at many different levels. Some will involve only minor changes; others may involve extensive alterations.

The calculation procedure model is a set of theories, rules and procedures that are used to solve a particular problem. Every single application of a CPM will involve a slightly different set of assumptions since every problem has some unique features. The similarity between the growth of scientific knowledge and engineering knowledge can now be recognized if we characterize the development of engineering knowledge as decision-making and problem-solving processes. Just as the falsification of bold conjectures is part of the logic of scientific discovery, so is failure of an artefact important in the growth of engineering knowledge of the CPMs. The process can be characterized as follows:

1. Problem
2. Conjectural solution (the synthesis of the CPM by recognition of some approximate similarity with previous problems or by speculation— usually within the current paradigm)
3. Appraisal of the consequences of the solution
4. Decision on a set of actions (i.e. design)
5. Carrying through of actions (i.e. manufacturing or construction)

6. Testing of solution (by performance of the artefact; if it fails, it is falsified)
7. Feedback concerning the dependability of the current paradigm

The components of this scheme are obviously not clear-cut and independent but the essential development is contained within it. The important testing phase is item (6). We have seen that the logic of scientific discovery suggests that the scientist should set up bold conjectures and attempt to falsify them. The engineer has no wish to follow the same logic because the conjectural solution is the CPM and to falsify that directly would require the engineered artefact to fail. However, it does follow, from the same logic, that when failure occurs it is important. This is because it is precisely then that the boundary of the total CPM, as applied to actual artefacts, is indicated. Even then the boundary will be very difficult to define exactly because failure will be due to a combination of circumstances: the role of any particular assumption, rule or procedure in the CPM will not be directly isolable; it may be difficult to isolate particular assumptions unique to that artefact from the more general assumptions associated with a particular CPM. Thus a CPM which has been used successfully for a number of years in this way is therefore not in any sense 'true', but is only weakly not falsified. In fact, a particular rule in a CPM may be false but its effect may be masked by the conservative assumptions made in the rest of the model.

In using and developing the CPM, engineers are interested primarily in safe, cautious conjectures (while acknowledging economic constraints) because the consequences of failure are so severe. Thus a CPM is rarely falsified directly in service; instead, great reliance is placed on partial testing of isolated aspects of it using idealized components in the precise conditions of a laboratory. The procedures are only falsified in the laboratory under conditions that do not completely reflect the conditions under which the actual artefact operates.

1.7 THE QUALITIES OF TRUTH AND SAFETY

It is possible to draw an analogy between the scientist's search for truth and the engineer's search for safety. Both truth and safety are qualities of what is being created; for the scientist truth is a quality of knowledge, for the engineer safety is a quality of an artefact.

At the most fundamental level of description, the differences between the nature of the work of engineers and scientists are not substantial; both are problem solvers. The actual differences are not due to the different nature of the methods each uses, rather they are due to the qualities of the objectives they pursue. The qualities of an engineered artefact will include, for example, function, safety, economy, reliability and environmental friendliness. The qualities of a scientific theory will include predictive power, explanation, truth, precision, simplicity and abstraction.

It would be possible to write extensively on the analogies between these two sets of qualities. For example, it is at least arguable that one of the functions of a theory is to predict. However, we are concerned here with engineering safety and we will restrict the discussion to an analogy between it and truth. The scientist predicts a result based on theory and then sets about testing that prediction in as precise a way as possible in order to progress towards true knowledge. As discussed previously, it is an unfortunate fact that, in strict logical terms, it will never be known whether it has been attained or not. Similarly, the engineer wants to progress towards a safe artefact and therefore pictures the likely scenarios for its behaviour. Engineering knowledge is used to make predictions and then the consequences of those predictions are interpreted in the light of the uncertainty known to be present. It does not follow that because the artefact has not yet failed it is therefore safe since again in strict logical terms the engineer can never know.

An important difference between science and engineering is that the consequences of error in the predictions made by the scientist and by the engineer are dramatically different. If during an experiment a scientific theory is falsified then the logical result is new knowledge. If an engineer's CPM is falsified, then an artefact has failed. Engineers are therefore interested in safe cautious theories that produce safe artefacts; scientists are interested in detailed accurate theories that produce true knowledge. Both are interested in solving problems. Engineering scientists tend to be dominated by the scientific interest in accuracy and, as a result, often frown on many of the necessary heuristics and rules in the CPM as being intellectually inferior. Designers rely on rules when science lets them down. Many misunderstandings arise because of a failure to appreciate this distinction.

The discussion so far presents us with a strange antithesis: it is the very success of engineering that holds back the growth of engineering knowledge and it is its failures that provide the seeds for its future development. Not only is it necessary therefore to identify the particular causes of an accident and the dominant causes of groups of accidents, but it is also important to identify the important changes in the current paradigm that have followed. The changes occur at many different levels with widely varying scope, as has been mentioned, and are often difficult to define in any precise sense. Many of the changes are well known and have been discussed individually at length. One of the important consequences of a heightened awareness of the changes is that new developments in research and practice can be seen as part of the continuing process of the growth of engineering knowledge. This aids an understanding and appreciation of the rules of those who contribute to that process and the uncertainty, which is inevitably part of the process, has to be suitably managed.

1.8 UNCERTAINTY MANAGEMENT

Most, if not all, of the large engineered facilities with which this book is concerned are large 'one-off' constructions or complex systems of artefacts as distinct from artefacts that are mass produced. This distinction between 'one-off' and mass production may, at first sight, seem rather trite but it does lead to profound differences in the quantity and quality of the information available to the engineer. If a product is to be mass produced it makes economic sense to test one or more prototypes; in fact, prototype testing becomes an essential phase of the design and development of the product. By contrast it is uneconomic to test a 'one-off' product to destruction and to use that information to rebuild. Thus the designer of a 'one-off' product obtains much less feedback about the performance of the product in the world outside of the laboratory than does his/her manufacturing counterpart. The resulting uncertainty largely surrounds the quality of any model, whether scientific or not, that the engineer uses to make decisions.

However, before we pursue an analysis of uncertainty in engineering systems it is worth referring back to the discussion of Sec. 1.4 concerning 'world views'. You will recall that it was argued that the world should be considered as a totality and not as two separate systems (human beings and physical objects). The important major differences between physical objects and human beings is that physical objects lack intentionality. Intentionality is the feature by which the states of our minds are directed at or are about objects other than themselves. This feature is why human systems are so difficult to analyse and to produce structured sets of theories that describe their behaviour.

Searle, in his 1984 Reith lectures,[11] discussed this relationship of human beings with the rest of the universe. He addressed questions such as, 'How do we reconcile the mentalistic concept of ourselves with an apparently inconsistent conception of the universe as a purely physical system?' Questions such as 'Can computers have minds?' or 'What is consciousness?' have become important in the development of artificial intelligence. It is not the purpose of this book to attempt a detailed discussion of these issues but it is important to recognize the fundamental importance to our consideration of the human involvement in engineering safety. In managing safety we must recognize that we do not understand sufficiently well the way in which human beings behave and yet that understanding must be central in predictions concerning safety. It is necessary therefore to move away from an emphasis on prediction of safety to an emphasis on the management of safety, certainly as far as human factors are concerned.

Of course it has been, in the past, much easier to deal with physical systems. The patterns that are observed concerning physical systems have been organized into engineering knowledge, as discussed earlier. The formal models of engineering science are expressed in the standard mathematical functions with which all engineers are familiar and which express one-to-one or many-to-one relationships. Attempts have been made to capture more complex relationships by the use of many-to-many mappings. For example, fuzzy relations and 'expert system' rules have been proposed. The uncertainty in these physical models is of two types: system and parameter uncertainties. System uncertainty is due to the lack of dependability of a theoretical model when used to describe the behaviour of a proposed artefact assuming a precisely defined set of parameters (or attributes) which describe the model. Of course, any system may be split into small subsystems if it is thought appropriate to do so for the problem being addressed. The models that lie at the most detailed level of analysis can be termed the system primitive models. Each theoretical model consists of a set of entities and relationships. An entity is anything of which it is required to keep a record; it may be physical or abstract. Each entity has a set of attributes which characterize it. If the attributes are measurable they may be familiar concepts such as length, weight, temperature, strain, etc., and are more commonly known as model parameters. The system uncertainty is complemented by parameter uncertainty which is due to the lack of dependability of theoretical propositions concerning the parameters, or attributes, of a theoretical model used to represent a proposed artefact, assuming that the model is precise. In engineering problems where prototype testing is thoroughly carried through, the system uncertainty is much reduced and the parameter uncertainty is dominant. In 'one-off' engineering both types of uncertainty are important and in some cases (e.g. geotechnics) the system uncertainty is dominant.

The central activity of both scientist and engineer is that of a decision maker. Whatever hypotheses are conjectured, whatever the problem faced and whatever the motivation of the problem solver, decisions must be taken on the basis of dependable information. So what is dependable information and how does the concept of dependability differ from that of truth?

The deterministic treatment of engineering calculations has its roots in the ideals of 'exact science'. We have seen that this is no longer tenable. It is now suggested that what really matters to an engineer is the dependability of a proposition. Of course, if a proposition is true then it is dependable, but if a proposition is dependable it is not necessarily true. Truth is a sufficient condition but not a necessary condition for dependability. Einstein demonstrated that Newtonian mechanics is not true but it is clearly dependable under certain conditions.

Sufficient conditions for dependable information have been discussed previously.[12] A conjecture is dependable if:

1. A highly repeatable experiment can be set up to test it.
2. The resulting state is clearly definable and repeatable.
3. The value of the resulting state is measurable and repeatable.
4. The test is successful.

These are sufficient but not necessary conditions because the proposition may not be false even though it is not possible to set up repeatable experiments. Deficiencies in any of the ways in which propositions can be tested or inductively applied obviously leads to uncertainty and a consequent loss of dependability.

Randomness is the uncertaintly left over when all of the patterns in the information have been identified. Thus randomness may be defined (following Popper) as the lack of a specific pattern and the concept of randomness is analogous to the concept of dependability of a theoretical conjecture. A highly dependable theory is one that has been tested many times and has passed almost all of those tests. A highly random sequence is one that has been tested many times to find out whether specific patterns are present and none have so far been found. As soon as a specific pattern has been found then the sequence is not random. In probability theory the observed tendencies for apparently random measures of data to group together, when measured many times under similar circumstances, are expressed using distribution functions. The most well known of these is the standard bell shape of the normal distribution. Thus it is possible to form a theoretical model of apparently very variable data. This has been the central purpose behind the development of reliability theory. However, it does address only part of the uncertainty, that is parameter uncertainty.

The emphasis in dealing with uncertainty in physical systems therefore becomes one of defining the circumstances in which a given model is appropriate for the problem at hand. It is a switch from the concept of truth to the concept of control or management. It moves away from a requirement for 'true' predictions of future scenarios, with or without uncertainty estimates, to the requirement for control of future events allowing for the inevitable uncertainties in our understanding of what might or might not happen. This is, of course, directly in line with our conclusions concerning human factors. Thus our philosophy is clear; while the science of engineering will allow us to make some predictions of risk they are inevitably partial and incomplete and the emphasis must be on management of safety.

1.9 INCOMPLETENESS

Risk has been defined earlier as being the chance of occurrence of an event or series of events together with the consequences of that event. So what do we mean by the proposition that the chances of some event are, say, 1 in 1000 or 0.001? If we toss a coin there is, more or less, a 50 per cent chance of it turning up heads or tails. The reason is that we assume that there are two possible states of the coin after tossing with equal chance of occurrence. Thus in any assessment of chance, the measure is relative to a set of possible events. The central difficulty in complex problems is just what constitutes the set of possible events? In statistical measurement this set is actual to the extent that over a period of time most of the events that can occur will occur. There is therefore an assumption of regularity. However, the assumption may well not be valid. This is particularly so with respect to rare events, since by definition they may not appear in a particular sample. Statistical sampling is the art and science of dealing with this difficulty.

In theoretical predictions of risk, based on scientific engineering knowledge, the population of possible events is infinite since, as Plato noted, 'How can we know what we don't know?' There is always a logical possibility that anything can happen. We can distinguish two kinds of theoretical models. A closed world model represents total knowledge about everything in a particular system and an open world model represents partial knowledge where some things are known to be true, some things are known to be false and others are simply unknown. Thus in a closed world every concept is either true or false and no undefined or inconsistent states are possible. In a closed world the information is complete in that all and only the relationships that can possibly hold among concepts are those implied by the given information. In an open world model there are four possible states of a concept, true, false, unknown and inconsistent, with degrees of uncertainty in between these extremes. Most mathematicians like to forbid inconsistencies but in practical problems the finding and settling of inconsistency is an important element of the problem-solving process. The relationship of these models with risk and uncertainty can be clarified by considering a classification of problem types. A problem will be characterized as a doubtful or difficult question to which there may be a number of possible answers. Each possible answer is a conjectural solution which has to be considered and evaluated in the decision-making process. Four types of problem are:

- Type 1. Where all of the consequences of adopting a conjectural solution are known for certain.
- Type 2. Where all of the consequences of adopting a conjectural solution have been precisely identified but only the probabilities of occurrence are known.
- Type 3. Where all of the consequences of adopting a conjectural solution have been approximately identified so that only the possibilities of ill-defined or fuzzy consequences are known.
- Type 4. Where only some of the consequences (precise or fuzzy) of adopting a conjectural solution have been identified.

The type 1 problem is the well-known one of decision making under certainty, that is determinism. The power of this simplest of assumptions is clear for physical systems such as dealt with by Newtonian mechanics. Most of the past successes of the applications of engineering science have relied on the fact that for certain regular and repeatable situations this model is appropriate in that it enables problems to be solved successfully. The type 2 problem is the extension of the type 1 problem to cases where a probability distribution over the set of possible consequences of a particular conjectural solution is available. This is termed in the literature as decision making under risk. Type 3 problems are an extension of the type 2 problems with an explicit consideration of vagueness or lack of information about the precise definition of the consequence of a conjectural solution.

The theoretical developments for dealing with each type of problem are impressive but nevertheless they all involve the restrictive closed world assumption that all of the consequences of a conjectural solution are known. Type 4 problems are those of real world problem solving. Since only some of the consequences are identified it is necessary to make an open world assumption since the entire sample space is not known. This has been termed decision making under ignorance; it might preferably be defined as open world decision making. There is always the possibility of unforeseen and unwanted consequences occurring after the adoption of a particular conjectural solution. It has been argued (Sec. 1.7) that the growth of knowledge is due to an evolutionary problem-solving process. Of course problem solving is not static, rather it is a continuing cycle consisting of the following stages: problem identification and definition, generation of alternative solutions, hypotheses, evaluation, choice, implementation, review of consequences and finally back to the beginning with a new problem definition. All of this happens in the context of a world view.

Thus, in summary, an emphasis on the control of future events rather than on a prediction of 'true' future scenarios does not imply a rejection of the scientific approach. It is merely that the whole process is seen in a new light. The issue related questions, the setting of objectives, the problem definition and the means by which the objectives are reached and the problems solved are therefore central. The way in which objectives are reached is the subject of quality assurance.

1.10 QUALITY ASSURANCE

'You cannot solve a problem until you know what the problem is. If you don't know where you're going then you'll never get there.' These are everyday maxims with which most people would agree but nevertheless many people seem to ignore.

One of the essentials of good management is the explicit setting of goals. For example, *The One Minute Manager*[13] sets out, with guidance for implementation, three simple principles for good management of people. They are effective goal setting, praising and reprimanding.

Quality is simply defined as the conformance to predetermined requirements.[13] Quality assurance (QA) is a means by which we try to ensure that we reach our goals. An essential goal of any business is to satisfy clients and to make profit. It ought to follow therefore that QA is good business. As safety is part of QA then it should follow that the proper management of safety is good business too.

So how do we recognize quality in a constructed project? If the requirements of each of the parties to a project are met then we have quality. The main concern of the client or owner is functional adequacy delivered on time and within budget. The main concerns of the designer are to have a well-defined brief, a fair contract with the client and a budget that enables proper staffing. The contractors require, among other things, good contract documents, timely decisions by the other parties to the project and a fair contract. The public and society at large require safety and other environmental considerations to be covered and they require conformance with the appropriate laws, regulations and other policies. These requirements are perhaps most likely to be met[14] when, at least:

1. There is open communication among all project partners.
2. The organizations and personnel for all phases of the work are appropriately qualified.
3. Lines of communication are well defined.
4. All members of the project teams have a serious interest in team performance.
5. Roles and responsibilities are well coordinated.
6. Conflicts are rapidly resolved.
7. There is an absence of litigation.

An essential requirement for QA will be that the procedures and practices adopted are appropriate for the problem at hand. If this is not the case then the system can become overly bureaucratic, inefficient and hence counterproductive. There is a risk of personal injury, damage to property, loss of resource (physical, human and financial), as well as legal liability so that errors can have serious consequences. These risks are managed through the quality of the work. The contracts deal with risk assumptions, risk avoidance and risk transfer mechanisms. These, together with limitations, indemnities, warranties and insurance, assign and dispose of inordinate risk. At the initial stages of a project when ideas are forming changes can be made to major design parameters for small cost. As the project develops and decisions are made which are consequential upon earlier decisions then there is less room for manoeuvre and changes can cost much more to implement. Thus it is extremely important for effective quality control to ensure that changes are considered at the appropriate stage of project development.

1.11 THE SCENE IS SET

In this chapter safety has been characterized as a problem for management. There is no single 'true' answer for any measure of the margin between the capacity of an engineered facility and the demands upon it. The uncertainties are deep rooted and intractable since there is always the chance that unintended consequences might occur. This, of course, should not be taken as an argument that advanced scientific treatments of safety, such as reliability theory, should be rejected—far from it. The argument is rather that the limitations (as with all theories) should be carefully documented so that the theories are used in appropriate circumstances. It is important to try to prevent significant misinterpretations of the results of theoretical calculations by engineers or lay people. Thus, for example, when a chance of failure of 1 in 1 million is theoretically calculated there is a great danger in interpreting that figure as a statistical measure.

We are now in a position to examine, in Part One of the book, the practical issues in more detail, particularly the role of design codes and of QA. In Part 2 we will interpret the theories of risk analysis and human factors as various aspects of a management problem. The way in which applications of these ideas are implemented in various industrial sectors are examined in Part Three and finally the whole topic of engineering safety is reviewed in Part Four.

REFERENCES

1. Magee, B.: *Popper*, Fontana Modern Masters, London, 1978.
2. Handy, C.: *The Age of Unreason*, Business Books, London, 1989.
3. National Economic Development Office: *Faster Building for Commerce*, London, 1988.
4. Fido A. T., and D. O. Wood: *Safety Management Systems*, Further Education Unit, London, 1989.
5. Avison, D. E., and G. Fitzgerald: *Information Systems and Development*, Blackwell Scientific, Oxford, 1988.
6. Popper, K. R.: *Conjectures and Refutations*, Routledge and Kegal Paul, London, 1976.
7. Hume, D.: *A Treatise on Human Nature*, Oxford University Press, Oxford, 1978.
8. Kuhn, T. S.: *The Structure of Scientific Revolutions*, University of Chicago Press, Chicago, Ill., 1962.
9. Stewart, I.: *Concepts of Modern Mathematics*, Penguin Books, London, 1975.
10. de Bono, E.: *Practical Thinking*, Penguin Books, London, 1976.
11. Searle, J.: *Minds, Brains and Science*, Harvard University Press, Cambridge, Mass., 1984.
12. Blockley, D. I.: *The Nature of Structural Design and Safety*, Ellis Horwood, Chichester, 1980.
13. Blanchard, K., and S. Johnson: *The One Minute Manager*, Fontana/Collins, London, 1983.
14. American Society of Civil Engineers: *Quality in the Constructed Project*, vol. 1, New York, 1988.

TWO

RISK ASSESSMENT

D. G. ELMS

2.1 INTRODUCTION

In an informal sense risk analysis has been used throughout the history of mankind. Risk is always associated with decision. Something has to be done; an action has to be taken. It might be trivial, as with crossing the street, or of great importance, as with siting and designing a major dam. In either case a choice has to be made as to what to do. The outcome is in the future, and is uncertain. Some outcomes will be better than others. Some might be good, some downright disastrous. A choice of possible actions must be made, and the choice means taking a risk. We assess the risks associated with each action and make the decision.

The process is mostly informal, using whatever information, experience and intuition is available. Much of the time this works well enough. However, there are also times when the risks are not well assessed and the resulting decisions are neither understandable nor rational. Particularly where there may be loss of life, this is not acceptable to a society demanding high levels of safety. Large commercial losses or damage to the environment must also be avoided. In such circumstances risks need to be better controlled.

There are two main strategies for controlling risk. One is to be more conservative in design to allow for uncertainties, which is, in other words, to assign more resources of money and materials to the engineering work. Indeed, engineers have many methods of tacitly controlling risk, such as the use of safety factors, permissible stresses or quality assurance. The second overall strategy is to put more effort into careful risk assessment, to maintain safety levels and reduce risk while refining designs and reducing costs. Both strategies are legitimate. The second has led to the development of methods for formal risk assessment.

Explicit techniques for risk assessment had their origins in the 1930s and 1940s. There were two main trends. One began in structural engineering and the other related to developments in operations research at the time.

In the structural field, the main early work was due to Pugsley,[1] based on a background in aircraft structures, and Freudenthal.[2,3] Significant contributions were also made by Wierzbicki, Baker, Torroja, Johnson, Shinozuka and others: Turkstra[4] gives a useful historical summary. The structural engineering thrust had a particular and idiosyncratic flavour for two reasons.

Firstly, structural engineering deals with risk problems in which the capacity of the system being analysed and the demand on it could be separated. Structurally, capacity and demand are represented by resistance and load.

Secondly, apart from major exceptions such as offshore platforms or aerospace structures, most structural engineering projects are relatively inexpensive and do not warrant the cost of individual risk assessment. As a result the greatest thrust in the development of risk analysis for structural engineering has been towards dealing with many structures at the same time by using risk analysis techniques to form better codes of practice. The requirements for code development are specialized and have given their own flavour to structural engineering risk assessment. The issues are interesting and important so will be explored in more detail later in the chapter.

Military and space requirements in the 1960s saw the development of a different approach deriving from earlier operations research work (for example, by Von Neumann[5]). The aerospace and electronics industries faced system reliability problems requiring assessment of the reliability of systems made up of many components, each with a known failure rate or reliability. The two groups followed somewhat different paths in that fault tree methods (developed in 1961 by H. A. Watson at the Bell Telephone Laboratories) were used at an early stage by aerospace engineers,[6] while the electronic industry used equivalent alternative approaches for another decade before using fault trees.[7] At this stage risk analysis techniques became particularly important in assessing the risks associated with nuclear power plants.[8] The chemical and process industry also began to use formal risk assessment methods at this time as they were ideal for dealing with the safety problems of large and complex chemical plants.

At present risk assessment techniques are being used widely. The aerospace, electronic, nuclear and chemical industries employ them, as indicated above. Structural engineering has mainly used risk assessment in the development of codes, but there are also major applications to individual structures such as offshore platforms. Other uses occur in the assessment of dam safety, urban planning, fire engineering and transportation engineering. A growing area is the use of risk assessment in dealing with environmental risk: many projects must complete a formal environmental risk assessment before permission to proceed can be given.

To carry out an adequate risk assessment is more difficult than it looks. This is not so much because the analytic techniques used are formidable— they are usually easier than they look—but rather because the conceptual issues involved are often hard to understand and deal with. It is easy to get answers, but to get good ones needs care, experience and an appropriately wary attitude. The rest of the chapter considers such issues, dividing them into questions of philosophy and of methodology, that is, into underlying ideas and more immediate questions of strategy.

We will start by looking in detail at the nature of risk.

2.2 RISK

The Nature of Risk

Risk is a curious and complex concept. In a sense it is unreal in that it is always concerned with the future, with possibilities, with what has not yet happened. If there is certainty there is no risk. There is a fairy-tale sense to it—the ungraspability of something that can never exist in the present but only in the future. Thus risk is a thing of the mind, intimately linked to personal or collective psychology even though as engineers we often try to give it the trappings of objectivity.

Another reason for its strangeness is that risk is a composite idea. It brings together three separate aspects: likelihood (or chance), consequences and context. All three contribute to any assessment or quantification of risk.

To illustrate the three aspects, consider this example. Suppose I want to cross a stream over a slippery log. There is a reasonably high chance I would fall off. If the stream were a trickle a few centimetres below the log, the consequences would be trivial so the risk would be small. If the stream were a raging torrent in a gorge a great way below, it would be a different matter: crossing would be a high risk which I probably would not accept. The likelihoods of falling would be the same in both instances, but the different consequences would produce very dissimilar levels of risk as far as I was concerned. On the other hand, if I wanted to cross the same gorge over a bridge, the chance of falling would be low and once again the risk would be small.

The third factor in risk is the context. This is often a question of who is assessing the risk for whom and in what circumstances; or it could concern the payoff—what it is hoped to gain. To continue the example, though I thought the risk of crossing the log over the deep gorge was unacceptably high if I had to do it myself, my assessment might be consideraby lower if it were you who had to cross. I might also fiercely dispute any assessment made by you of the risk I myself would face if I had to do the crossing.

A significant difficulty in working with risk is that the word 'risk' is often given a negative overtone—that risk is in some sense a bad thing. This is unfortunate as it could just as readily be given a positive connotation, for we do not voluntarily take on a risk without expecting some benefit we would otherwise be without. The benefit might flow directly from something achieved, but the benefits of accepting risk could as easily be indirect. Excessive safety, for instance, inevitably means that some of the finite fund of resources available to a society have been withheld from other uses. Health, welfare, education, functional efficiency and aesthetics must all compete with safety for a share of the overall resources. It could even be argued that to invest too much in safety, and to design buildings, as it were, with gold-plated reinforcing bars, would be morally wrong. A corollary that follows could be that if no failures occur, ever, engineers are not doing their jobs properly. We accept risk in order to achieve something, and so it is an indicator of progress and improvement.

As risk is an elusive and easily misunderstood idea, it must be discussed more deeply. To begin with, we shall look in more detail at the three components of risk: chance, consequences and context. We will start by considering chance in its specific and formal usage: probability.

Probability and Its Nature

Probability has had a long history.[9] In a sense the history has been a development of understanding. It has involved the interplay of philosophers, mathematicians and practitioners—the first to get the ideas right, the second to ensure a rigorous framework and the last to relate it all to reality and practical usefulness. Perhaps the best discussion is a succinct article by Good.[10]

Various definitions of probability are used. I shall categorize them into three: structural, frequentist and subjective. The first, structural probability, derives from the structure of the problem, from its logical or physical characteristics. The nature of a die, for instance, is to have six identical faces, so that the probability of a six being thrown is $1/6$; or, given that five men and three women are candidates for a prize, the probability of a woman winning it, in the absence of other information, must be $3/8$. No measurements have to be made for this kind of probability, and there is no subjectivity present. The result derives from the nature of the problem itself, from its structure. The underlying model has a specific and causal connection between its parts. Note, though, that this type of probability is ideal, and may not be a true estimate of likelihood: the die might be loaded, and this could only be checked by experiment, by making a large number of trials and assessing the frequencies of the outcomes.

For this reason there are those who say that the only legitimate definition of probability is frequentist; that is that probability is a limit deriving from observation of long runs of identical events. Given the number of cars passing a given point, for instance, and observing the number of accidents occurring over a substantial time, the annual frequency of accidents could be estimated which could be expressed as the probability of an individual car having an accident. However, here, too, there are difficulties. In practical terms, it is usually hard to ensure that the observations are taken under identical conditions over a long period of time. In the traffic accident situation, the traffic density might change seasonally and over the years. In any case it is often not easy to know how many observations to take, to know how long is long enough, especially where the accidents are relatively infrequent. The real problem with a pure frequentist view is that no underlying model is assumed, no causal connection between variables. In practice, though, simple observations are not enough: hypotheses and assumptions must be made as to the nature of the model being assumed for the situation being tested. These assumptions are, unfortunately, sometimes hidden.

A more important limitation is that there are many engineering situations in which we need to use probabilities and assess risk, but where it is not possible to have repeatable observations. An engineer might want to estimate the probability of an older highway bridge collapsing in an earthquake within the next ten years. It is both possible and legitimate to make such an estimate, but there can be no question of obtaining a frequency-based probability. This is not to say that the engineer will make an estimate purely on the basis of subjective experience. There are many possible sources of contributing information: the seismicity of the area can be estimated, laboratory test results could be found on, say, the strength of unconfined concrete piers, the general standard of workmanship and repair of the bridge could be taken into account and so on. However, in the end, the engineer would have to combine all the relevant pieces of information and make an estimate, and in this sense it would be a subjective estimate of probability. The number would have to be consistent with the axiomatic definition of probability so that the normal probability theory mathematical operations could be applied (see, for example, Ang and Tang[11]), and it could be improved as an estimate in the light of new information using a Bayesian approach, but it would still contain an inevitable subjectivity.

I can see no way round it as the only appropriate kind of probability to be used, for its breadth of definition includes the other two. Neither would I wish there to be a more objective definition. Subjectivity is inevitable, so it is better for it to be overt and not hidden. In any case, subjectivity in the form of experience and intuition is central to the skill of a good engineer, though it must be well grounded in fact and reality.

Consequences

That part of risk we have called 'consequences' does not have the philo-sophical problems associated with probability. There are, however, many practical problems.

The consequences of an event must be measured in terms of a value system. The most straightforward value system is the binary measure of simple failure, where all that needs to be known is the probability of the event occuring. Either a building collapses, or it does not; or a train crashes, or a ferry is lost. This sort of risk problem is relatively straightforward. Even so there is often the difficulty that the theoretical model used for analysing the problem does not show such clear-cut behaviour. For instance, there is no obvious way in which a computer model of a ductile building will 'collapse' in an earthquake, and so an arbitrary definition of collapse has to be made to relate the model behaviour to the required reality.

More often risk will be concerned with more fundamental results such as loss of life, monetary loss or environmental damage. The consequences must then be expressed in terms of a specific value measure. A difficulty arises if more than one has to be taken into account in the same analysis. This can be done by arbitrarily assigning monetary value to life loss or environmental damage. Sometimes it is necessary to do so. However, in many cases it turns out that the different measures of risk will be used in separate contexts. This simplifies the problem in that the value measures can be kept separate. Even so, some things are not easy to quantify—injury, for instance, as opposed to loss of life. Either a life is lost or it is not, but an injury could be of many degrees. Similarly, though some environmental matters can be quantified, such as an increase of carbon dioxide emission or noise level, others are not so easily handled—a loss of aesthetic value, for instance, or the long-term effects of destroying a forest or polluting a watercourse. There is no simple answer to such problems, but method-ologically there is less difficulty if the risk analysis is carried out in two parts, the first dealing with the probability of a disaster happening and the second analysing the consequences should it occur.

There is also a problem in comparing long-term and immediate conse-quences. The results could be quite different depending on the choice of discounting factor. In any case there is the question of whose view should be taken into account. Many people put little weight on long-term threats and give greatest importance to immediate risks. People are notably reluctant to give up smoking: the consequences are well documented and grave, but they are not immediate. However, we are now straying into the third component of risk, its context.

Context

Every risk assessment has a context. Without it, it would not make sense.

Without fully understanding the context, a risk analysis would be bound to fail, or to be inadequate in some way. By 'context' I mean everything that is affected by the analysis of the risk situation, and which affects it. The context includes people; indeed, the people concerned are often its most important part.

The idea of context is related to that of 'world view', discussed in Chapter 1. Both are to do with setting the frame of reference of a problem, and they are similar in that though they are centrally important, they are easily overlooked from a conventional viewpoint.

Risk analysis is almost always required in a context of risk management. Risk management is concerned primarily with controlling risk. It is closely related to quality management in its approach. It seeks to balance risk against resources in some way so as to achieve the lowest overall risk for a given investment and to ensure that specific risks are bounded in that no single possibility of failure or disaster has a risk level greater than a specific maximum level. Whereas risk management provides the overall context, the immediate context of a risk analysis is usually related to decisions that have to be made. Thus risk analysis can properly be seen as one part of a decision-making process. As a part of risk management, the goals and aims of what is being done are very important and in fact they can be said to drive the whole process. However, we are here getting close to questions of methodology rather than the overall ideas which are being discussed at this point.

The second though not independent part of the context of risk analysis is the people, the actors concerned. There are many of these. Clients, users, the public, people immediately affected, groups such as firms, local authorities or interest groups, and those commissioning or carrying out the analysis, all are part of the context of risk analysis and have to be considered. Many will have different goals and points of view. Some will perceive the same situation to have a very different risk. As it can be said that risk only makes sense insofar as it is perceived by someone, we should be aware of the different sorts of perception, which we could call different types of risk. This turns out to be an important point in communication, as people may be using quite different definitions of risk. We will look at the matter shortly as a separate section. Before that, though, note that very often, in fact more often than not, a risk analysis is carried out in a political context, using 'political' in a broad sense.

The context of a risk analysis gives bounds, reasons, purpose and interactions. Whatever is being done must be congruent with the context and take account of it in all its relevant detail, otherwise the whole analysis is likely to prove irrelevant and useless.

Kinds of Risk

A number of different types of risk can be distinguished.[12] We will consider four: individually perceived risk, collectively perceived risk, calculated risk and 'real risk'. The last is put in inverted commas because there is some question as to whether it is a legitimate concept. There is also the question of whether an 'acceptable risk' can be set as a standard by, say, some national authority, the difficulty being to distinguish to which kind of risk it refers.

Perceived risk is the risk that one thinks is the case. It might be personal risk to oneself, as with the possibility of personal injury, or the risk to other people or things. Risk is after all the chance of adverse happenings. Though it could be injury and loss of life, it could also be property damage or loss, financial loss, as with an investment going awry, or environmental damage. The essential point here is to ask whose perception it is and why the risk is being perceived.

These questions of who and why are crucial. 'Who' are those likely to suffer risk. 'Why' refers to the reasons why risk needs to be considered, which is almost always in the context of decisions that have to be made. The importance of perceived risk is that the perceivers, even if they do not make the primary decisions, are likely to affect the decisions through the political process.

The perception of risk associated with a particular situation depends on a number of factors over and above objective or intersubjective considerations. Some of them are as follows:

- Voluntary/involuntary nature of risk
- Familiarity with the situation
- Number of people involved
- Manner of death
- Cultural context
- Personal context
- Nature of communication
- Long-term versus short-term exposure
- Immediacy of consequences

To discuss them briefly, first, there is the degree to which the risk is voluntary. People object to having a risk thrust upon them even though they would be happy to take the same level of risk voluntarily, demanding, for instance, much higher safety standards in public transport than for their own cars. Part of the reason for this is the belief that if one is in control, the risk can be avoided by one's own skill.

Familiarity tends to reduce perceived risk which is why so many of the accidents in a machine shop, say, occur to the most experienced operators.

As to the number of people involved, the public reacts more strongly to a disaster in which many lose their lives than to the same number of lives lost individually, in road accidents for instance. This may be partly a result of the influence of the news media in their reporting of incidents.

There is generally a stronger adverse reaction to some sorts of death than to others. Death by fire is seen as more horrifying than death in a road accident, and death as a result of a nuclear incident is even worse.

The cultural context in which a risk situation exists affects its perception. Historically, for instance, the West has come to view death as far more significant than it did 50 years ago. Religious and metaphysical beliefs have a strong influence on the perceived importance of life.

Perceived risk is very much affected by personal context—whether it is one's own or someone else's risk, for example, or the magnitude of one's need to achieve some goal. If the need is great, then the risk often seems to diminish.

The way in which information about risk is received strongly affects its perception. Media coverage emphasizing the dangers and drawbacks of a project would affect one's understanding of risk, especially if it were conveyed in emotional terms. Likewise an overenthusiastic description of the advantages of a project could conceal its dangers and lead to an underestimation of risk.

Long-term exposure to a hazard is seen as much more serious than short-term exposure. To live near a chemical or nuclear plant is more a cause for concern than the more transient risks of, say, car travel, as the risk has to be lived with all the time and there is no way to get away from it, either for oneself or for one's family.

Finally there is the matter of the immediacy of results. It is highly hazardous to smoke. However, many smokers are prepared to accept the risk as the consequences are not immediate but are likely to show themselves in the distant future. The future problems are discounted compared, in this case, with the immediate pleasures.

Besides individually perceived risk, there is also collective perception. An interesting question here is whether there is still a direct connection with decision making. Probably there is, as it is now the social group that is faced with the need to make the change or not. Perhaps the group is also threatened by change. It is not that everyone in the group sees risk in the same way or even as having the same severity. Individuals still make the decisions. However, in a way the whole thing is best seen in the light of the decision-making processes of the group. This is a political matter. There has to be broad agreement as to values and directions within the group. It is a question of normative values, to some extent, as it concerns the trust the group has through its various processes in the decision-making ability of selected members.

What is particularly interesting is the way in which ideas of risk are communicated within a group, so that there is some consensus of perception. Such a perception is not necessarily either reasonable or rational.

'Calculated risk' is the risk level obtained by the use of a quantitative risk assessment procedure. It is likely to be a calculated probability multiplied by an assessed or defined consequence. It is produced by constructing a numerical model with its attendant approximations and assumptions. The model will use data which are bound to be less than perfect. The quality of the model and the quality of the data combine to produce a result whose quality cannot be greater than that of either model or data. Almost certainly the result will show a lower risk than reality, for one of the major effects of the analysis model is either to leave out important aspects of the problem or not to take them fully into account. For instance, human error or a large number of individually highly unlikely system failure possibilities may have been omitted. The underestimation is often severe. For example, for major bridge failures, typical calculated failure probabilities are of the order of 10^{-6} per year, while Brown[13] estimated the actual failure rate as 10^{-2} to 10^{-3}, which is several orders of magnitude larger. For this reason, observed and calculated risks should never be compared directly without assessing the basis of the figures with great care.

Let us now turn to the idea of real risk, or 'true risk' as it could also be called. It is a controversial idea. Some believe it is a reasonable and useful idea. Others deny its existence and feel its use is confusing and misleading. It really depends on one's basic outlook when tackling problems. The assumption underlying the concept of real risk is that if only all the relevant information were known about probabilities and consequences, then the risk so calculated would be the real risk, with the perceived or calculated risk, which is what we would actually know, being a modification of the real risk; the difference is due to a lack of information, poor models or wrong information (such as inaccurate or misleading news reports). This point of view rests on several further assumptions. Firstly, the system must be stable in time, as otherwise essentially statistical information cannot be gathered. Secondly, the information must be measurable and records must be available. Finally, the time-scale of the occurrence of information must be such that it could be collected. In the case of earthquakes, for instance, the incidence of major events is infrequent so that the data we have are necessarily poor. On the other hand, traffic accidents are sufficiently frequent to allow the possibility of collecting good data. The real risk of traffic accidents could thus be thought of as an asymptote attainable with sufficient data gathering, while for earthquakes, the idea of a real risk seems almost to depend on a metaphysical assumption of a divine being (or totally objective omniscient engineer) outside the system who would know the information which we ourselves could not possibly obtain. There is therefore a major objection to the use of 'real risk', and it could be seriously misleading. Nevertheless, when thought of as an unattainable asymptote, it could have some usefulness.

There is also the question of whether it is possible or desirable for a regulatory authority to define a level of acceptable risk as a guideline for design. In a sense, modern structural codes adopt this approach in specifying a target risk level for their codes. Indeed, as a zero risk is impossible, there is much to be said for specifying an acceptable maximum or a target guideline (the two are somewhat different: a maximum level of risk might be required for a single facility or system, whereas a target is an average to be attained over many structures built to the same code requirements). Nevertheless, there are problems associated with setting an allowable risk level. First of all, it must necessarily be arbitrary, though work has been done to try to estimate the level that seems to be accepted by society as a whole by, for instance, looking at the levels of traffic risk at which major investment of resources seems to be needed to reduce the accident rate. This type of approach could be a good rough guide. However, a level obtained by observation could not be used directly as a standard for calculated risk, because of the incommensurability between calculated and observed risk mentioned earlier. Any standard of acceptable risk should presumably reflect the wishes of society. An immediate problem is, whose wishes? This raises difficult moral and social questions. Then again, people do not necessarily regard different types of hazard as having the same severity—deaths by traffic accident, by fire or by nuclear incident would be viewed differently and in increasing order of gravity. The magnitude of an accident is also a factor, as people are more averse to large disasters than to the same number of people killed in a large number of small incidents. To deal with this latter problem, some attempts have been made to specify acceptable risk limits as lines on a frequency/magnitude ($F-N$) diagram. An $F-N$ curve is a cumulative plot of the magnitude of disaster events, measured in terms of lives lost against frequency. The Netherlands Ministry of the Environment, for instance, specifies an upper limit of acceptable risk as $FN^2 = 10^{-2}$ and a lower limit of $FN^2 = 10^{-3}$.

Generally, *some* standard would be helpful. Indeed, it would be necessary, for how else would an engineer know how safe to build and how much resource to spend on safety. In any case, in an era of litigation, engineers and contractors need standards for their protection. There is otherwise a risk that extreme and expensive conservatism will prevail, which cannot be good for any community. Nevertheless, for reasons given above, any standards of acceptable risk must be both specified and used with care.

Ways of Specifying Risk

The way in which risk is specified is important, both for communicating it to others and also for thinking about it oneself. It is helpful to classify risk into two main types: risk to human life, and all other kinds, such as economic risk or environmental risk.

There are various ways of describing risk to human life, and all of them have their place. We will look at three, though note that we are considerably simplifying the issue.

Firstly, there is individual risk, the risk to an individual person who might be affected. This could be expressed as lives lost per 10 000 per year, though sometimes it is transformed to a reduction in life span by so many days. One source has given the annual risk of death per 10 000 as 3.3 for coal mining and 12 for flying as aircrew. These measures show the general level of risk of an activity or situation.

As a measure of the riskiness of a particular activity to an individual, the *fatal accident rate* (FAR), sometimes also known as the *fatal accident frequency rate* (FAFR), is used. This is defined as the number of deaths per hour of exposure divided by the number of people at risk multiplied by 10^8. The FAR is intended as an instantaneous measure, just as, say, miles per hour is a measure of velocity. It will differ throughout the day for an individual, depending on the activity. For example, FAR values for sleeping, eating, driving a car or riding a motorcycle are 1, 2.5, 57 and 660 respectively. For work in the chemical industry the FAR value is about 5 and in the construction industry about 67. A locomotive engineer has an FAR of about 13 while driving.

However, society is even more concerned with preventing major disasters than it is with providing safety for individuals. A risk measure reflecting this is the societal risk graph or $F-N$ curve, introduced briefly in the previous section. An example is given in Fig. 11.2.

Economic risk can be handled using cost–benefit analysis and expected (i.e. average) values of risk, though the quantification of costs and benefits is often difficult. However, this approach cannot easily be applied to questions of safety and loss of life because of the moral issues involved, even though a weighing of costs and benefits must be implicit in any risk situation. A limiting risk approach is better for safety issues. It is often more appropriate for environmental risk as well.

2.3 RISK ANALYSIS

Introduction

We now turn away from general ideas to detailed comments on risk assessment. However, we are faced with the immediate problem that the applications of risk assessment are wide ranging, with different objectives, terminologies and technical demands. The nature of a quantified risk assessment for a petrochemical plant would be different from that for many environmental risk assessments and very different from the risk analysis involved in the development of a structural design code. Therefore, as this chapter must cover all risk assessment, it is not possible to give a detailed list of specific tasks; in any case, specific applications are dealt with later in the book. Instead, I shall discuss fundamental factors that all risk assessments seem to have in common.

Common Elements of Risk Assessment

There are four underlying ideas common to all risk assessments that need to be discussed in detail. They are:

1. There is a need for tight discipline.
2. The development of a risk assessment is cyclical.
3. The process is a team effort.
4. There are a number of tasks common to most assessments.

The need for tight discipline Naturally, all engineering tasks need to be approached with disciplined thinking. Woolly thinking produces woolly results. Nevertheless, a tight and consistent methodological approach seems particularly necessary for risk assessment problems. It needs to be stressed at all levels. A major reason for the importance of discipline seems to be that 'risk' is a complex and sophisticated concept. It thus needs a high degree of attention to its meaning and appropriate usage, which is the reason for the emphasis on its philosophical underpinnings earlier in the chapter. At the overall level, a systems approach is needed; that is a clear overview must be kept in focus while at the same time paying attention to detail. There is an implication here that it is important to get the complete system defined and understood. A tightly disciplined approach is also needed at the detailed level, where in a sense the analyst is playing a game with the problem in hand according to a set of rules. The rules are flexible and can be adapted to the task in hand, but, once set, they should be accepted rigorously. Here again the 'game' is more complex than most engineering activities, thus requiring increased attention to consistency.

The development of a risk assessment is cyclical The idea of risk assessment as a game leads on to the fact that the activity is not linear, but moves back and forth as the game proceeds. An alternative metaphor suggested by Donald Schon in *The Reflective Practitioner*[14] is that a conversation develops between the engineer and the problem. The point is that in practice the development of a risk assessment, particularly a quantitative risk assessment, does not progress linearly, but in a series of cycles or iterations as understanding grows. There are two implications: that the iterative process must be taken into account when planning a risk assessment and that different tasks interweave and run in parallel rather than following a logical and clearly defined progression.

The process is a team effort A risk analysis usually requires input from a number of people with different expertise. Clarity of communication and good management are therefore important.

There are a number of common tasks As mentioned above, we cannot give a detailed list of things to be done that apply to all types of risk assessment. Nevertheless, if we stay at a sufficient level of generality we can identify a number of common components or tasks. To do so is consistent with the aim of the chapter, which is to give a general understanding of risk assessment rather than a recipe for doing it.

Calculating Risk

Let us assume that someone, a client, wants to commission a risk assessment, perhaps to determine the safety level of a proposed facility or operation, or at any rate to obtain an estimate of the risk involved in an intended action. The tasks that must be done are to:

1. Establish the purpose
2. Learn about the problem
3. Decide on the scale
4. Develop risk models
5. Obtain the data
6. Do the risk assessment
7. Communicate the results

Note that although the points are presented as a list, they would not necessarily be carried out in that order. The procedure would normally be iterative, with insights gained feeding back into the system. Often a major function of a risk analysis is that it is a powerful learning process.

We shall now discuss the different tasks in detail.

Establishing the purpose The first step must always be to establish the aim of the project and what the results will be used for. A clear understanding of the purpose is essential and drives the project at every level. Often the client is not fully clear about the purpose. The real reason for wanting an analysis may be hidden. It might, for instance, be political. This would be a legitimate enough reason, but it must be understood overtly by both client and analyst. The client may also have in mind several reasons for wanting a risk assessment. This is always difficult as separate needs are not always reconcilable. Dissimilar requirements might need different levels of quality in the results, different models or different means of quantifying the results. In such cases priorities need to be established with the client. The danger here is the obvious one that vague or conflicting requirements will lead to vague results which will satisfy no single specific need.

Learning about the problem One of the main tasks in any risk analysis is to learn about the problem. Partly it requires the analyst to find out about the process that is being analysed—about, for instance, the operation of a plant, the ways in which a structure could fail or the nature of a rail transport network. There is more to it than that, though. It is also necessary to understand the context of the problem and its constraints, and, in particular, what could go wrong.

Some people seem to be able to learn about a complex engineering problem quickly and reliably, and to be able to pick out its essence in a relatively short time. Others find it difficult. From this it can be assumed that there is a specific skill involved, which is itself learnable. Without wishing to expand on the matter, as the subject is extensive, there are certain tricks that can help, such as asking the right key questions, using a consistent grammatical structure for descriptions or following through in detail what is processed by a system to see what happens.

The first task in learning about the system is to discover the essential nature of the problem, initially in general terms but eventually in getting to the essence of things—to what the problem is about. This has to be considered in some depth, and it is emphasized here as it is not an obvious thing to do for many people, for whom the surface appearance of a problem is sufficient.

A particular and important aspect of this is to explore the hazards and identify what can go wrong. Hazard identification has been systematized in some areas of application, earning sometimes unfortunate acronyms such as Hazops (hazard and operations studies) or Hazan.

The next task is to identify the type of problem. Risk problems can be categorized into different types, needing different approaches. A useful classification divides them into capacity/demand and system problems. In the first, the demands applied to a system can be separated from its capacity to withstand them. Structural problems are usually like this. Wind, gravity and other loads present the demand, and the structure has a certain capacity to resist them. The two are independent, though each can be made up of many parts. The components of a structure contributing to its capacity, for instance, can be very many, interacting in complex ways.

In contrast, system risk problems consist of systems with many components, each of whose individual reliabilities can be estimated and whose joint effect on the reliability of the whole system depends on the nature of their interaction and the way in which they are put together to form the whole system. Examples are electronic circuits, complex mechanical systems and chemical processing plants. Risk assessments of *localized* systems (such as a petrochemical plant) need significantly different approaches from those for *distributed* systems (such as a rail transport network).

A further categorization of risk problems is into qualitative and quantitative (or probabilistic) risk analyses (the latter called QRAs or PRAs). Even though risk analysis is normally thought of in quantitative terms, qualitative studies in which various items have their risks ranked rather than quantified can be valuable, and are often more appropriate than quantitative analyses, especially where data are sparse and poor, as with some environmental problems. Such an approach will often use the same logic as a quantitative analysis and would require the same rigour of thought.

Important constraints on a risk assessment are time and money: when it has to be completed and how much it would cost. The feasibility of being able to stay within these constraints is related to the scale of the study, which is discussed later .

A risk assessment often needs analysis models. These are concerned with modelling the reality of the systems being assessed. For example, to estimate the risk faced by a building structure, the building must be idealized. It might be enough to use a simple model where the risk of failure is only calculated for a single beam or column. However, for some situations that would not be enough, and a more complex model would be needed that dealt with multiple modes of failure and the behaviour of the building as a whole. The choice of analysis models depends on the purpose of the exercise and what is required of it.

An important aspect of an analysis model is that it must be associated with an event definition for use in a risk analysis. Again using structural risk as an example, a failure event has to be defined at which some limit state is transcended. Sometimes this is obvious, as when an actual fracture occurs, but more often there is an arbitrary aspect to the choice of a failure event so that it must be defined with some care: failure of a structure in an earthquake, for example, might have to be defined as exceeding a limiting deflection, which would have to be the equivalent in an analysis model of collapse in reality.

Finally, there is the important question of learning about the actors, the people who are going to be involved in the risk assessment or be affected by it. There are those primarily needing the results, who are perhaps commissioning the assessment, and those who are secondarily involved. The latter group includes politicians, pressure groups and the public. All have to be borne in mind. There have been many cases where a project has had to be aborted, sometimes expensively, because some of the potential actors were neglected or because the results of risk studies were communicated in an inappropriate way incompatible with the ability of the general public to understand them. Thus a risk assessment must be aimed correctly at an early stage.

Deciding the scale A major risk assessment is expensive. It is an exercise that should not be entered into lightly. In fact, it is almost worth while making a general rule that no major analysis should be carried out without first doing a scoping study and a pilot study. It is analogous to commissioning sketch plans for a building before deciding to proceed to working drawings. However, there is a difference: it could well be found that a scoping study or pilot study has provided sufficient information and a full-scale risk assessment is no longer required.

The basic reasons for a scoping or a pilot study are to establish the nature of the problem. The scoping study has a role in determining the nature and quality of the data available and discovering the extent of the problem as a whole. A pilot study is useful for checking out the methodology of the study and seeing whether the data are adequate and the results appropriate. It is important to understand the difference between the two: essentially, a scoping study is a shallow pass over the whole problem, while a pilot study is a full-depth investigation of a small part of it.

At whichever level the study is carried out, once the scale has been set the rest of the study must be consistent with it. The appropriate scale is really determined by being consistent with:

1. The objective of the analysis
2. Data availability
3. The quality of the quantitative models used and
4. Constraints such as time or money

Developing risk models Risk models produce quantified risk estimates. Firstly, there is the question of the most appropriate model type. The two most frequently used approaches for producing probabilities of failure are fault tree and event tree models, though there are others. There are advantages and disadvantages to both, though there is insufficient space to discuss them fully at this stage. Often, it makes sense to combine the two by, for instance, using fault trees to obtain probabilities of failure and then analysing the consequences with event trees.

Once the overall model type is established, the next step is to develop its structure. This needs careful definition of the events in a tree and decisions on the appropriate levels of detail and disaggregation of the problem. The event definition is the more important in that the whole risk assessment is vulnerable to errors. A helpful approach is to try to state every event in the consistent grammatical form of something happening: 'switch fails', 'abutment collapses' and so on. This might seem simple, but in fact it is a surprisingly powerful tool for ensuring a model is internally self-consistent.

When in doubt, it is better to make a model more rather than less detailed. Assuming that as part of the risk assessment process a sensitivity analysis will take place, which is particularly easy with fault tree models as they tend to be transparent, then considerations of sensitivity will soon point up aspects of the model that are in too much detail.

Sensitivity of the results to input data is usually important in making risk management decisions—how best to reduce risk, for instance, or how to balance investments to produce the minimum risk.

Obtaining data The data needed for the analysis must be reviewed at an early stage in setting up the project, because if the required data do not exist or take too long to obtain, the proposed model and its degree of detail must be reconsidered. It is not a simple question, as data can be obtained in different forms with different degrees of quality. Some might be hard data, to do with the structure of the system (the company, for instance, has 16 aircraft), they might be statistical (there are 23 flights a day, on average) or they might be anecdotal (the track is blocked on average once every two months). Data should be corroborated wherever possible, particularly where they are doubtful. Questions of possible dependence (in a probabilistic sense) are important and must be resolved. Sometimes, probability information can only be obtained using a separate analysis.

There is in fact a considerable art in getting the most out of data that are often sparse or of low quality. This is where a systems approach is useful, as the mass of data should be seen as a unified whole with the model rather than as a linear string of independent items. Data can often be bounded or checked with reference to the pattern of the whole. Where this happens, the least reliable data items can have their reliability improved, and surprisingly good results can be obtained from unpromising beginnings.

Doing the assessment It would seem trivial to run through the analysis once the quantitative model has been set up and the data acquired and in place, but rather more than that is in fact required. It is never a question of setting up the model and then running it. As development is iterative, the model grows and develops from its first rough beginnings. Firstly, it must be established that it works correctly. A necessary, though not sufficient, check on this is that all the results should make sense both with regard to expectations and with respect to each other. Corroboration and confirmation are needed wherever possible. Then, almost certainly, a sensitivity analysis is required to discover what parameters contribute most to the results. Items of poor-quality data can be dealt with by using bounds or distributions on them, which will give distributions for the results. For large models this is essentially a Monte Carlo exercise. Above all, there must be a component of play when the model is used to learn more about the system.

Communicating results The final task in a risk assessment is to communicate the results. This must be done carefully, as they can easily be misinterpreted. Several points need to be considered.

Firstly, there is the question of the most appropriate way to convey a quantified risk estimate. For risk estimates involving loss of life this was discussed above.

The actors involved must all be taken into account, just as when carrying out the initial planning of the risk assessment. This could mean communicating the results in different ways to different groups of people. Communication is often more helpful during the course of a project than when left to the end, especially if there is likely to be interaction between the analyst and the people affected by the project. In any case, there will be a need for communication throughout the project with various people because of the iterative nature of the risk assessment as discussed above.

2.4 SUMMARY

The chapter has given an overview of risk assessment, concentrating on common features, on context and on conceptual foundations. Detailed applications and techniques are covered in later chapters. As risk assessment cannot stand alone without a context of use, the next steps in the story are also covered in chapters dealing with risk control and risk management. Finally, though quantitative risk assessment is a powerful tool, it has significant limitations, discussed in Chapter 19, which must be well understood before using it in practice.

REFERENCES

1. Pugsley, A. G.: Concepts of Safety in Structural Engineering, *J. Inst. Civ. Engrs*, vol. 36, no. 5, pp. 5–51, 1951.
2. Freudenthal, A. M.: The Safety of Structures, *Trans. ASCE*, vol. 112, p. 125, 1947.
3. Freudenthal, A. M.: Safety and the Probability of Structural Failure, *Trans. ASCE*, vol. 121, pp. 1337–1397, 1956.
4. Turkstra, C. J.: *Theory of Structural Design Decisions*, Solid Mechanics Division Study no. 2, University of Waterloo, Waterloo, Ont., Canada, 1970.
5. Von Neumann, J.: Probabilistic Logics and the Synthesis of Reliable Organisms from Unreliable Components, *Automata Studies*, Annals of Mathematics Studies no. 34, Princeton University Press, Princeton, NJ, pp. 43–48, 1956.
6. Mearns, A. B.: Fault Tree Analysis—The Study of Unlikely Events in Complex Systems, *Systems Safety Symposium*, sponsored by the University of Washington and the Boeing Company, Seattle, Wash., June 1965.
7. Fussell, J. B., G. J. Powers, and R. G. Bennetts: Fault Trees—A State of the Art Discussion, *IEEE Trans. on Reliability*, vol. R-23, no. 1, pp. 51–55, 1974.
8. United States Nuclear Regulatory Commission: *Reactor Safety Study (USNRC, WASH 1400)*, USNRC, Washington, 1975.
9. Maistrov, L. E.: *Probability Theory, A Historical Sketch*, trans. by S. Kotz, Academic Press, New York, 1974.
10. Good, I. J.: Kinds of Probability, *Science*, vol. 129, no. 3347, pp. 443–447, 1959.
11. Ang, A., H.-S., and W. H. Tang: *Probability Concepts in Engineering Planning and Design*, vol. 1, *Basic Principles*, Wiley, New York, 1975.
12. Royal Society: *Risk Assessment—Report of a Royal Society Study Group*, Royal Society, London, 1983.
13. Brown, C. B.: A Fuzzy Safety Measure, *J. Engng. Mech. Div., Proc. ASCE*, vol. 105, no. EM5, pp. 855–872, 1979.
14. Schon, D. A.: *The Reflective Practitioner*, Temple Smith, London, 1983.

THREE

DESIGN CODES

T. V. GALAMBOS

3.1 INTRODUCTION

Structures must be 'safe' and 'serviceable'. A building, for example, must possess a 'structure' which provides strength and stiffness so that the system can perform the duties for which it was destined.

By 'safety' we mean that the artefact, be it a building, a bridge or an aeroplane, will not break of fail during its intended life in any manner that would kill or harm its users or cause them severe economic loss. The term 'serviceability' covers the requirement that the occupants of the structure will not suffer discomfort or economic loss due to the everyday forces and demands to which the structure is subjected. Safety and serviceability can be easily achieved if there is no consideration of the economic cost. The pyramids are an example of such engineering. However, a well-designed structure should be just safe, just serviceable and be optimal in cost. Complete adherence to this optimality principle is seldom possible in practice. However, safety must always take precedence.

Structural design is the art and science of creating a satisfactory structure. In antiquity and up to perhaps the beginning of the nineteenth century the component of art and experience were predominant. Modern structural design practice rests squarely on both experience and scientific prediction. Even if veteran design professionals rely strongly on experience and intuition, society demands eventually a documented scientific justification for the final product.

While it is easy to agree in principle that every structure should be safe, serviceable and economical, it is indeed very difficult to get engineers, owners and occupants to come to terms with the specific definitions and criteria to which designs must conform.

Throughout most of recorded human history the builder or his guild decided on the criteria for a satisfactory design. The builder's practical experience and his word that the structure was safe assured the people who commissioned the work. Most of the time they were right. If the structure failed, then the builder paid the price: jail or the gallows. As industrialization spread throughout the world in the nineteenth century the old way of doing business no longer worked. Who was to blame for all the boilers that blew up on the Mississippi steam boats? Who should be hanged for the collapse of the many railroad bridges that fell down in the 1890s? Technology was too complex and responsibility was too diffused, and more structured methods were needed to protect society. No matter how reliable the consulting engineer, nor how learned the professor, it did not matter. Two designs by two different designers should obey the same criteria of proportioning. Out of this desire for an ordered and safe building environment came the emergence of design codes around the turn of the twentieth century. For about the past hundred years structural design has been regulated in a more-or-less uniform and legal manner. This chapter is a description of the purpose, the philosophy, the format and the structure of design codes. Particular emphasis will be placed on the relationship between the codes and the safety of structures.

3.2 THE FUNCTION OF DESIGN CODES

The Design Code Is a Standard

The function of a design code is to regulate design so that the resulting artefact is safe, serviceable and economical. It also ensures uniformity of all designs for a certain type of structure. This is a simplistic statement of a very complex organism, as we shall see in the ensuing discussion.

The name 'design code' is only one of several popular designations. Other nomenclatures are 'design standard', 'design specification' or the term 'norm', which is used with German or French codes. The most unambiguous names in the English language are 'design codes' and 'design standards'. The word 'specification' has many other connotations. Particularly close is its use in describing parts of construction contract documents, and so it should be used with caution when describing design codes.

A design code, then, is a common standard against which all structures of the same type are to be measured. By this very definition the code must be a 'minimum' standard. The actual design may have members that are stronger and stiffer than those required by the code, but weaker or less flexible elements are not acceptable.

The Role of the Design Code in the Design Process

The structural design process may be characterized by the following steps:

1. General planning of the structure type
2. Preliminary design of feasible alternatives
3. Selection of loads
4. Analysis of the alternates to determine overall deformation and stability, and internal forces
5. Checking the preliminary design against the applicable design code
6. Repeated modification, reanalysis and code checking until a satisfactory design is achieved.

In this process the code plays the role of a controller to assure that all structures in that particular population of buildings obey the same minimum standards. The creative job of the engineer is in planning, load definition, preliminary design and structural analysis. Code checking is a necessary drudgery. However, it provides assurance to the responsible building official that there is compliance with the design code and so the designer is therefore safe from blame should anything go wrong which has been covered by the code. Code conformance is equated with structural safety in the minds of the engineer, the government and the public. In actuality this is not quite true. In reality, conformance to the code assures society that there is only a very small but acceptable chance that a structural malfunction can occur.

The Nature of Design Codes

Design codes are not entirely primary design documents. Depending on the type of code, it may or may not define the loading that must be the basis for the code. For example, the American Institute of Steel Construction (AISC) code for steel buildings[1] refers the designer to the American National Standards Institute (ANSI) load code[2] or to the applicable local building code for the loads, while the standard of the American Association of State Highway and Transportation Officials (AASHTO) for highway bridge design[3] gives a complete definition of all loading cases that must be considered. All design codes with which this writer is acquainted refer back to materials standards (American Society for Testing Materials, ASTM, in the United States) and welding standards (American Welding Society, AWS), etc.

A design code is thus a document resting on other documents, or it is a document that is parallel to other standards which must also be considered.

Whether or not a design code is a legal document depends on many things. The name code implies that the user, either voluntarily or because of legal constraints, agrees to abide by it. The design code is actually not a legal document until it is adopted by a legally binding building code of the appropriate jurisdiction.

The practice in the United States may differ somewhat from the custom in other countries, but the process of code development is similar everywhere.

Development of Design Codes in the USA

Structural design codes in the United States are developed and maintained by voluntary associations representing a particular structural materials industry, e.g. the American Concrete Institute (ACI), the AISC, the American Iron and Steel Institute (AISI—it maintains the cold-formed steel codes), the Aluminum Association (AA), the American Institute of Timber Construction (AITC), etc., or a particular structure type, e.g. AASHTO for highway bridges, American Railroad Engineering Association (AREA), etc. Professional associations, such as the American Society of Civil Engineers (ASCE) and the American Society of Mechanical Engineers (ASME) also promulgate design standards. The writer believes that even though many such voluntary associations exist in all countries, they do not take such an independent role in design code development as in the United States. Their members are more apt to participate in the relevant government code writing bodies.

In the United States these voluntary associations each maintain a 'code committee' or 'specification committee' which actually develops and is ultimately responsible for the design code. Membership of these committees is voluntary and unpaid. The size and composition is carefully monitored to include an appropriate proportion of producers, fabricators, designers, researchers and owners. These committees develop and maintain the design code through meetings, sponsorship of research when needed, voluntary work by researchers in member organizations or universities, or by contract work. Even though the codes may change officially only every five or so years, the work proceeds continually so that each code is a living, changing, active organism.

Approval of the code by the membership of the code committee is strictly regulated by consensus rules. Votes are formally recorded and all negative votes must be resolved by discussion and compromise. A code, then, as it leaves the code committee is a document that all members of the committee have approved affirmatively. This is the case everywhere in the world. The basic scientific, technical and professional group responsible for the technological, scientific and mathematical soundness of the codes must unanimously support its creation, because once the document leaves the womb of its creators, it takes on its own life. This life is principally political.

In the United States the code is first approved by the predominantly non-technical boards or directorates of the particular voluntary organization. It is then approved for use by regional model building codes such as the Uniform Building Code, the Southern Building Code, Building Officials Congress of America, etc. These model building codes, or the building codes maintained by individual cities or other jurisdictions, are finally adopted by elected legislative bodies. Thus the design code becomes law and is mandatory for use in the design of structures in the particular legislative area, be that a city, a state or province, a country, a continent (as the EUROCODES will be) or the whole world (International Standards Organization, ISO).

Whatever the political ramifications and complications, and wherever in the world, whatever the interrelationships, for each design code there is initially a competent technical group that is beyond politics and conscientiously attempts to develop and maintain an up-to-date safe and economical design code. The members of this committee represent the best representatives of their respective technical fields.

To conclude this section on the function of design codes several quotes from codes about their own function and purpose will be cited:

From the AISC Specification[4] Preface:

> The AISC Specification for the Design, Fabrication and Erection of Structural Steel for Buildings has evolved through numerous versions from the 1st Edition, published June 1, 1923. Each succeeding edition has been based upon past successful usage, advances in the state of knowledge, and changes in engineering design practice. The data included has been developed to provide uniform practice in the design of steel framed buildings.

and

> The AISC Specification is the result of the deliberations of a committee of structural engineers with wide experience and high professional standing. ... Each specification change is based upon essentially unanimous affirmative action on the part of the full Committee.

From the proposed new AASHTO Highway Bridge Code:[5]

> The provisions included in these Specifications are intended for use in the design, evaluation and rehabilitation of fixed and moveable highway bridges. ... Emphasis is placed on the concept of safety through redundancy, ductility and scour protection. The design objectives identified herein are intended to provide for serviceability from construction through the service life of the bridge.

and

> Bridges shall be designed for the limit states defined herein to achieve the objectives of Safety, Serviceability, and Constructability. Safety requires that the resistance of a bridge exceeds a series of load combinations that may occur during the design life of the bridge,

assumed to be 75 years. . . . Serviceability requires that the bridge responds within specified limits to repeated load and environmental effects throughout its service life, and that the bridge be repairable. Constructability requires that the bridge can be safety erected to a condition which is consistent with the strength or service limit states. The requirements of economy and aesthetics shall be satisfied.

From the Preface of EUROCODE 3:[6]

The Commission of the European Communities (CEC) intends to produce European Codes—the EUROCODES—for the design and execution of buildings and civil engineering structures. These codes are intended to establish a set of common rules as an alternative to the differing rules in force in the various Member States.

Design codes thus represent the best professional consensus of the practices of design and construction which are minimally safe, serviceable and economical. By the very nature of the process of maintaining such codes they tend to be conservative and may lag behind the research front by years or even decades.

3.3 THE SCOPE, CONTENT AND STRUCTURE OF DESIGN CODES

The Scope of Codes

The purpose of structural design codes is to provide rules and criteria for the design of structures. Included in these are the requirements of safety and serviceability, as well as the necessary clauses to define loads and select materials and the recommendations for safe and economical fabrication and erection.

The scope of the code is thus far broader than just concern for safety, although safety is first and foremost. The code covers the whole spectrum of operations from design through construction, even providing in the case of bridges the criteria for inspection and evaluation during the service life. However broad the scope of the design code, it does not cover all of the activities of the design engineers, who must have the additional tools of materials science, structural mechanics, applied mathematics, as well as the skills of structural computation together with experience. A design code by itself is not sufficient to design any structure; it is part of the total task of creating a successful project.

The Content of Codes

The broad scope of the design codes is reflected in their content. For illustration the main headings of the EUROCODE 3[6] for steel structures and the AISC Load and Resistance Factor Design (LRFD) code[1] are presented as Tables 3.1 and 3.2, respectively. Both of these codes cover the same type

Table 3.1 Table of contents for EUROCODE 3[6]

1. Introduction
    1.1 Object
    1.2 Scope
    1.3 Assumptions
    1.4 Units
    1.5 Symbols
2. Basis of Design
    2.1 Fundamental Requirements
    2.2 General Design Concept
    2.3 General Rules Concerning Limit State Design
    2.4 General Rules Relating to Actions and Their Combinations
    2.5 Material Properties
    2.6 Durability
    2.7 Calculation Models and Experimental Models
    2.8 Compatibility of Quality
3. Materials
    3.1 General
    3.2 Structural Steels
    3.3 Connecting Devices
4. Serviceability Limit States
    4.1 General
    4.2 Deflections
    4.3 Dynamic Effects
5. Ultimate Limit State
    5.1 General
    5.2 Sections
    5.3 Components
    5.4 Systems
6. Connections
    6.1 General
    6.2 Connections Made with Bolts, Rivets and Pins
    6.3 Welded Connections
    6.4 Hybrid Connections
    6.5 Column Bases
    6.6 Connection in Thin-Walled Elements
7. Fabrication and Erection
    7.1 Scope
    7.2 General
    7.3 Material Specification
    7.4 Preparation
    7.5 Bolted Connections
    7.6 Welded Connections
    7.7 Tolerances
8. Test Loading
9. Fatigue
    9.1 Scope
    9.2 Basic Principles
    9.3 Fatigue Loading
    9.4 Fatigue Stress Spectra
    9.5 Fatigue Strength
    9.6 Safety Concept
    9.7 In-Service Inspection and Maintenance

Table 3.2 Table of contents of AISC LRFD Code[1]

A. General Provisions
B. Design Requirements
C. Frames and Other Structures
D. Tension Members
E. Columns and Other Compression Members
F. Beams and Other Flexural Members
G. Plate Girders
H. Members under Torsion and Combined Forces
I. Composite Members
J. Connections, Joints and Fasteners
K. Strength Design Considerations
L. Serviceability Design Considerations
M. Fabrication, Erection and Quality Control
APPENDICES
COMMENTARY

---

of construction: steel frames made from fabricated hot-rolled shapes and plates. The topics covered are essentially the same. The differences are: the AISC code covers steel–concrete composite construction, while EUROCODE has an entire separate code on this subject. EUROCODE places much more emphasis on proof testing. EUROCODE tends to place all criteria in sequential order, while the AISC standard places everyday design rules in the main text, relegating the less frequently occurring design requirements to appendices. The AISC standard also has an extensive commentary to provide explanations. No doubt EUROCODE will also follow with a similar item once the complete code has been fully ratified.

There is no question that it is neither possible nor desirable to devise a code that covers all possible design eventualities. No matter how thick the book, some designer will uncover something that is missing. For this reason the codes deal with the most frequently occurring situations. General provisions permit the use of more sophisticated analyses which will obey the spirit of the code as regards safety and serviceability. In the opinion of this writer the present generation of codes has probably reached the limit of tolerable bulk and complexity. More of this complication will make the codes a modern dinosaur. Future design codes should concentrate on providing general principles and deemphasize detailed requirements.

The Structure of Codes

The contents and the basic safety philosophy are, of course, crucial to a good design code. So is, however, the structure of its content. Take the case of the AISC Specification of 1979:[4] an entirely new standard had been adopted by AISC in 1961. In the ensuing 18 years there were around a dozen meetings of the specification committee, there were three new editions of the code, with numerous supplements in between, and there were no fundamental structural changes. The result was that the 1979 edition is a crazy-quilt of patchwork additions that kept engineers in a constant state of confusion. Because of this unstructured complexity, the chance of errors increased greatly. The effect of such errors is, naturally, not included in the codes themselves: perfect execution is assumed.

Structure and clarity of presentation is thus vital for a good code. Modern codes have remedied this shortcoming. For example, the AISC LRFD code[1] was structured according to the concepts of decision theory, and decision tables and flowcharts are provided in the computerized version of the code and in the Manual accompanying the code, respectively. While code structure would appear to have nothing to do with safety, it really does promote or hinder orderly and clean calculation, thus adding to or subtracting from the volume of human error.

The next section of this chapter will focus on the code implementation of safety principles. Before that, however, some words about economy are appropriate. The main decisions about the economy of individual structures are made a long time before the code checking operation and during the planning and the preliminary design stages. However, a code that has too many conservative criteria can lead to overall economic waste, and thus to the demise of an entire segment of industry. The design codes, therefore, must not only promote uniformity of design across the whole population of similar structures but they must also give considerable attention to economic equalization while keeping a uniform level of safety.

3.4 SAFETY CONSIDERATIONS IN DESIGN CODES

Definition of Structural Safety for Design Codes

We have seen in Chapter 1 that structural safety is a very broad concept, encompassing far more than the narrow definition we will adopt here. In the 'big picture' safety includes quality control, avoidance of human error, robustness against unexpected catastrophe and many more attributes. The definition in design codes has little to do with all this. The definition we adopt is as follows: 'A structure is safe if during the expected life of the structure the chance of exceeding a limit state set by the design code is acceptably small.'

Among all the major calamities that could beset a structure, this appears to be about a negligible complaint. However, the design codes take care of a lot of detailed requirements which, if ignored, would cause a multitude of problems during the life of the structure. The main concern is that at the time of design we do not know with certainty the properties of the structure nor the lifetime magnitudes of the loads.

We do know these vital quantities vary from those we assume in design. Somehow this uncertainty must be accounted for. Traditionally the codes have provided 'safety factors' for this. The following sections will discuss various ways in which safety factors are developed and used. It should be reiterated that safety factors are no protection against gross human error, lack of judgement, inexperience, greed, carelessness and other unfortunate happenings which cause the predominant share of the known structural failures.

Allowable Stress Design

Conventional wisdom has it that the greater the ignorance about an event, the larger the factor of safety should be. In the beginning of the scientific building process engineers assessed, as best they could, the strength of the structure. They then divided this strength by 6, 4 or 2 or any other judgemental and experiential number to obtain a safe load. The selection of the factor of safety depended on the confidence of the estimate of the strength.

In the second half of the nineteenth century the theory of elasticity began to take hold on the practice of structural design engineers. This theory assumes linearity between loads and the resulting forces or deformation magnitudes in the structure, as well as between the forces and the resulting stresses. The design philosophy which evolved out of the application of elasticity theory is called 'allowable stress design' (ASD). Simply stated, ASD computes the stresses σ by linear theory for the maximum loads that can be expected during the life-span of the structure, and it compared these stresses to 'allowable stresses' σ_{all} which are a fraction of limiting stresses σ_{lim}. These are defined as the stress levels where linear elastic theory ceases to apply, that is where the material yields or the structure becomes unstable. The design criterion is defined as

$$\sigma \leqslant \sigma_{all} = \frac{\sigma_{lim}}{FS} \tag{3.1}$$

The abbreviation FS is the 'factor of safety'. The magnitude of this factor, of course, is one of the crucial issues in design codes; the other is the definition of σ_{lim}. How is such a factor developed? It essentially evolved historically, from high values when a technology is just starting to gradually lower values until a lower ceiling, dictated by common sense and by successful and unsuccessful experience, is reached. The evolution of the allowable stress for mild steel is illustrated in Table 3.3. For essentially the same material, made by practically the same process, the basic allowable stress in the United States increased by about 60 per cent in 70 years of evolution. Improved quality control in the mills, as well as increased confidence in the design

Table 3.3 Evolution of the allowable stress for mild steel structures in the USA

Year	Minimum yield stress, ksi (MPa)	Factor of safety	Allowable stress, ksi (MPa)
1890	28.6 (197)	2.00	14 (97)
1918	27.5 (190)	1.72	16 (110)
1923	33 (228)	1.83	18 (124)
1936	33 (228)	1.65	20 (138)
1963	36 (248)	1.67	22 (152)

process due to accumulated experience, led to this increase in the allowable stress.

A vast majority of the civil engineering structures that exist today have been designed by ASD. Most engineers practising today feel comfortable with the method. The underlying philosophy is simple: Under the design load (also known as the 'working' load), which represents a credible maximum expected value during its lifetime, the response of the structure is shown to be linear. The stresses are well below any limit at which linear theory no longer applies. With one set of loads and with one set of linear calculations the problem of strength and serviceability are simultaneously verified. Everything that is determined about the structure is within the everyday experience of the engineer. No wonder that this method has such a strong attraction and no wonder that there is such a persistent resistance to change to more complex methods of design! Has not ASD been spectacularly successful in the past hundred years?

Evolution of Limit States Design

The traditional interpretation of ASD is:

1. At service loads all parts of the structure are linearly elastic.
2. If the service loads are chosen to be high enough so as to have a small chance of being exceeded and if the allowable stresses are selected to be a small enough fraction of a limiting stress, then the structure will have an excellent chance of serving out its alloted time without experiencing damage or distress.

There are a number of objections to this way of looking at the design safety problem from scientific, probabilistic and economic standpoints:

1. Stress and strain are not always linear, e.g. the stress–strain curve of concrete is non-linear even at small stresses.

2. Time effects (creep and shrinkage of concrete and wood), environmental effects (effect of moisture on wood strength, corrosion of metals) and loading rate effects are apt to introduce non-linearities in space and time.
3. Load effect and deformation are not always linear.
4. The load–deformation behaviour past the theoretical limit of linear response may be ductile (b and c in Fig. 3.1, with a very large reserve (c) or a small reserve (b) of postyield capacity) or brittle (a in Fig. 3.1).
5. Under some circumstances it is necessary to utilize the energy absorption capacitance of the non-linear range to resist earthquakes or blasts.
6. The chance of exceeding the limit state of the onset of non-linearity depends on the statistical characteristics of the loads, the materials, the idealizations used to devise a computational model, etc. The reliability of the elements within the structure or the reliability of different structures can thus vary considerably.
7. If all the structures designed by ASD have a consistently good record of performance, then there must be many members of this set that are overdesigned; that is if the worst designs are just acceptable, then all the others are too expensive.
8. New construction materials and design techniques must undergo years of trial and error until an acceptable safety factor can evolve.

These, and many other shortcomings of ASD, were generally known among researchers for some 75 years, and efforts to devise a design method that would practically accommodate these objections began in the 1930s in the Soviet Union (Streletsky) and in the 1940s in England and in the United States (Pugsley and Freudenthal). The resulting method is known as 'limit states design' (LSD), because the focus is shifted from the service condition to the limit of structural usefulness.

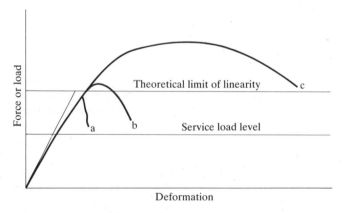

Figure 3.1 Illustration of non-linear force–deformation behaviour of structures.

The first LSD codes began to appear in the Soviet Union and other East European countries in the 1940s.[7] The code of the American Concrete Institute was the first North American design standard to appear in the LSD format in the early 1960s. By the early 1970s enough research work had been performed on both the probabilistic basis of the codes and on amassing the statistics and the behavioural models of the limit strength of structures for the way to be opened for the general acceptance of LSD. Presently (early 1990s), LSD codes are in use almost everywhere in the world.

The intellectual, theoretical and mathematical basis exists in the new LSD codes to account for all the objections raised against ASD. However, due to practical constraints this is not yet fully realized in current (1990) LSD standards. The resulting documents would be still too complex for design office use.

Limit States Design Methods

Limit states design operates as follows: the engineer calculates the limiting capacity of the structure or of its constituent elements (beams, columns, connections, etc.). This 'limit strength' ('ultimate strength', 'collapse strength', 'maximum capacity', are some other terms used) is then reduced to account for the chance that the strength is less than that computed for the nominal material properties, the handbook dimensions and the computational model used in the code. The factored strength is then compared to the computed load effect due to the appropriate maximum loads, which are then magnified to account for the uncertainties of loads that will act on the structure during its lifetime. The design condition is that

$$\phi R_n \geqslant \gamma Q_n \tag{3.2}$$

where $\phi < 1.0$ is the 'resistance factor' (also named 'capacity reduction factor' or, in many European codes, e.g. in EUROCODE, $\phi = 1/\gamma_m$, where γ_m is the 'material factor'), $\gamma > 1.0$ is the 'load factor', R_n is the code-specified nominal resistance and Q_n is the computed nominal load effect (shear, bending moment, axial force, etc.). Both the resistance and the load effect refer to the limit state condition and their calculations consider both material and geometric non-linearities and initial imperfections. If the limit state is the cessation of elastic response and the structure is initially perfect and constrained from non-linear behaviour, then LSD is equivalent to ASD. However, LSD looks to the limit and ensures that actual loading is comfortably below the limit, while ASD says that under actual loading all is well and thus at the limit all will be well also. The basic differences of the two methods are illustrated in Fig. 3.2. The resistance R is characterized by a non-linear load deflection curve and a probability distribution, and the load effect Q is also characterized by a distribution curve. Both Q and R are random quantities. The nominal values R_n and Q_n and the factors ϕ and γ

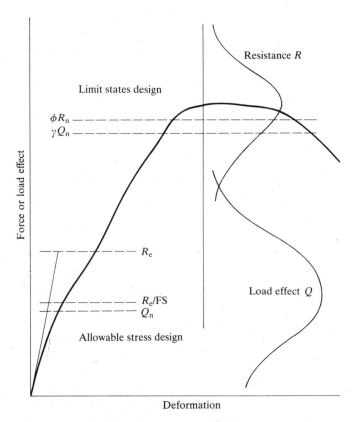

Figure 3.2 Comparison of ASD and LSD methods.

are specified in the LSD code, while the elastic limit R_e and the factor of safety FS are from an ASD code. The latter ignores non-linearity but is generally conservative.

It was realized early in the evolution of LSD that some types of loads are more precisely known than others. For example, self-weight (dead loads) has a smaller variability than, for example, occupancy (live) or wind loads. The concept of multiple load factors (also known as partial factors) was then introduced. The design criterion of Eq. (3.2) can now be expanded to the following form:

$$\phi R_n \geqslant \sum_{i=1}^{m} \gamma_i Q_{in} \tag{3.3}$$

For example, in the AISC LRFD code,[1] the following load factors are used:

Dead load factor: 1.2
Live load factor and snow load factor: 1.6

Wind load factor: 1.3
Earthquake load factor: 1.5

These factors not only reflect the fact of load variability but, in the case of wind or earthquake loading, also an implicit recognition that the ductile structure does not only resist load but also absorbs energy.

Once multiple load factors were introduced, another problem needed attention. Transient loads, such as those due to occupancy or wind or earthquake loads, are not likely to take on their lifetime maximum values simultaneously. Within the current LSD codes this phenomenon is taken care of in one of the following ways:

1. *American Concrete Institute Code:*

$$\phi R_n \geqslant \psi \sum \gamma_i Q_{ni} \tag{3.4}$$

where ψ is the 'combination factor' equal to 1.0 when Q_{ni} are gravity loads (dead, live or snow loads) and 0.75 if wind or earthquake loads are also present. Wind loads and earthquake loads are never assumed to take on their maximum lifetime values simultaneously.

2. *The Canadian Standard S16.1 for Steel Structures:*

$$\phi R_n \geqslant \gamma_D D_n + \psi (\gamma_L L_n + \gamma_{W/E} Q_{W/E} + \gamma_T T) \tag{3.5}$$

In this equation the subscript n denotes nominal values and D, L, W, E and T are dead, live (includes occupancy and snow), wind, earthquake and temperature loads, respectively. The load combination factor ψ takes on the value of 1.0 when only L, W/E and T act, 0.7 when two L, W/E and T act, and 0.6 when all three act.

3. *The ANSI A58.1 Load Code:*[2]

$$\phi R_n \geqslant \gamma_D D_n + \gamma_1 Q_{ni} + \sum_{i>1}^{m} \gamma_{ir} Q_{ni} \tag{3.6}$$

where Q_{ni} are the transient loads: occupancy, snow, wind, earthquake and temperature induced loads. One of these, Q_{ni} is assumed to be at its maximum lifetime value with the appropriate load factor, while the others are at their instantaneous values (i.e. values they are likely to assume at any arbitrary instant in time). For the sake of simplicity the same nominal values based on the maximum lifetime are used with reduced load factors γ_{ir}. The transient loads are then rotated to position 1 until the critical load combination is determined. For example, if dead, live, snow and wind loads act, then the following combinations apply:

$$1.2D_n + 1.6L_n + 0.5S_n \tag{3.7a}$$

$$1.2D_n + 1.6S_n + 0.5L_n/0.8W_n \tag{3.7b}$$

$$1.2D_n + 1.3W_n + 0.5L_n + 0.5S_n \tag{3.7c}$$

Similar rules for combination of loads are recommended for the EUROCODE, with different factors.

Limit state design examines the condition of the structure at failure, comparing a reduced capacity with an amplified load effect for the checking of safety. Since safety is related to the condition when the structure becomes useless, an additional check for serviceability must also be performed. Modern LSD codes, while representing more rationally and accurately the true behaviour of the structure, are more complicated than the ASD codes because several combinations of loads must be analysed and the checking must include a variety of non-linear effects. Without computers we could not efficiently implement LSD codes.

From one safety factor in ASD we now have a whole catalogue of load factors and resistance factors. It took the better part of a century to evolve the ASD safety factors, and now we have to ensure the appropriateness of many factors from both the standpoint of safety and economy! The translation from an ASD to an LSD code is accomplished by a process called 'calibration': before we can properly describe calibration, we must first explain the role of probability in code development.

Probabilistic Concepts

All of the parameters that enter into the determination of the nominal resistance R_n and the nominal load effects Q_{in} have certain degrees of uncertainty which derive from the following:

1. Load intensities and load locations are random by their very nature. At best, we can know only their probability density in time and space; at worst, we can guess at their expected maximum value from common sense or experience. Loads do not conform to the uniformly distributed and concentrated idealizations favoured in the diagrams of textbooks. Loads from different sources act together in random ways.
2. In order to be able to perform structural analysis, radical simplification must be made in modelling the actual structure. There are in any structure innumerable such idealizations, and their combined effect results in uncertainties of the computed load effects.
3. Material properties are subject to random variations, even though proper quality control measures exclude most faulty and understrength materials.
4. The conceptual resistance models contain many idealizations and assumptions that result in uncertainties.

In modern structures and with the use of modern methods of analysis and modern materials, these uncertainties are not wildly fluctuating chaotic quantities. However, there are not insignificant variabilities which have coefficients of variation of 5 to 20 per cent for resistances and 10 to possibly as much as 40 per cent for load effects. Traditionally safety factors were employed in order to make the consequences of unavoidable understrength and/or overload harmless.

The idea that probability theory can be directly used to determine the reliability of the structure has evolved in parallel with the maturing of the LSD methods. By the early 1990s the application of probability theory in structural design has matured so that many textbooks are now devoted to the subject (e.g. Ref. 8), and the subject is widely taught in engineering schools.

The probabilistic methods, stripped of all complications, can be described as follows (Fig. 3.3). The probability that the resistance R is less than the load effect Q, that is that a limit state is exceeded, is the probability that Q is in the region X and $X + dX$, that is $p_Q(X)$, times the probability that $R < X$, that is $F_R(X)$, where $F_R(X)$ is the cumulative distribution

$$F_R(X) = \int_{-\infty}^{X} p_R(x)\,dx \qquad (3.8)$$

integrated over the whole domain

$$p_F = p(R < Q) = \int_{-\infty}^{\infty} F_R(X)p_Q(X)\,dX \qquad (3.9)$$

In order to evaluate Eq. (3.9) we must know the probability density functions of R and Q, and R must be statistically independent of Q. The design criterion is then to check that the probability of exceeding a limit state is less than or equal to an acceptable probability of failure. For example, if both R and Q are independently normally distributed, then it can be shown that

$$p_F = \Phi\left[-\frac{\bar{R} - \bar{Q}}{(\sigma_R^2 + \sigma_Q^2)^{1/2}} \right] \qquad (3.10)$$

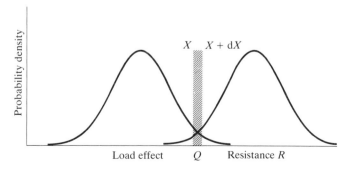

Figure 3.3 Definition of probability of failure.

where Φ is the standardized normal cumulative distribution function which can be looked up in tables, $\bar{R}$ and $\bar{Q}$ are the mean values and σ_R and σ_Q are the standard deviations of R and Q, respectively. Alternatively, it is more convenient to use instead of the probability p_F the 'reliability index', or 'central safety factor':

$$\beta = \frac{\bar{R} - \bar{Q}}{(\sigma_R^2 + \sigma_Q^2)^{1/2}} \tag{3.11}$$

This reliability index β is the number of standard deviations between the failure point (where $R = Q$) and the mean of $R - Q$, that is $\bar{R} - \bar{Q}$ (Fig. 3.4). The relationship between β and the probability of exceeding the limit state p_F is

$$p_F = \Phi(-\beta) \tag{3.12}$$

if R and Q are independently normally distributed. For example, if $\beta = 3.0$, $p_F = 0.001\,35 = 1/741$. A low value of β implies a high probability of failure, while a high value of β signifies a low probability of failure.

It so happened in the development of probabilistic methods of structural design that the reliability of structures is generally designated by the reliability index β (a number usually between 2 and 5) rather than by the probability of failure p_F (a number between 0.022 75 and 0.000 000 3).

The reality of structural capacity and the actual loads are, of course, far more complex than the simple description presented here (see Ref. 8, for example). However, the simplistic idea that one can compare the reliability of one structure to that of another structure by knowing just four quantities ($\bar{R}$, σ_R, $\bar{Q}$, σ_Q) has resulted in the probability-based design methods known as 'first-order reliability methods' (FORM). Considering the fact that previously it took decades of trial and error, and finally the arbitrary selection of factors of safety by a code committee on the basis of judgement and

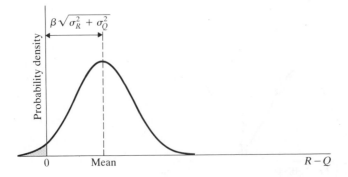

Figure 3.4 Definition of the reliability index.

compromise, FORM offers a quantum jump improvement in the ability to create new design codes. It and its more sophisticated successor SORM (for 'second-order reliability method') provide the tools that have been used in the development of modern LSD codes.

One could think of structural design in which the code would specify a target reliability index β_T and the designer would prove, by analysis based on FORM or SORM using the relevant statistical data, that the actual reliability index β exceeds β_T. Such a method of design is called a level II design method. Level I methods are the traditional design procedures that use load factors and resistance factors.

Calibration

It is generally agreed among design code writers that civil structural practice at the beginning of the 1990s is not at a stage of development where level II methods can be promulgated for everyday design. However, it is practical to use such level II methods to develop the partial factors necessary for the level I methods. Thus probabilistic sophistication, tempered by experience and judgement, can aid indirectly in the development of the more economical LSD codes.

The key concept is that similar types of structures should have essentially the same reliability against exceeding a limit state. Connection with the experience of the past is to insure that the reliability of the expanded set of structures in the new code is the same as that of a proven member of the set of structures designed by the old code.

The calibration process has three basic parts:[8] judgement, fitting and code optimization.

Judgement is the application of accumulated experience with a given type of structure, as illustrated in Table 3.3 for the evolution of the factor of safety for steel beams. As understanding of behaviour expanded, as successful experience accumulated and as the control over the production of the material increased, the factor of safety was reduced and the guaranteed minimum value of the yield stress was increased. It is evident from this table that the factor of safety over the past half-century had been essentially constant at the value of 5/3. From this we can conclude that experience with this factor has been satisfactory for many years and that a greater or lesser reliability than implied by the value of FS = 5/3 contravenes past satisfactory structural safety and economic experience. In the development of new design criteria it is thus not desirable to depart radically from this reliability. Structural types such as simply supported beams furnish us with a fixed point from the proven past.

Fitting is a match of a new structural design code to some point in the parameter domain in the previous code. Classical examples of this approach are the load factors provided for Part 2 of the AISC 1979 Specification[4] for plastic design of steel structures and the load factor design part of the 1989 AASHTO Specification for highway bridges.[3] In the former case the same load factor is employed for the plastic design of statically determinate and indeterminate structures as is used for the first yield limit state of statically determinate beams in the ASD portion of the same code. In the latter case (i.e. for bridge design) the load factors for the new code were chosen to give the same beam sizes in a simple-span bridge for the LSD and the ASD methods of design when the span equals 12 m. In both instances the applicability of the domain of constant reliability was extended to include a larger population of structure. This is illustrated in Fig. 3.5 for the 1979 AISC Specification. From this figure it is evident that the ASD method is needlessly conservative for statically indeterminate structures which are made up of compact elements capable of forming a plastic mechanism.

Code optimization is calibration by a process of optimization. Such an optimization was performed for the development of the load factors in the ANSI A58.1 1982 Load Code.[2,9] As a first step the scope of this code was defined to encompass building structures of all traditional building materials (steel, concrete, wood, masonry). For these structural members the applicable limit states were identified and the prevalent loads and load combinations were defined. Next, FORM probability analyses were performed over the whole domain of materials, limit states and loads to determine the variation of the reliability index in the then-current building construction world. The next step in the operation consisted of three judgemental decisions: (1) selection of the *code format*, (2) choice of the *code objective* and (3) selection of the *target reliability indices*.

A particular load and resistance factor design (LRFD) format was finally chosen from a number of available alternatives. This format has been discussed previously and is defined by Eq. (3.6). The code objective was to develop a level I code with the appropriate load factors γ and resistance factors ϕ such that a level II (i.e. FORM) probabilistic analysis would show

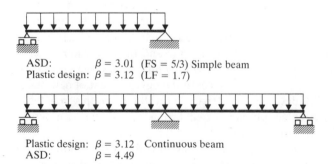

ASD: $\beta = 3.01$ (FS = 5/3) Simple beam
Plastic design: $\beta = 3.12$ (LF = 1.7)

Plastic design: $\beta = 3.12$ Continuous beam
ASD: $\beta = 4.49$

Figure 3.5 Calibration of plastic design for Ref. 4.

a constant reliability equal to the target reliability. This target was chosen on the basis of the FORM analyses performed on the then-current design codes.

It should be emphasized that these last three steps, that is the selection of code format, code objective and target reliability, are judgemental operations which involved representatives of all interested parties, e.g. code writers from all the individual materials specifications in the United States. Other choices could have resulted in an equally valid level I design methodology. Thus while the Canadian steel design code or the EUROCODE are based on the same probabilistic premises, the code format and the target reliability are different.

As it turned out, for the US ANSI A58.1 1982 Load Code it was not possible to arrive at one single target reliability index and, at the same time, to achieve consistency with past economic practice. The FORM analyses of current design indicated that the most prevalent reliability index was $\beta = 3.0$ under gravity loads. Using this value as the target for load combinations which also included wind or earthquake loads resulted in structures of greater weight than the weight of the then-current designs. A compromise was eventually reached and the following target reliabilities were chosen for the ANSI A58.1 1982 Load Code:

Gravity loads: $\beta_T = 3.0$
Gravity plus wind loads: $\beta_T = 2.5$
Gravity plus earthquake loads: $\beta_T = 1.75$

Following are the target reliabilities inherent in other modern probability-based design codes. For the Canadian codes for steel and concrete buildings and bridges, $\beta_T = 3.5$, based on a 30-year life of the structure. The proposed EUROCODE has a value of $\beta_T = 3.5$ for normal construction. The target reliability index for the ultimate limit states in the proposed Nordic Code (for Denmark, Finland, Iceland, Norway and Sweden) is $\beta_T = 4.3$. At this time of code evolution it is not yet clear whether these divergent values signify real differences in reliability or whether the differences result from variations in the definition of loads and in the projected life of the structure.

The next step in the calibration process for the American Load Code was the choice of the frequency of occurrence of a particular kind of building material, type of member and kind of limit state. This data space was the *demand function* and was the best estimate of the likelihood of the different situations prevalent in practice. The optimum load factors were then determined as the minimum of the squares of the weighted differences between resistances obtained from the target reliability index and the assumed variable load factors and resistance factors. These optimal factors were then subjected once more to judgement and discussion until finally the load factors in Eqs (3.7a) to (3.7c) were proposed and then approved by unanimous ballot.

The complete set of ANSI A58.1 1982 load factors are presented in Table 3.4, and the process of code calibration is flowcharted in Fig. 3.6.

In US practice the load code, which was discussed above, is separate from the design codes for the various materials used in building construction. For example, in the AISC LRFD Specification[1] the ANSI A58.1 1982 load factors were used, together with the recommended target reliability indices and the FORM probabilistic methodology, to develop resistance factors ϕ consistent with the statistical data available on the ultimate limit states for members and connections. A list of these factors is given in Table 3.5. A reanalysis by FORM (or SORM where required) of the final LRFD code reveals the degree to which equalization of reliability across the various structural members and connections in this code was achieved. Table 3.6 lists the values of the reliability indices for the case where only dead load and live load act on the structural elements, and for the nominal live load to dead load ratio $L_n/D_n = 1.0$. For this case the reliability index should be 3.0 to be consistent with the premises of the load code.

A review of Table 3.6 reveals that the new LRFD code was not at all successful in attaining uniform reliability since the β values vary from a low

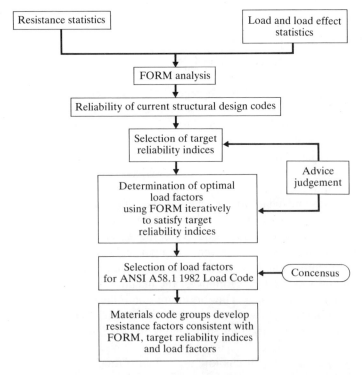

Figure 3.6 Flowchart of calibration procedure for developing the load factors of Ref. 2.

Table 3.4 Load factors and load combinations[1]

$1.4D_n$

$1.2D_n + 1.6L_n$

$1.2D_n + 1.6S_n + (0.5L_n \text{ or } 0.8W_n)$

$1.2D_n + 1.3W_n + 0.5L_n + 0.5S_n$

$1.2D_n + 1.5E_n + (0.5L_n \text{ or } 0.2S_n)$

$0.9D_n - (1.3W_n \text{ or } 1.5E_n)$

D = dead load

L = live load

S = snow load

W = wind load

E = earthquake load

n = nominal (code specified) value

Table 3.5 Resistance factors in AISC LRFD Code[1]

Tension members: yield limit state, 0.90

fracture limit state, 0.75

Compression members: 0.85

Flexural members: 0.90

Compact composite beams: 0.85

Welds: 0.90, 0.80 or 0.75, depending on type of weld

Bolts: tensile and bearing strength, 0.75

shear in bearing-type connections, 0.65

shear in friction-type connections, 1.00

Shear rupture strength in a connection, 0.75

Webs and flanges with concentrated forces:

local flange bending, 0.90

local web yielding, 1.00

web crippling, 0.75

compression buckling of web, 0.90

sidesway web buckling, 0.85

Table 3.6 Reliability indices for AISC LRFD Code for $L_n / D_n = 1.00$

Type of element	Reliability index
Tension member, yield limit state	3.0
Tension member, fracture limit state	4.1
Rolled beam, flexural limit state	2.5–2.8
Rolled beam, shear limit state	3.4
Welded beam, flexural limit state	2.5–2.9
Welded beam, shear limit state	3.3
Welded plate girder, flexural limit state	2.6–2.9
Welded plate girder, shear limit state	2.3
Columns	2.7–3.6
High strength bolts, tension	5.0–5.1
High strength bolts, shear in bearing	5.9–6.0
High strength bolts, tension and shear	5.8
High strength bolts, eccentric joints	4.8
High strength bolts, slip-critical joints	1.6–2.0
Fillet welds	4.4
Eccentric welded joints	3.9
Welded connections, flange bending	2.6
Welded joints, local web yielding	4.1
Welded joints, web buckling	4.0
Welded joints, web crippling	2.6–2.9

of 1.6 to a high of 6.0, a spread of about four orders of magnitude in the probability of failure. On closer examination, however, some justification for the differences can be brought out:

1. The range of low β values (1.6 to 2.0) for slip-critical joints can be attributed to the fact that this is a serviceability limit and not an ultimate limit. Such β values are essentially in line with values for floor deflection or lateral drift limit states.[10]
2. The limit states for connections and connectors (fracture of a tension member at its end, bolts and welds) have generally higher β values than the members. This is by a deliberate decision so that failure should occur not in the joint but in the member. This is a customary practice inherited from previous codes. The spread of β values for connections and fasteners, excepting the slip-critical joints, is from 2.6 to 6.0—still a far too broad range. The reliability indices for flange bending ($\beta = 2.6$) and web crippling (2.6 to 2.9) are definitely too low, and a reduction of the resistance factor ϕ is indicated for the next edition of the code. High-strength bolts have very high reliability indices (4.8 to 6.0). Consideration should be given to an increase of the ϕ-factors to bring the β values more in line with those for the welds.
3. Beams and columns have β values varying from 2.3 to 3.6. Welded plate girders have uncomfortably low β values, and so the resistance factor should be reduced. Columns have too wide a range of β values. This is because the AISC Code uses a single-column curve. This will not be the case for the EUROCODE, where a much greater equalization is possible through the use of five column curves.

3.5 CONCLUSIONS

In this chapter we have presented the role of design codes in the overall safety of large constructed projects. It was shown that 'factors of safey' in allowable stress design codes and 'partial factors' in limit states design codes serve the purpose of accounting for the unavoidable uncertainties of the strength of the structure and the loads that act on it.

The illustrations of the development of probability-based limit states design codes were taken from American experience and practice, because of the background of the author. However, essentially the same development and the same theoretical basis underlies the modern limit states design codes of Canada (e.g. S161.1 and others), Great Britain (BS 5400), the Nordic Code in Europe, the proposed EUROCODE and the design codes of the Soviet Union and Hungary. The code format and the implied comparative levels of reliability may vary somewhat from code to code, but reliability theory has provided a common ground through which codes of different jurisdictions can be compared. Through such efforts as EUROCODE or ISO standards it is hoped that the real differences in reliability can be eventually eliminated.

Conformance to codes is but one aspect of the many features of the safety of large constructed projects which are discussed in this book.

REFERENCES

1. American Institute of Steel Construction: *Load and Resistance Factor Design Specification for Structural Steel Buildings*, AISC, Chicago, 1986.
2. American National Standards Institute: *Minimum Design Loads for Buildings and Other Structures*, ANSI A58.1, New York, 1982 (revised by American Society of Civil Engineers as ANSI/ASCE 7-88 Standard).
3. American Association of State Highway and Transportation Officials: *Standard Specifications for Highway Bridges*, AASHTO, Washington, D.C., 1989.
4. American Institute of Steel Construction: *Specification for the Design, Fabrication and Erection of Structural Steel for Buildings*, AISC, Chicago, 1979.
5. Draft of LRFD Specification for Highway Bridges, a document not yet open for public use.
6. Commission of the European Communities: *EUROCODE No. 3, Common Unified Rules for Steel Structures*, P. J. Dowling *et al.* (eds), 1984.
7. Ivanyi, M.: Design Concepts of New Hungarian Codes, *Int. Coll. Stability of Steel Structures*, Budapest, 25–27 April 1990.
8. Madsen, H. O., S. Krenk, and N. C. Lind: *Methods of Structural Safety*, Prentice-Hall, Englewood Cliffs, N.J., 1986.
9. Ellingwood, B., J. G. MacGregor, T. V. Galambos, and C. A. Cornell: Probability-Based Load Criteria: Load Factors and Load Combinations, *ASCE J. Struct. Div.*, vol. 108, no. ST5, pp. 978–997, May 1982.
10. Galambos, T. V., and B. Ellingwood: Serviceability Limit States: Deflection, *ASCE J. Struct. Engng.*, vol. 112, no. 1, pp. 67–84, January 1986.

FOUR

QUALITY ASSURANCE

M. MATOUSEK

4.1 THE NEED FOR SYSTEMATIC QUALITY ASSURANCE

Recent building collapses and increasing damage to structures have raised questions about quality, and about safety in particular. A number of spectacular accidents have made headlines in the press. These include, for example, the collapse of the Congress Hall in Berlin (West Germany), the failure of the roof of a swimming pool in Uster (Switzerland), the collapse of a bridge in Lustenau (Austria), the collapse of a block of flats in Castellaneta (Italy), the collapse of a suspension bridge in Lully-sur-Loire (France), the collapse of a steel bridge in the State of Connecticut (USA), the earthquake catastrophe in Armenia (USSR), etc. The failure of structures and of technical installations or artefacts in particular can also lead to *environmental problems* and even to *environmental disasters,* such as the chemical disaster in Bophal, the nuclear power plant accident in Chernobyl, the huge fire in Schweizerhalle, etc.

In addition to accidents affecting safety and environmental compatibility, there are also many small incidents that only affect the serviceability for use or durability of a structure. This can include cracks, chipping, formation of condensation and mould, etc.

Damage to structures is estimated to be 3 to 6 per cent of the construction costs. In addition to this property damage, there is also personal damage, consequential damage (delays, breaks in production, loss of market shares, etc.) and damage to the environment. These costs may exceed the cost of direct damage many times over. As regards damage to the environment, nowadays it is often completely impossible to put a value on this, or to repair it. Damaging the environment may even lead to it being completely destroyed.

There is a time limit on liability, and even if the guilty party is established before the expiry of the time limit, often he/she either no longer exists (bankruptcy) or is financially not in a position to pay for the repair of the damage. The owner must often pay for damage after the time limit has expired. Current practice shows that the costs of repairing damage are very high. The costs of settling the cause of the damage (experts' reports, court costs) should also not be underestimated.

The failure of buildings and other artefacts is not just a present-day phenomenon. Structural failures and the resulting diasaters also occurred in earlier times, such as the collapse of churches and bridges, the bursting of dams or the destruction of cities following fires and earthquakes. Many old buildings are nonetheless still in good condition. This is the result not just of the many years of experience but also of the simple building methods used and the skilled craftsmanship of the workers.

The situation is now very different. New buildings have to meet new, considerably more complex requirements. They are more complicated and more susceptible to failures. New materials and new technologies are used. With all this rapid innovation, experience is lacking. In addition, building workers are now often only semi-skilled labourers rather than trained workmen. Systematic quality assurance is the exception rather than the rule. Builders and building consultants today assume that quality specifications in technical standards and the obligation to produce careful workmanship in accordance with the plans are sufficient to ensure quality. Only costs and deadlines are discussed (Fig. 4.1). Quality is thus more or less taken for granted. The number of accidents clearly shows that this way of looking at the matter is inadequate.

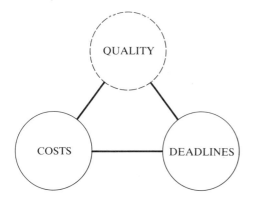

Figure 4.1 Actual situation: only costs and deadlines are discussed.

In order to prevent damage and to guarantee the necessary level of quality, it is essential to plan and implement a system of quality assurance. This fact has been recognized in time and has led to research being carried out throughout the world. The results of this research are already being incorporated into standards. Experience in quality assurance in other industries such as electrical engineering, mechanical engineering, electronics, etc., has also been evaluated and is now being used in corresponding quality assurance standards. Quality assurance is, in this connection, of an international significance that reaches beyond the borders of individual nations. Quality assurance work was thus coordinated and international standards on quality assurance have been prepared.[1,2] On the basis of these standards, a system of procedures and certain tools and methods are now available. However, it is essential that systematic quality assurance (which can be abbreviated to QA) should be implemented and applied in the best possible way. The following will deal with the basic background to QA. It is based on the results of damage studies and research work, and experience in the application and implementation of QA in the building and construction industry.

4.2 SAFETY—AN IMPORTANT QUALITY CHARACTERISTIC

What Is Quality?

In construction, the term 'quality' is one of the commonest catchwords. However, it is rarely clear what is actually understood by quality. The problem lies in the fact that the term is mainly used as an absolute. Quality in the absolute sense describes the totality of the features and characteristics of an object or a service. We speak of too much or too little quality or better and poorer quality. Seeing quality as an absolute can lead to a product or service being suitable for a variety of uses but having characteristics that are superfluous in actual use and may even be a disadvantage in relation to the particular intended use.

The term 'quality' must be seen in more relative terms and be made to relate to the actual purpose of the building and the relevant services. Quality is therefore described as the totality of the features and characteristics of a product or service that bear on its ability to satisfy stated or implied needs.[1] The aim is to achieve only those quality characteristics that are necessary, not those that are possible.

Quality Characteristics

The use of a concept of quality related to needs or purposes assumes that quality is described in terms of definite quality characteristics. This has only happened rarely to date. It is only in recent standards that separate quality characteristics are stated clearly.[3] Basically, there are four quality characteristics: serviceability, safety, environmental compatibility and durability.

Serviceability guarantees the use of the artefact for the agreed purpose and under the agreed conditions of use. The use is defined on the basis of agreed threshold values and applies in particular to usability (deformation, dimensional tolerances, leak tightness, vibrations), appearance, form and installation and processing.

Safety related primarily to the danger to human life and also to the risk of property damage resulting from the failure of structures and technical installations, and indicates which hazards can be eliminated by what measures. Since not all hazards can be eliminated, certain hazards must be accepted as risks. These risks are then offset by the eliminated hazards— safety. Depending on the hazard, a distinction is made between technical safety (load-bearing capacity, fire safety, safety of mains supplies, operating safety, etc.), physical safety (protection against criminal activity, sabotage) and safety in relation to accidents suffered by employees (prevention of accidents) and dangers to health from noxious substances.

Environmental compatibility covers the effects of the artefact on the environment (air, soil, groundwater, surface waters, etc.) during the construction phase, the operating phase, the demolition phase and particularly as a result of failures and disasters, and the measures to be taken to reduce the effects to acceptable levels.

Durability ensures that serviceability and safety and environmental compatibility are maintained during the intended period of use.

The quality characteristics are specified on the basis of the purpose, which in turn is based in particular on financial and time constraints. If funds are limited, the needs, and consequently the purpose, of the structure must be adjusted accordingly. It is clear from this that costs are not a quality characteristics but rather the financial consequence of the quality characteristics that have been specified. Unfortunately, quality and cost are not always separated. Consequently, it is impossible at the moment to say how much of the cost of a structure or technical installation is accounted for by individual quality characteristics—serviceability, safety, environmental compatibility and durability.

The Particular Importance of Safety

Among these quality characteristics, safety is of particular importance. This can be seen clearly from the division of property damage according to quality characteristics (limited to the load-bearing structure), shown here in percentage terms:[4]

- 94 per cent sudden failure of the load-bearing structure for buildings (mainly safety problems)

● 6 per cent unsatisfactory condition of the structure, such as cracks, deflection, corrosion, wear, etc. (mainly problems of serviceability and durability)

Many building specialists today still equate safety with the 'safety factor'. This is hardly surprising, since the safety factor is basically the only safety concept that the building specialist encounters during training and in practice. It is thus assumed that structure is guaranteed safe if the calculated safety factor corresponds with that given in the standards documentation.

It is not sufficient to regard safety as a concept limited to mathematical verification in this way. This view may hide a possible lack of safety. What is the use of a safety calculation if, for example, the decisive actions are not taken into consideration or the measures taken are improperly implemented or ineffective? Studies of accidents and structural collapses clearly show that structures can fail despite a 'safety calculation'. Safety is a quality characteristic and should therefore not be restricted to being a mathematical factor.

4.3 THE STRUCTURE OF QA

The Main Reason for Lack of Quality

The quality of artefacts is basically determined by all the work done by those involved in the construction process. From the original intention to build through to demolition, the construction process involves a large number of people—builders, architects, engineers, technical experts, draughtspeople, specialist contractors, secondary trades, etc. Since everyone makes mistakes, it can be assumed that failures will also occur in such a complex process, so that the desired level of quality may not be achieved.

This assumption is confirmed by accident studies at home and abroad. These show clearly that damage is mainly caused by mistakes made by those involved in the building work. Damage analysis[4] shows that 90 per cent of the cost of damage and 85 per cent of the number of accidents causing death and injury are caused by errors, the remaining 10 or 15 per cent being caused by consciously accepted risks. Only a very small proportion of the damage caused by error can be traced back to hazards of which science and technology were unaware at the time (e.g. the effects of vibration, stress crack corrosion).

In this connection, any difference between target and actual human performance that exceeds permitted tolerances is described as an error. Depending on the qualitative evaluation of this difference, a distinction can be drawn between three types of error: missing work, faulty work and insufficient work. The damage studies on buildings[4] show that these defect types can be divided as follows (given as a percentage of the cost of the damage):

- 46 per cent missing work, such as failure to carry out calculations and tests, missing reinforcement, missing conduits, etc.
- 43 per cent faulty work, such as wrong components used in the wrong place, mistakes in calculations, mistakes in measurements, etc.
- 11 per cent insufficient work, such as insufficient insulation layers, air-conditioning plant not large enough, not enough reinforcement, etc.

The figures show that almost 50 per cent of errors can be eliminated with very little expenditure, with monitoring to check completeness. However, our knowledge of the types of error is insufficient to counter these errors effectively. The cause and sources of these errors must be determined.

Sources of Errors and QA Measures

Errors are characterized by three factors: firstly, by the phase of the construction process during which they occur, secondly, by the persons involved in the process and the way in which they are organized and, thirdly, by human behaviour. These three factors can be identified as sources of errors and studied further. They can be described as follows:
- Sources of errors in the technical procedures of the construction process, such as faulty calculations, missing plans, wrong components, etc.
- Sources of errors in the organizational sphere, such as inadequate work specification, insufficient demarcation of areas of competence and responsibility, lack of information flow, insufficient cooperation, etc.
- Sources of error in the personnel sphere or in the field of human behaviour, such as lack of skills, carelessness, negligence, forgetfulness, mistakes, etc.

Once the sources of error have been examined, it is then possible to counter the errors systematically by taking particular measures—by QA [5] Errors can basically be prevented or detected in time and put right. This means that QA consists not only of inspections but also of measures to prevent errors. QA can therefore be described as all of the actions needed to prevent errors or to detect and correct errors.

The measures to prevent errors are determined by the sources of errors and are therefore divided into measures taken:

- In the technical procedures of the construction process, such as use of needs analysis specification of quality requirements, application of use analyses, risk analyses, utilization plans, safety plans, environmental reports, systematically compiled calculations and plans, guidelines for building works, guidelines for use and operation, building manuals, etc.

- In the organizational sphere, such as use of progress schedules, organigrams, function diagrams, job specifications, communication and documentation systems, information booklets, meeting concepts, variation procedures, etc.
- In the personnel sphere, such as use of requirement and ability profiles, assessment and selection of employees, familiarization periods, additional training, consideration of staff absence, specification of consequences of failure to carry out work, etc.

In addition to measures to prevent defects, measures to detect and correct errors should be used as required. These will not prevent the actual errors, but will detect them in good time and put them right. Major damage is thus avoided. The damage study[4] showed this clearly: 85 per cent of the cases of property damage and 90 per cent of the cases of personal injury could have been avoided if inspections had been carried out in good time. Detection of errors in time consequently requires systematic planning and execution of inspections and checks, using suitable auxiliary material, such as inspection plans, inspection guidelines, check-lists, minutes and reports.

Optimum Specification of QA Measures

In addition to achieving the desired reduction in the risk of damage, the use of measures to prevent, detect and correct errors (QA measures) is related to cost. It is pointless if, for example, the inspections cost more than repairing the damage itself. QA measures should therefore be used in the best possible way in the light of the *risk of damage* and the *QA costs*. The expenditure on QA will then be smaller in the case of simple structures involving a low risk of damage than for complex structures involving high risks. It is obvious that it will be necessary, and sensible, to allow for a considerably higher expenditure on safety than for the other quality characteristics.

At the moment, QA meaasures are not often planned and implemented systematically. This unsatisfactory situation must change. QA should be planned into every building project through a quality plan, and implemented accordingly. In addition, everyone involved in the construction process should be introduced to systematic QA by the use of quality manuals. The new QA standards can form an important basic foundation for these.[1,2]

4.4 SYSTEMATIC QA PLANNING

Quality Plans

The quality plan sets out, for a particular building project, who is responsible for QA, what QA measures are proposed in the technical, organizational and personnel sphere, who will be producing and implementing these and how feedback is to be guaranteed. The quality plan should be used by the building as a management tool to allow quality in the construction process to be supervised and to intervene in this process when necessary.

The quality plan is phase oriented and can be subdivided as follows (see Fig. 4.2):[6]

1. *QA organization and QA management.* A report is made of how the QA organization is structured and who is undertaking which QA tasks.
2. *QA measures.* For each phase of the construction process, QA measures are laid down for the technical, organizational and personnel spheres. As construction quality is introduced and maintained, the QA measures should be specified in more detail for the following phases:[6] study phase ('FOCUS quality'), planning and preliminary design ('DEFINE quality'), design ('SPECIFY quality'), planning of construction ('OFFER and DECIDE quality'), construction ('CONTROL quality'), delivery ('VERIFY quality'), use ('KEEP quality'). In connection with the QA measure, the following QA documents are of particular importance: utilization plan, safety plan, environmental report, inspection plan, building manual. These documents are discussed in more detail in Sec. 4.5.
3. *Feedback.* Feedback ensures that information on the application and implementation of QA is evaluated and that corresponding improvements are made.

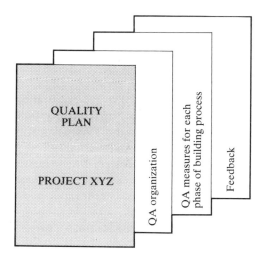

Figure 4.2 Elements of a quality plan.

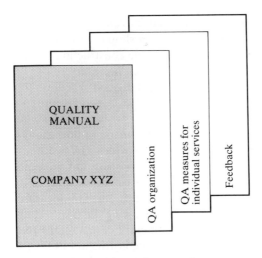

Figure 4.3 Elements of a quality manual.

Quality Manuals

The planning, realization and use of buildings assume that certain defined tasks have to be carried out. In order to guarantee the quality of the individual tasks, it is necessary that everyone who carries out a task (contractors, suppliers, manufacturers, planners, etc.) prepares a quality manual (see Fig. 4.3).[6] This should show the way in which anyone providing a service sees and implements QA in a company for the services that are provided. The quality manuals are consequently task-oriented in contrast to quality plans.

These quality manuals have been used for a long time in the manufacturing industry. They are an exception in the construction industry, but will become essential for those providing services in the future.

QA Standards as a Basis

The importance of QA has been recognized and has led to the preparation of corresponding QA standards for products and services.[1,2] In this connection, ISO standards 9004 and BS 5750 are particularly important. These standards cover all activities that affect the product or service. Activities are divided into the following phases: marketing, layout and design, procurement, process planning and process development, production, testing, packing and storing, sale and distribution, installation and operation, technical support and maintenance, removal after use.

In the QA standards, the quality system is basically made up as follows:

- Quality management (responsibility, organization, funding and personnel operations)

- Documentation of the quality system (quality handbooks, quality plans, quality records)
- Auditing the quality system (audit planning, implementation, production of report)
- Independent checking of the quality system
- Personnel (training, qualifications, motivation)

The new QA standards are an important foundation for the planning and implementation of QA. Although the QA standards were generally produced for products and services, they can also basically be used for QA in structures and large-scale technical facilities, especially for preparing quality plans and quality manuals.

4.5 SOME IMPORTANT QA DOCUMENTS

Utilization Plan

The aim of the utilization plan is to define the builder's requirements for suitability for use, to agree the service life and the conditions of use and to specify the measures needed. These requirements will relate in particular to deformation, dimensional tolerances, aesthetic effect, vibrations, etc. The agreed conditions of use will include, on the one hand, the agreed type of use and, on the other, all the influences that can be expected during the period of use or service life. The utilization plan is therefore the starting point for selection of the right structural concept. The final decision as regards the structural concept will, however, be determined by safety and durability and, depending on the installation, by environmental factors.

Safety Plan

Structures are generally planned and built without any awareness of precisely what hazards they could involve and what measures could be taken to counter these. The use of safety plans is intended to prevent these mistakes in the future.

The safety plan basically has the following structure:[7]

1. *Specification of safety goals.* Safety goals are given, in the initial instance, by safety requirements in laws, regulations, guidelines, etc. Risk acceptance and safety costs should also be borne in mind when working out safety goals.
2. *System analysis.* The artefacts are treated as self-contained systems and the individual components are described.
3. *Hazard analysis and evaluation of risk.* The hazards connected with the

artefacts are determined and the risk evaluated. The hazards are basically of the following types:

(a) Hazards from the natural environment, such as snow, storms, avalanches, earthquakes, etc.

(b) Hazards from the technical environment, such as fire collision of vehicles, explosions, overloading, etc.

(c) Hazards from failure of the system components, such as columns, beams, foundations, reinforcement, installations, etc.

(d) Hazards from sabotage and criminal activity

(e) Hazards from materials dangerous to human health and risks of accidents in the workplace

4. *Planning safety measures.* The hazards that exist are evaluated with regard to the safety goals and the most suitable safety measures are laid down. When laying down these measures, the existing risk must, in the first instance, be reduced to accepted levels. After this, a decision is made by evaluating the relationship between risk reduction and safety costs to determine which risks are to be eliminated by safety measures and which are to be consciously accepted.

5. *Feedback.* The safety plan is to be kept up to date at all times. Feedback ensures that the experience gained from accidents and the latest scientific and technical knowledge are included in the safety plan and corresponding improvements are made.

Basically, safety plans are to be prepared for entire technical facilities, including production. However, depending on the nature of the problem, they may relate just to individual components (load-bearing structures, installations, operating equipment). The scope of the safety plan thus depends on the type of technical facility and its level of complexity.

Environmental Report

For artefacts that could cause appreciable harm to the environment, environmental compatibility needs to be studied more closely, and the basic situation set out in an environmental report. The report will indicate the possible effect on the environment of the artefacts and the antipollution measures needed to reduce this to acceptable levels. Basically, the environmental report can be divided up as follows:

- Need for the artefact and its purpose
- Existing environmental pollution (actual situation) of air, groundwater, surface waters, soil, noise levels, etc.
- Environmentally oriented description of the artefact, and in particular a description of the building structure, the manufacturing process and the flow of material

- Effects on the environment during individual phases—construction, operation, cleaning and demolition—and an indication of environmental protection measures
- Effects on the environment resulting from possible accidents and disasters and an indication of environmental protection measures
- Long-term environmental pollution in the individual phases and those resulting from possible accidents and disasters

The environmental report is intended to enable planning application departments and those involved in the building process to take environmental compatibility specifically into consideration as a quality characteristic.

Inspection Plan—Manufacturing and Construction

The inspection plan should give specific details of the inspections provided for in the utilization and safety plan and the environmental report. The inspection plan is particularly important for detecting errors in the manufacturing process and construction. In practical terms, the inspection plan can be structured as follows:

- General summary of inspections, showing what inspections are to be provided for which processes and who is responsible for these
- Detailed description of inspections, in which the background to the inspections is described in more detail (content of tests, equipment needed, tolerances, documentation of tests, etc.)
- Inspection instructions and check-lists, giving the detailed instructions for the individual inspections
- Completed inspections file, where all minutes and reports of inspections carried out are kept

When specifying inspections, the question always arises of the number and content of these inspections. On the one hand, inspections help to reduce risks but, on the other hand, they involve expenditure. Care must therefore always be taken to ensure that the cost of inspections is in proportion to the risk of error or accident. The basic principle should be: the greater the risk, the more thorough the inspections should be.

Building Manual

An instruction booklet is always supplied with every piece of household equipment, saying how the equipment should be used, inspected and maintained. This kind of instruction booklet is not usually supplied, for example, with buildings. This mistake should be rectified by the production of building manuals, to guarantee the quality of the building while it is in use. Basically, the building manual can be divided up as follows:

- Regulations for use, setting out areas of competence and responsibility and regulations governing use
- Risk file, which lists the consciously accepted risks, measures to reduce damage and the persons at risk
- Inspection and maintenance plan, specifying the procedure for monitoring use and the risks involved, and inspection and maintenance of building components
- List of principle documents, giving all the most important construction documentation and where it is kept
- Procedures in the case of change of use, changes to the building and rebuilding work
- Feedback
- Documentation, containing details of inspections carried out, maintenance work, changes to the building, check-lists, reports, lists of plans, safety documents, etc.

Production of building manuals means that damage during the time of use can be specifically prevented. Errors such as not using the building for the intended purpose, lack of risk monitoring, insufficient maintenance, unauthorized alterations, etc., can be prevented or detected in good time.

4.6 IMPLEMENTATION OF SYSTEMATIC QA

Quality assurance should be regarded primarily as the responsibility of the builder. A builder should ensure that the project is assessed in the future, not just on the basis of costs and deadlines, but also in terms of quality. The builder should therefore pursue the three related aims of *quality*, *costs* and *deadline*. These three elements can be described as forming a triangle (Fig. 4.4): quality, costs and deadline. Only if quality is clearly separated from costs and deadlines can projects and project extensions be judged in terms of quality and the best solution chosen.

The builder will make the necessary funds available and assign the QA obligation to specialist subcontractors, while monitoring how this is applied. For normal building projects, the builder will make the project manager responsible for QA. The project manager will work out the quality plan with the subcontractors, instigate and supervise the planning and implementation of the QA measures and support the preparation of quality manuals by the suppliers and contractors. In the case of special, high-risk projects, it is advisable to hand the QA work over to an independent QA organization.

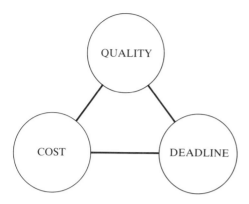

Figure 4.4 Quality, cost and deadline as three dependent aims.

Passing on the QA from the builder to specialists and subcontractors assumes that they—especially the project manager—have received some training internally or externally in the field of QA. It is not enough to ask for a safety plan or an environmental report, for example, if the people requesting and supplying these documents do not know what they should contain or how they should be prepared. Project managers themselves must therefore be able to work out and to apply QA measures. Only then can they hand over the QA work to individual suppliers and support them as regards QA.

4.7 DEVELOPMENTS AND OUTLOOK

Quality assurance in construction is developing rapidly. This development has been stimulated by structural accidents and by research work, especially in the area of safety. Various conferences and congresses have dealt with QA recently, including the International IABSE Conference on 'Quality Assurance within the Building Process' (Switzerland, 1983), Joint SIA/SAQ Conference on 'Quality Assurance in Building' (Zurich, 1984, 1990) and International IABSE Symposium on 'Safety and Quality Assurance of Engineering Structures' (Tokyo, 1986).

The findings thus obtained are incorporated into *standards*. New QA standards have been prepared and many QA measures are already part of technical standards and regulations, such as utilization plans, safety plans, environmental reports, inspection plans and building manuals.

Quality assurance cannot be regarded merely as a practical task. Training in QA should become an integral part of vocational training in the future, from apprenticeships to college training.

The introduction of systematic quality assurance is bound to involve some teething problems, such as employee resistance, changing habits, fear of additional expenditures, etc. However, in the long term, neither the developer nor society in general can afford any longer to build without systematic quality assurance. Inadequate or poor quality costs money. It makes more sense to spend part of this money on quality assurance than to have the expense of repairing defects and damage later. The knowledge is there. It is time to apply it in practice.

REFERENCES

1. *Quality Vocabulary*, British Standard BS 4778, 1987, or corresponding International Standard ISO 8402, 1986.
2. *Quality Systems*, British Standard BS 5750, 1987, or corresponding International Standards ISO 9000, ..., 9004, 1987.
3. The International Organization for Standardization: *General Principles on Reliability for Structures*, International Standard ISO 2394, 1986.
4. Matousek, M., and J. Schneider: *Untersuchung zur Struktur des Sicherheitsproblems bei Bauwerken* (Study on the Structure of the Safety Problems in Buildings), Institut für Baustatik und Konstruktion ETH Zurich, Report no. 59, Birkhäuser Verlag, Basle and Stuttgart, 1976.
5. Matousek, M.: *Massnahmen gegen Fehler im Bauprozess*, Institut für Baustatik und Konstruktion ETH Zurich, Report no. 124, Birkhäuser Verlag, Basle and Stuttgart, 1982. Translated by the University of Waterloo into English: *Measures against Errors in the Building Process*, Canada Institute for Scientific and Technical Information, Ottawa, 1983.
6. *Quality Assurance for Building*, Synthesis Report, CEB Comite Euro-International du Beton, Bulletin no. 184, May 1988.
7. Matousek, M.: Safety Plans for Buildings, Structures and Technical Facilities, *Proceedings of ICOSSAR '89, the 5th International Conference on Structural Safety and Reliability*, San Francisco, Calif., August 1989.

PART
TWO

THE THEORY

PROBABILISTIC RISK ASSESSMENT

B. R. ELLINGWOOD

5.1 INTRODUCTION

Engineering decisions concerning the performance of constructed facilities must be made in the presence of uncertainties that arise from inherent randomness in the demands on the facility and its capacity to withstand those demands, imperfect modelling of complex systems, insufficient data and lack of an experience base. While many of the factors that determine the performance of engineered systems are uncertain, they nonetheless exhibit statistical regularity. Probability and statistics provide a framework for dealing with such uncertainties rationally.

The idea that statistical variations in engineering parameters should be considered when setting design criteria is not new. For example, codes and standards used in structural design specify design values of loads and material strengths that are obtained from probability distributions that are assumed to describe such parameters. Design wind speeds and snow depths are usually based on 50-year mean recurrence interval (MRI) values; such values have a probability of 0.02 of being exceeded in any given year. Dams are designed to withstand 100 to 500-year MRI floods; structures to withstand 500 to 1000-year MRI peak ground accelerations due to earthquake; concrete mixes to yield compressive strengths with a 10 per cent probability of being under specified strength; and so on. These criteria address statistically the possibility of an unfavourable load or strength. Underlying such criteria is the notion that in the presence of uncertainty, absolute reliability is an unattainable goal.

Risk is the natural consequence of uncertainty and thus is inherent in all human activities and projects. The most general definition of risk includes the notions of probability of an unfavourable event or hazard and the consequence of the event in economic or human terms. Since uncertainty cannot be eliminated, the management, if not elimination, of risk through proper design is a major engineering goal. The most common engineering approach to risk management in the past has been to apply a factor of safety in design calculations. In building design and construction, it is known that any structure will fail given a sufficiently large load. A traditional design approach might be to estimate the load conservatively and then design for a load that is twice as great. No one knows what failure probability is associated with the design resulting from this approach, only that failures are rare and that risks are acceptably low. It is easier to make something safe than to estimate the inherent risk.

This approach works well as long as technology evolves slowly and there is opportunity to learn from experience in developing and revising consensus-based engineering standards. However, the past two decades have made it clear that simply specifying conservative values of demand and/or system capacity is insufficient for managing risk. Intuition often fails when rare events determine the basis for design. Many current safety issues involve new technologies where the cumulative operating experience is insufficient to provide information on likely performance of a facility during extreme events and where the consequences of failure are perceived to be unusually severe. If the capital investment in a facility is large, it may be difficult to correct mistakes that are uncovered. For advanced technologies and for applications where operating experience is insufficient to provide a convincing demonstration that safety objectives are met, a more sophisticated and systematic approach is required.

Risk and reliability analysis provide a collection of analytical tools that engineers and decision makers can use to manage risk. These tools can be used to evaluate vulnerability of existing facilities to unexpected demands and to set performance criteria for design so that the probability of unacceptable performance is acceptably small. The remainder of this chapter describes some of the mathematical tools that can be used in the analysis of risk and reliability of engineered facilities and problems that might be encountered. The applications cited apply mainly to structural engineering and the performance of structures. However, the technique can be applied to any demand-capacity problem.

5.2 CLASSICAL RELIABILITY ANALYSIS

The conceptual framework for the application of risk and reliability analysis in structural engineering is provided by classical reliability theory described by Freudenthal and coworkers,[1,2] Ang and Cornell,[3] and others. The loads (demands) on the structure and the resistance (capacity) are modelled as random variables, and it is assumed that the statistical information necessary to define their probability laws is known.

In the simplest conceptualization, we can envisage an overall resistance R and an overall structural action due to the applied loads Q. The resistance and load effect may be those for a system as a whole or for a component within the system; here, we need not distinguish between these cases, provided that R and Q are expressed properly in dimensionally consistent units. We might envisage R and Q as being units of stress (kPa) or generalized force (kN, kN m). More generally, Q might be peak earthquake ground acceleration, in which case R is the ground acceleration at which the component or system fails (such a definition is the basis of seismic fragility modelling, to be discussed in Sec. 5.5), velocity or another response parameter.

The component or system continues to perform as long as its resistance exceeds the effect of the loads placed on it; conversely, failure occurs when the resistance is less than the load. The condition $R = Q$ is denoted the 'limit state function' of the component or system. The limit state, denoted by the event $R < Q$, represents a condition in which the system fails to fulfil its intended purpose in some manner. Most engineered systems have several limit states, ranging from unserviceability to catastrophic failure. The identification of the limit state is an essential ingredient of reliability analysis and must precede any probabilisitic evaluation of uncertainty in the response of the system. The development of mathematical relationships to describe the limit state(s) of an engineered system requires a thorough understanding of the basic system operational characteristics. For a structure, this means that the limit state must be firmly grounded in principles of structural mechanics, validated with the aid of experimental observations.

If the probability distributions of R and Q are known, the limit state probability or probability of failure can be determined as[2]

$$P_{\mathrm{f}} = P[R < Q] = \int_0^\infty F_R(q) f_Q(q) \, \mathrm{d}q \qquad (5.1)$$

in which $F_R(q)$ is the cumulative probability distribution function (c.d.f.) of R, defined as

$$F_R(q) = P[R < q] \qquad (5.2)$$

and $f_Q(q)$ is the probability density function (p.d.f.) of Q, obtained by differentiating its c.d.f., $F_Q(q)$. The convolution in Eq. (5.1) is illustrated in Fig. 5.1. Note that the c.d.f., as a probability, is bounded between 0 and 1, while the p.d.f. is a continuous version of a frequency function or histogram. The limit state probability P_{f} provides a quantitative measure of safety of the component or system that takes explicit account of the uncertainty

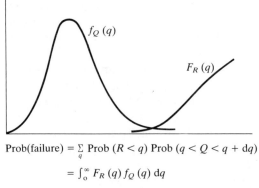

$$\text{Prob(failure)} = \underset{q}{\Sigma} \, \text{Prob}\,(R < q)\,\text{Prob}\,(q < Q < q + dq)$$

$$= \int_0^\infty F_R\,(q)\,f_Q\,(q)\,dq$$

Figure 5.1 The probability of failure as a measure of risk.

reflected in the probability laws of R and Q. Such a quantitative measure of safety is lacking in the traditional judgemental safety factor approach to risk management.

If R and Q both have normal distributions, the margin of safety, $M = R - Q$, also has a normal distribution. The limit state probability may be expressed as[4]

$$P_f = P[R - Q < 0] = P[M < 0] \tag{5.3a}$$

$$= \Phi\left(\frac{m_R - m_Q}{\sqrt{\sigma_R^2 + \sigma_Q^2}}\right) \tag{5.3b}$$

$$= \Phi\left[\frac{(m_R/m_Q) - 1}{\sqrt{(m_R/m_Q)^2 V_R^2 + V_Q^2}}\right] \tag{5.3c}$$

in which m_R, σ_R are the mean and standard deviation ($\sigma_R^2 = $ variance) for R and similarly for Q, V_R and V_Q are the coefficients of variation in R and Q, and $\Phi(\cdot)$ is the standard normal probability integral, which is tabulated in most texts on statistics. The ratio m_R/m_Q is denoted the central factor of safety. The coefficient of variation, defined as the standard deviation divided by the mean, is a convenient dimensionless measure of uncertainty. If R and Q are both described by lognormal distributions, the overall factor of safety, $N = R/Q$, also has a lognormal distribution and the limit state probability can be expressed as

$$P_f = P[R/Q < 1] = P[\ln N < 0] \tag{5.4a}$$

$$= \Phi\left\{\frac{\ln[(m_R/m_Q)\sqrt{(1 + V_Q^2)/(1 + V_R^2)}]}{\sqrt{\ln[(1 + V_R^2)(1 + V_Q^2)]}}\right\} \tag{5.4b}$$

$$\approx \Phi\left[\frac{\ln(m_R/m_Q)}{\sqrt{V_R^2 + V_Q^2}}\right] \tag{5.4c}$$

The latter approximation is accurate provided that V_R and V_Q are less than about 0.30. Other distributions may be specified for R and Q. When this is done, Eq. (5.1) usually must be evaluated numerically.

Equations (5.3) and (5.4) show that the limit state probability is a function of the central factor of safety, m_R/m_Q, and the variabilities V_R and V_Q, all of which are dimensionless. The same result is obtained if other distributions for R and Q are chosen. Thus, risk can be managed by adopting strategies that increase basic design conservatism (increase m_R/m_Q), ensure minimum quality in design and construction of the facility (reduce V_R) and control facility usage (modify and perhaps reduce V_Q).

Structural loads generally vary randomly in time. The strength also can be time dependent as a consequence of structural ageing and deterioration of construction materials due to environmental stressors, damage due to extreme events such as earthquakes and fatigue damage resulting from repetitive loading conditions. Accordingly, the probability that a component or system continues to operate successfully during an interval of time $(0, t)$ is dependent on t. Consider, as an example, a component with random capacity, R, subjected to a sequence of discrete stochastic load events, Q_i, $i = 1, \ldots, n$, during interval $(0, t)$. Let us assume that the intensities, Q_i, are identically distributed and statistically independent random variables, each of which is described by the cumulative probability distribution $F_Q(q)$. Such a description of a stochastic load history provides a reasonable model of extreme events that occur infrequently in time and have a relatively short duration. Scenarios involving such events often provide the basis for design of engineered facilities. If there is no change in the R during $(0, t)$, the reliability function, defined as the probability of successful performance during $(0, t)$ is expressed as

$$L(t) = P[R > Q_1 \cap R > Q_2 \cap \cdots \cap R > Q_n] \tag{5.5a}$$

$$= \int_0^\infty F_Q^n(x) f_R(x) \, dx \tag{5.5b}$$

in which $f_R(x)$ is the probability density function of R. Conversely, the limit state probability would be

$$P_f(t) = 1 - L(t) \tag{5.6}$$

If the occurrence of the events can be described by a Poisson point process, the number of events to occur in $(0, t)$, $N(t)$, is described by

$$P[N(t) = n] = (\lambda t)^n \exp(-\lambda t)/n! \qquad n = 0, 1, 2, \ldots \tag{5.7}$$

The reliability function $L(t)$ is then obtained as

$$L(t) = \int_0^\infty L(t \mid N(t) = n, R = r) P[N(t) = n] f_R(r) \, dr \tag{5.8}$$

Equation (5.1) provides a theoretical basis for the evaluation of safety and performance. Risk is managed by assigning a small probability, P_f, to the limit state event(s). Figure 5.1 shows that this goal can be attained by adjusting the positions and shapes of the probability laws describing R and Q. For this to be a sound basis for decision making, all uncertainties in design must be vested in the probability laws that describe R and Q, and these probability laws must be known. However, in structural safety analyses, these probability laws are seldom known exactly. Failures fortunately are rare and limit state probabilities are low. Consequently, data to describe system behaviour during extreme conditions, described by the lower fractiles of R and upper fractiles of Q, are scarce. The limit state probability is very sensitive to the choice of distribution of R and Q at these extremes, as illustrated in Fig. 5.2. Moreover, the overall resistance and load may themselves be functions of random variables, that is

$$R = g_R(X_1, X_2, \ldots, X_k) \tag{5.9a}$$

$$Q = g_Q(X_{k+1}, \ldots, X_n) \tag{5.9b}$$

in which the parameters $X_1, \ldots, X_n$ are random variables. The functions g_R and g_Q generally are non-linear, and while the distributions of X_i may be known, the distributions of R or Q may be difficult to obtain. The numerical

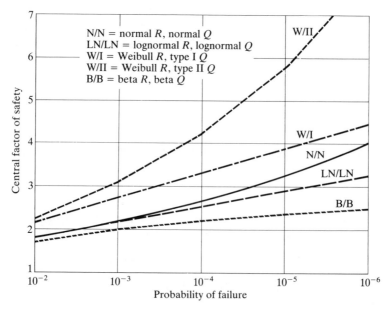

Figure 5.2 Dependence of central factor of safety on choice of probability distributions for load and resistance ($V_R = 0.15$, $V_Q = 0.20$).

problems in evaluating Eq. (5.1) are substantial, even with recent advances in computational techniques.

5.3 FIRST-ORDER, SECOND-MOMENT RELIABILITY ANALYSIS

The difficulties in evaluating limit state probabilities motivated the development of first-order, second-moment (FOSM) reliability analysis methods, beginning in the late 1960s. To illustrate the basic idea of the FOSM method, note that the margin of safety defined in Eqs (5.3), $M = R - Q$, is a random variable, with the probability density $f_M(m)$ (as of yet unspecified), illustrated in Fig. 5.3. The mean and variance of M can be written as

$$m_M = m_R - m_Q \tag{5.10a}$$

$$\sigma_M = \sqrt{\sigma_R^2 + \sigma_Q^2} \tag{5.10b}$$

with m_R and σ_R^2 the mean and variance of R, and similarly for Q. The probability of failure, P_f, is the shaded area to the left of zero in Fig. 5.3. As we move the position of $f_M(m)$ by changing either m_M or σ_M, P_f also changes. More specifically, an increase in m_M (with σ_M held constant) or a decrease in σ_M (with m_M held constant) causes P_f to decrease and thus increases the reliability. This trend will hold regardless of the precise functional form of $f_M(m)$. Thus, the following inequalities are equivalent measures of safety:

$$P[R - Q < 0] < P_f \tag{5.11a}$$

$$m_M - \beta\sigma_M > 0 \tag{5.11b}$$

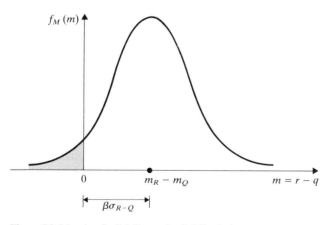

Figure 5.3 Margin of reliability and reliability index.

The parameter β appearing in Eq. (5.11b) is denoted the reliability index. Lower values of P_f correspond to higher values of β.

If the distribution of $R - Q$ is known, the relation between P_f and β can be determined unambiguously. For example, if R and Q are described by normal distributions,

$$\beta = \frac{m_R - m_Q}{\sqrt{\sigma_R^2 + \sigma_Q^2}} \qquad (5.12)$$

and

$$P_f = \Phi(-\beta) \qquad (5.13a)$$

$$\beta = \Phi^{-1}(1 - P_f) \qquad (5.13b)$$

in which Φ^{-1} is the percentage point function of the standard normal probability integral.

When the probability laws of R and Q cannot be determined exactly, β is still a useful comparative measure of reliability. The second-moment properties of random variables (variance, standard deviation or coefficient of variation) provide the most basic descriptions of the uncertainty represented in full by their probability distributions. Equation (5.12) shows that β depends on the first- and second-order statistics (means and coefficients of variation) of the random variables rather than on their complete distributions (hence the 'second-moment' in FOSM). As a result, β is not as informative a measure of reliability as P_f because it neglects higher-order statistical information contained in the full distributions. On the other hand, as a measure of reliability, β is an improvement over traditional approaches to dealing with uncertainty, which essentially ignore the information on uncertainty contained in the second-order statistics and use judgemental factors of safety instead.

We turn now to a general formulation of reliability analysis that is more suitable for complex problems. A limit state of a system can be envisaged as the inequality,

$$G(X_1, X_2, \ldots, X_n) < 0 \qquad (5.14)$$

in which the function $G(\mathbf{X}) = 0$ is denoted the limit state surface and X_i are the basic random variables that describe the material strengths, dimensions and loads due to the normal use of the facility, environmental conditions and possibly accident or abnormal conditions. The function $G(\mathbf{X}) = 0$ separates the failure ($G < 0$) and the safe ($G > 0$) domains. P_f can be written as

$$P_f = \int \cdots \int_D f_{\mathbf{X}}(x_1, x_2, \ldots, x_n)\,dx_1 \ldots dx_n \qquad (5.15)$$

in which D is the region in which $G(x_1, \ldots, x_n) < 0$.

Assume that the random variables X_i are statistically independent. In order to simplify the FOSM analysis, the variables x_i are transformed into a space of unit random variables through

$$U_i = \frac{X_i - m_i}{\sigma_i} \qquad (5.16)$$

The variables U_i are also statistically independent with zero means and unit standard deviations. In the space of unit variables, the limit state function becomes

$$g(U_1, U_2, \ldots, U_n) = 0 \qquad (5.17)$$

with the limit state occurring when $g(\mathbf{U}) < 0$. The original and transformed formulations of the safety analysis are illustrated in Fig. 5.4.

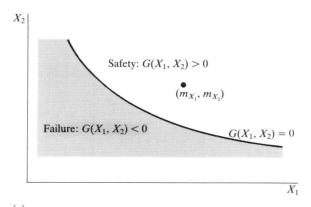

(a)

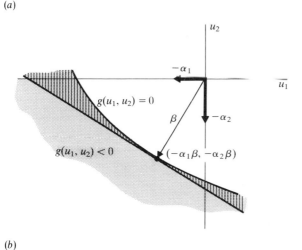

(b)

Figure 5.4 Formulation of reliability analysis in original and standardized variable coordinates.

The reliability index β is defined as the minimum distance from the origin in the unit variable space to the surface defined by $g(\mathbf{u}) = 0.$[5] This definition is a logical extension for a multivariate analysis of the basic definition of β in Eq. (5.11b) and Fig. 5.3. The reliability index can be obtained as the solution to the constrained optimization problem,

$$\beta = \min(\mathbf{u}^{\mathrm{T}}\mathbf{u})^{1/2} \qquad (5.18a)$$

$$\text{subject to } g(\mathbf{u}) = 0 \qquad (5.18b)$$

using any one of a number of techniques.[6] The point on the surface $g(\mathbf{u}) = 0$ corresponding to the minimum distance is denoted the checking point and is expressed as

$$\mathbf{u} = -\boldsymbol{\alpha}\beta \qquad (5.19)$$

in which $\boldsymbol{\alpha}$ is the vector of direction cosines describing the orientation from the origin of the unit vector along which β is measured, and the negative sign arises because $\boldsymbol{\alpha}$ is in the direction of decreasing $g(\mathbf{u})$. The solutions for $\mathbf{u} = -\boldsymbol{\alpha}\beta$ generally lie in the lower range of the distribution of resistance variables and in the upper range of the load distributions.

To show that this procedure is consistent with the earlier development, let us consider the limit state

$$G(R, Q) = R - Q = 0 \qquad (5.20)$$

Making the transformations to the unit variables r and q, by

$$r = \frac{R - m_R}{\sigma_R} \qquad (5.21a)$$

$$q = \frac{Q - m_Q}{\sigma_Q} \qquad (5.21b)$$

the limit state in the unit variable space is

$$g(r, q) = m_R + \sigma_R r - m_Q - \sigma_Q q = 0 \qquad (5.22)$$

The solution for β and $\boldsymbol{\alpha} = (\alpha_r, \alpha_q)$ is

$$-\alpha_r = -\frac{\sigma_R}{\sqrt{\sigma_R^2 + \sigma_Q^2}} \qquad (5.23a)$$

$$-\alpha_q = +\frac{\sigma_Q}{\sqrt{\sigma_R^2 + \sigma_Q^2}} \qquad (5.23b)$$

$$\beta = \frac{m_R - m_Q}{\sqrt{\sigma_R^2 + \sigma_Q^2}} \qquad (5.23c)$$

Equations (5.23c) and (5.12) are identical.

The limit state probability can be obtained by integrating the joint PDF of the reduced variates (r, q) over the domain identified by the lightly shaded area shown in Fig. 5.4. If R and Q are normal random variables, then r and q are also normal and P_f can be obtained directly from Eqs (5.12) and (5.13).

When the limit states $G(\mathbf{x})$ and $g(\mathbf{u})$ are non-linear, $\boldsymbol{\alpha}$ and β must be determined iteratively rather than in closed form. Moreover, the limit state probability cannot be determined precisely from Eq. (5.13), even if r and q are jointly normal, as the integration is performed only over the lightly shaded portion in Fig. 5.4 and not that part of the domain that is shaded darkly. In other words, the reliability analysis we have performed corresponds to a linear approximation of the limit state function $g(\mathbf{u}) = 0$, linearized at the checking point $\mathbf{u} = -\boldsymbol{\alpha}\beta$, rather than the function itself (hence the 'first-order' in FOSM). Provided that the function $g(\mathbf{u}) = 0$ is not highly non-linear, the probability content neglected in the darkly shaded area is small and Eq. (5.12a) may provide a reasonable approximate to P_f. In that sense, the FOSM method can be thought of as an approximate tool for numerically integrating Eq. (5.15).

If two or more random variables $\mathbf{X} = (X_1, X_2, \ldots, X_n)$ are correlated, with covariance $\text{Covar}[X_i, X_j] = \rho_{ij}\sigma_i\sigma_j$, then the unit variables likewise are correlated, with a covariance matrix C_u containing elements $\text{Covar}[U_i, U_j] = \rho_{ij}$. The reliability index is defined as

$$\beta = \min(\mathbf{u}C_u^{-1}\mathbf{u})^{1/2} \tag{5.24}$$

in which the inverse of the covariance matrix C_u is used as the metric on the unit normal space. The remainder of the solution is obtained as before, in Eqs (5.18) and (5.19).[7]

FOSM methods were originally developed to circumvent the need to specify full distributions of random variables. Accordingly, β may not be a particularly informative measure of safety for limit states involving variables that are described by PDFs that are positively or negatively skewed in appearance. To account for general distribution shape in a first-order context, any variable, X, can be transformed to a unit normal variable, U, through the transformation[8]

$$U = \Phi^{-1}(F_X(X)) \tag{5.25}$$

in which $F_X(X)$ is the distribution function of X. Once this transformation is accomplished, the analysis proceeds as before. Techniques are available to deal with correlated non-normal variates X_i and X_j, but require the joint distribution function of X_i and X_j.[8]

5.4 NUMERICAL METHODS

The evaluation of the limit state probability requires that the joint probability density function $f_X(\mathbf{x})$ be integrated over the domain of $\mathbf{x}$ in which $G(\mathbf{x}) < 0$.

If $G(\mathbf{X})$ can be expressed as a sum of normal random variables or as a product of lognormal variables, the multidimensional integration can be reduced to a one-dimensional integration [cf. Eqs (5.3) and (5.4)], which can be completed with the assistance of tabulated values of the standard normal probability integral. If $G(\mathbf{X})$ is non-linear or if the random variables are non-normal, however, the integration is difficult and usually cannot be performed in closed form. Although specialized techniques may be used in some instances to reduce the dimension of the integration,[6] for complex problems involving many random variables we usually have to fall back on some variant of Monte Carlo simulation.

A Monte Carlo simulation is a numerical experiment.[9] Monte Carlo methods provide a powerful array of tools for analysing the behaviour of complex engineered facilities. Applications can be found in areas ranging from system reliability analysis to hazardous waste disposal and radiation transport. Simulation often provides insight on system behaviour not obtained by other methods. In contrast to closed-form solutions, which usually involve numerous simplifying assumptions, Monte Carlo methods allow the analyst to work with as general a model of the engineered system as time and knowledge will permit. Constraints are likely to be imposed by computational considerations; however, computation has become very inexpensive relative to professional services during the past decade.

The starting point in any Monte Carlo simulation is the development of mathematical models that describe the behaviour of the system and probabilistic models that describe the stochastic nature of the engineering variables of interest. One can choose whatever probabilistic models seem appropriate. Once the distributions of the variables are identified, random number generators are available in standard statistical analysis packages to generate the sequence of variates needed for the simulation.[9] In the absence of empirical data, distributions must be chosen on theoretical or intuitive grounds, and sensitivity studies must be conducted as part of the risk analysis to determine the effect of distribution on the measure of risk. The results of a Monte Carlo simulation can be analysed, like any other experiment, using classical statistical analysis techniques.

Basic Monte Carlo Simulation

Monte Carlo simulation can be regarded as a technique for numerical integration. Since integrals can also be evaluated by analytic or numerical methods, reverting to Monte Carlo simulation implies either a very complex integration or an inability to represent the problem in integral form.

Consider the function of random variables,

$$Y = g(X_1, X_2, \ldots, X_n) \qquad (5.26)$$

Represented in integral form, the mathematical expectation of random variable Y is

$$E[Y] = J = \int_0^\infty \cdots \int_0^\infty g(\mathbf{x}) f_\mathbf{x}(\mathbf{x}) \, d\mathbf{x} \qquad (5.27)$$

Now let $\mathbf{X}_i = (X_{1i}, X_{2i}, \ldots, X_{ni})$ represent an outcome from one simulation out of N trials and let $Y_i = g(\mathbf{X}_i)$. Repeating the experiment N times, the expected value (mean) of Y would be estimated as

$$\hat{J} = \frac{1}{N} \sum_{i=1}^{N} g(\mathbf{X}_i) \qquad (5.28)$$

Thus, the Monte Carlo simulation has a direct integral counterpart. The expected value of the estimator $\hat{J}$ is

$$E[\hat{J}] = E\left[\frac{1}{N} \sum_{i=1}^{N} g(\mathbf{X}_i) \right] = \frac{1}{N} NE[g(\mathbf{X})] = J \qquad (5.29a)$$

so that the estimate $\hat{J}$ is an unbiased estimator of J. Convergence of $\hat{J}$ to J as N becomes large is ensured by the weak law of large numbers. The sample variance is given as

$$S^2 = \frac{1}{N} \sum_{i=1}^{N} [g(\mathbf{X}_i) - \hat{J}]^2 \qquad (5.29b)$$

while the mean-square error in the estimate $\hat{J}$ is given by

$$E[(J - \hat{J})^2] = \frac{S^2}{N} \qquad (5.29c)$$

The limit state probability [Eq. (5.15)] can be written as a special form of mathematical expectation. To see this, define an indicator function as

$$I_f = \begin{cases} 1 & \text{if } (x_1, \ldots, x_n) \in F \qquad (5.30a) \\ 0 & \text{if } (x_1, \ldots, x_n) \notin F \qquad (5.30b) \end{cases}$$

The failure probability can then be expressed as

$$P_f = \int_0^\infty \cdots \int_0^\infty I_f(\mathbf{x}) f_\mathbf{x}(\mathbf{x}) \, d\mathbf{x} \qquad (5.31a)$$

$$= E[I_f] \qquad (5.31b)$$

Thus, to compute the probability of failure by Monte Carlo simulation,

$$\hat{P}_f = \frac{1}{N} \sum_{i=1}^{N} I_f(\mathbf{X}_i) = \frac{N(G < 0)}{N} \qquad (5.32)$$

in which $N(G < 0)$ is the number of occurrences of $\mathbf{X}$ in which $G(\mathbf{X}) < 0$ and N is the total number of Monte Carlo trials.

Using the De Moivre–Laplace theorem, the 95 per cent confidence interval on the estimate $\hat{P}_f$ is obtained from a normal sampling distribution:

$$P[\hat{P}_f - 1.96\sqrt{P_f/N} < P_f < \hat{P}_f + 1.96\sqrt{\hat{P}_f/N}] \qquad (5.33)$$

For example, if $P_f = 10^{-3}$ and $N = 100\,000$, the 95 per cent confidence interval on P_f is $\pm 0.2\hat{P}_f$. Clearly, very large samples are required to estimate small limit state probabilities accurately.

Variance Reduction Techniques

The mean-square $E[(J - \hat{J})^2]$ in Eq. (5.29c) measures the accuracy of a simulation. There are two ways to reduce the mean-square: (1) increase N and (2) reduce S^2. Increasing N may become very costly in analysing safety of complex engineering systems in which the desired limit state probabilities are small [cf. Eq. (5.33)]. Variance reduction techniques aim at reducing S^2 for samples of a finite size by either modifying the random sampling process or utilizing prior knowledge in formulating the problem.

Importance sampling is one such approach to variance reduction that has been used successfully in structural reliability studies.[10] Consider the integral in Eqs (5.15) and (5.32) and suppose that the random sampling occurs not from $f_X(\mathbf{x})$ but from another density, $h_V(\mathbf{x})$.

The integral P_f can be written as

$$P_f = \int_0^\infty \cdots \int_0^\infty \frac{I_f(\mathbf{x})f_X(\mathbf{x})}{h_V(\mathbf{x})} h_V(\mathbf{x})\,d\mathbf{x} = E\left[\frac{I_f(\mathbf{x})f_X(\mathbf{x})}{h_V(\mathbf{x})}\right] \qquad (5.34)$$

and thus the estimator $\hat{P}_f$ becomes

$$\hat{P}_f = \frac{1}{N}\sum_{i=1}^N \frac{I_f(\mathbf{x}_i)f_X(\mathbf{x}_i)}{h_V(\mathbf{x}_i)} \qquad (5.35)$$

The mean-square error can be shown to become vanishingly small for given N if we choose $h_V(\mathbf{x})$ as[9]

$$h_V(\mathbf{x}) = \frac{I_f(\mathbf{x})f_X(\mathbf{x})}{P_f} \qquad (5.36)$$

The function $h_V(\mathbf{x})$ is known as the 'importance sampling function'. Of course, since P_f is not known, there is some judgement involved in choosing $h_V(\mathbf{x})$. The effectiveness of the method depends on how good an importance sampling function can be selected. Points in the simulation should be sampled from the region of the domain of integration that contributes most to the integral.[10]

Other variance reduction techniques are available.[9] Among those that have found application in risk and reliability assessments are correlated sampling, antithetic variates and stratified sampling. One particular stratified sampling technique is known as Latin hypercube sampling, and has been widely used in probabilistic risk assessments of nuclear power plant systems (see Sec. 5.5).

Other Methods

First-order reliability analysis, as described above, can be viewed as an approximate technique for numerical integration of the joint density function of random variables X.[8] The first-order analysis involving non-normal random variables [Eq. (5.25)] is tantamount to replacing the non-normal probability distribution for random variable X by a normal distribution at the checking point for that variable.[11] Since this fitting takes place in the region of the distribution of X that contributes most to the integral in Eq. (5.15), the limit state probability $P_f = \Phi(-\beta)$ determined from such an analysis is often very close to the exact limit state probability.

It is interesting that structural reliability analysis has come nearly full circle over the past 25 years in the way that probabilistic information is treated. Early formulations of structural reliability[1,2] were full-distribution methods. Because of the paucity of supporting data and difficulties in performing the necessary numerical analysis, these full-distribution methods were set aside in favour of FOSM methods. Now, with improvements in computation and with availability of additional data to define characteristics besides means and coefficients of variation, full-distribution methods again are becoming favoured in risk and reliability analysis. This reflects, in part, the growth in the use of reliability techniques, which has motivated the development of computational methods and acquisition of supporting data.

5.5 IMPLEMENTATION OF RELIABILITY THEORY IN ENGINEERING ANALYSIS

Applications

The past two decades have seen a growth in the application of probabilistic risk assessment and reliability in numerous areas, including design code development and evaluation of critical facilities.

Reliability-based structural codes The gradual acceptance by standard writers of limit states design over the past two decades has made it possible to develop probability-based design procedures and common load requirements that can be used with different construction technologies. In several new standards in the United States, Canada and Western Europe, probabilistic methods have been used to take inherent variability and uncertainties in loads and structural strengths into account. These advances in the technical basis for codes have been received enthusiastically by some groups; others, however, have been more reticent in their acceptance.

Probability-based limit states design requires four basic types of information:[12,13] (1) a database to describe probabilities of occurrence and intensity of occupancy and environmental loads; (2) probabilistic models of strength; (3) models to describe the response of the structure; and (4) procedures for computing the reliability measures (limit state probabilities or reliability indices) associated with various limit states for members, components or the system as a whole. With this information, one can devise safety checking procedures based on prescribed target reliability levels.

A structural system or component can be defined by its nominal (code-specified) material strength properties, dimensions and loads. These nominal design variables can be represented as

$$\theta = (F_y, F_c, \dots, A_s, l, \dots, D, L, W, S, \dots) \tag{5.37}$$

in which F_y, F_c are strengths of steel, concrete or other material, A_s, l are geometric parameters and D, L, W, S are dead, live, wind, snow or other loads. If the limit state $G(\mathbf{X}) < 0$ is defined for a particular structure by θ in terms of the (random) loads, strengths and dimensions, $\mathbf{X}$, then P_f can be evaluated from Eq. (5.15) or β can be obtained from Eq. (5.17). Either way, the reliability of the structure can be analysed once the structure is defined by θ.

In reliability-based design, the process is reversed. The code performance objective involving the design variables, θ, stated in probabilistic terms, is

$$P_f(\theta) \leqslant P_{f0} \tag{5.38a}$$

$$\beta(\theta) \geqslant \beta_0 \tag{5.38b}$$

in which P_{f0} or β_0 are target limit state probability or reliability index set by the profession or by a regulatory authority. The goal of probability-based design is to define a structure, defined by nominal variables θ, through the use of a set of design equations of the form

$$\phi_i R_i > \sum \gamma_j Q_j \tag{5.39}$$

in which R_i and Q_j are nominal strengths and loads, and ϕ_i and γ_j are resistance and load factors determined so that reliability goals of the code [expressed through Eqs (5.38)] are met, within limits, for all structures falling within the purview of the code. These load and resistance factors can be set by a mathematical optimization procedure that minimizes the squared deviation of $\beta(\theta)$ from the target.[13]

Considerable research has gone into developing the statistical database on loads and strengths needed to implement the above analysis.[12] Target reliabilities were established by evaluating members designed with existing codes; those members were selected for which there was professional consensus that past performance had been acceptable. Figure 5.5 illustrates

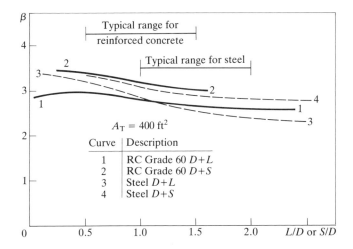

Figure 5.5 Reliability index for steel and reinforced concrete beams. *(Source: J. Structural Safety, vol. 1, no. 1, pp. 15–26, 1982.)*

this process for steel and reinforced concrete beams designed using structural design standards in common use in the United States in the late 1970s. Note that the reliability index β is calculated for a 50-year period of reference. An examination of reliability measures associated with existing design criteria for common construction materials reveals that these measures vary considerably according to structural member, failure mode, construction material and load combination. However, it was found that values of β for many members in which the limit state is relatively ductile, such as beams in flexure, tended to fall in the range 2.5 to 3.0 (on a 50-year basis), higher values being observed for gravity load combinations and lower values being observed for combinations involving wind load.

Thus, design strengths and load combinations were chosen for probability-based limit states design so that reliabilities for members would fall within this range for most ordinary building construction. A partial set of general load requirements for combinations involving dead, live, snow and wind loads is presented below:

$$1.2D + 1.6(L \text{ or } S) \tag{5.40a}$$

$$(0.9 \text{ or } 1.2)D + 1.3W + 0.5L \tag{5.40b}$$

A comparison of reliability indices using existing and new criteria for steel beams is presented in Fig. 5.6. A more detailed discussion of these concepts and their application to steel design can be found in Chapter 2. These criteria are no more difficult to apply in routine design than traditional criteria. They are, however, more amenable to revision as additional data become available.

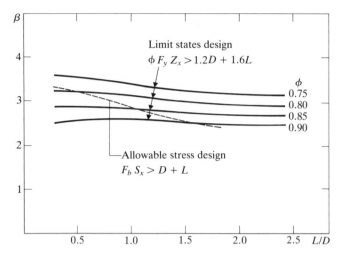

Figure 5.6 Comparison of reliability indices for steel beams using existing and probability-based design requirements. *(Source: J. Structural Safety, vol. 1, no. 1, pp. 15 – 26, 1982.)*

Most reliability analyses conducted to date for general code development purposes have dealt with individual members, where the limit states and structural data are relatively well defined. The use of a reliability index rather than a limit state probability avoids some of the difficulties noted earlier with the sensitivity of the reliability measure to the distribution extremes and the scarcity of data. Since the target reliability measure is obtained by calibration to existing practice rather than by comparison to other societal risks, only a relative rather than an absolute measure of risk is required.

Code requirements are one tool for managing risk. By their nature, they are written to apply to a broad class of facilities. Because of their broad scope, there occasionally are problems when codes are used to evaluate specific engineered systems, particularly when the system falls outside the experimental base of the code.

Seismic probabilistic risk assessment of nuclear plants In contrast to structural code development, a probabilistic risk assessment (PRA) examines the performance of one engineered facility to a specified set of hazards. The end result of a PRA is a probability of unacceptable system performance; this probability can be used to evaluate the relative significance of various natural and man-made hazards and the role of engineered safety features in mitigating system failure. A seismic PRA of a nuclear plant focuses specifically on the earthquake hazard. It incorporates information on uncertainties in the seismic hazard at the plant site, dominant accident sequences leading to plant damage and possible release of radionuclides, and capacity of structures

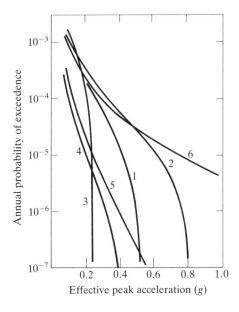

Figure 5.7 Annual probability versus peak ground acceleration at Limerick Station site.

and equipment to withstand earthquake ground motion.[14] Some of these uncertainties are inherent in nature, while others arise from modelling assumptions and limitations in the supporting technical data.

The seismic hazard is described by a complementary c.d.f. describing the relation between a ground shaking parameter (often, peak ground acceleration) and the probability that it is exceeded annually at the plant site. Figure 5.7 illustrates the seismic hazard for the Limerick Generating Station (LGS) located in south-east Pennsylvania. A family of curves is used to describe the hazard and its uncertainty; the underlying earthquake source mechanisms in the Eastern United States are uncertain, and each curve is associated with a set of postulated seismotectonic events. Such curves and their weightings are arrived at through expert opinion.

The plant logic model relates the failures of individual structural, mechanical and electrical components and systems to the end event, herein taken as damage to the reactor core. The logic model, in the form of event and fault trees, is reduced for probabilistic analysis to a Boolean equation which expresses the end event in terms of unions and intersections of component failure events. For the LGS, the core melt event, CM, can be expressed approximately by a group of events, S1 to S17, that denote seismic failure of specific structural, mechanical or electrical components, and events DGr, Wr, Cr and SLCr that denote random non-seismic equipment failures:

$$CM = S4 + S6 + S1*[A + (S3 + Cr)*(S10 + SLCr) + (S17 + Wr)]$$

$$(5.41a)$$

in which

$$A = S11 + S12 + S13 + S14 + S15 + S16 + DGr \qquad (5.41b)$$

The probabilistic description of the seismic capacity of each component appearing in Eq. (5.41) is referred to as a seismic fragility. The fragility is the c.d.f. describing the component probability of failure, given a value of peak ground acceleration, a. A common method for describing component fragility is to use a family of lognormal distributions defined with three parameters: median capacity A_m, logarithmic standard deviation V_R describing inherent (irreducible) randomness and logarithmic standard deviation V_U describing modelling uncertainty. Figure 5.8 illustrates the fragility family for the LGS reactor enclosure structure [component S4 in Eqs (5.41)]. The multiplicity of curves arises from uncertainty in the median, A_m, assumed to be described by V_U.

Using the individual component fragilities in Eqs (5.41), a plant-level fragility family can be determined. These plant-level fragilities are convolved, at random, with the hazard curves in Fig. 5.8 using the Latin hypercube sampling technique mentioned in Sec. 5.4 and rank-ordered to obtain a frequency distribution of annual core damage probability. This frequency distribution, shown in Fig. 5.9, graphically illustrates the difference between a point and an interval estimate of risk. The range in the frequency distribution is a reflection of the uncertainties in modelling the seismic hazard and the fragilities. The 5- and 95-percentile estimates are 2.7×10^{-8} and 2.4×10^{-5}

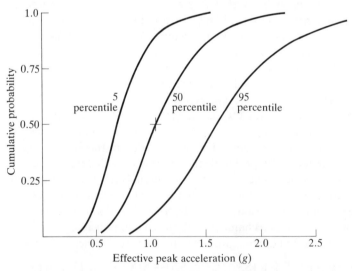

Figure 5.8 Lognormal fragility model for Limerick Generating Station reactor enclosure structure.

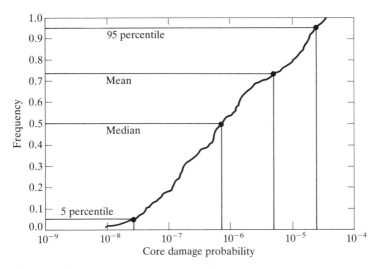

Figure 5.9 Distribution of core melt probability.

per year, spanning a range of three orders of magnitude. The median (50-percentile) estimate is 7.2×10^{-7}, while the mean estimate is 5.0×10^{-6}; the latter occurs at approximately the 75th percentile of the frequency distribution.

Probabilities of this order of magnitude are difficult to give an actuarial interpretation because of limitations in the supporting database. The bottom line risk estimate is the weakest part of the PRA and undue emphasis on its numerical value in comparison with other societal risks detracts from the overall benefits to be derived from the PRA process itself. There is no other comparable structured framework for analysing the role of uncertainty in the performance of a complex engineered system.

Barriers to Implementation

While the mathematical tools for conducting a risk analysis are at a reasonably advanced state of development, the results of the risk analysis are not always robust. There are a number of conceptual and practical difficulties facing the engineer who desires to use these methods as decision tools. Most of the technical barriers are related to the need in the usual probabilistic risk assessment to deal with statistically rare events, the concomitant difficulties in acquiring the necessary statistical data to make the assessment sufficiently credible and the difficulty in interpreting small probabilities for decision purposes.

Lack of data Modern risk and reliability analysis is data intensive, and the analysis of uncertainty plays a central role. Some uncertainty measures have little empirical basis at present. In part, this is due to the approximate nature of the mathematical models that describe any complex system. More important, however, are uncertainties and limitations in the data used to describe the incidence, magnitude and consequence of statistically rare events. Because of the uncertainties in modelling and in the data, the numerical estimates of risk when expressed in terms of annual probabilities, may span several orders of magnitude. Moreover, it may be impossible or economically infeasible to gather sufficient supporting data to reduce these uncertainties in risk in any significant way.

Expert opinion sometimes can be used to develop probabilistic models of phenomena in cases where it is not feasible to develop the supporting data by other means. This is accomplished by means of a structured question and answer process involving a panel of experts. This process can be designed to elicit professional technical consensus from the panel while minimizing affective conflict between the panel members. Among its recent applications in structural engineering have been the development of probabilistic seismic hazard curves for the Eastern United States, and revisions to the uniform live loads in American National Standard A58.1-1982, *Minimum Design Loads for Buildings and Other Structures*. Data based on expert opinion are amenable to updating by Bayesian methods[4] if subsequent information can be located.

Limit state probabilities as a basis for decision Limit state probabilities or reliability indices are the quantitative measures of performance that are missing in traditional code development. Accordingly, engineering decisions or reliability-based design must be based on an idea of what limit state probability or reliability index is acceptable. These target reliabilities should depend on the mode of failure (failure may develop slowly enough to take remedial action or it may occur suddenly) and the consequence of a failure (failure may lead to collapse, extended costly withdrawal from service or minor inconvenience). The reliability targets may not be the same for all limit states if the consequences of reaching the limit states are different.

In support of the first generation of probability-based design criteria for ordinary building construction,[12,13] measures of reliability were determind for steel and reinforced concrete structural members that generally had performed acceptably when designed by traditional methods. Using these measures as targets calibrated the reliability-based criteria to design procedures that have proved satisfactory in the past. Calibration studies provide a useful starting point for probability-based design criteria. If the reliabilities associated with existing structural components that perform essentially identical functions vary greatly, the design criteria are not internally consistent. In the absence of data to suggest that elements with relatively low calculated reliabilities perform poorly in service, it follows that the elements with higher reliabilities may be overdesigned. Thus, unduly conservative design practice can be eliminated without sacrificing performance. Inasmuch as only comparative measures of reliability are needed to render this judgement, FOSM methods are nearly as useful as full-distribution methods for making such improvements.

The process of code monitoring and adjustment used to adjust the reliabilities that are inherent in conventional design specifications may not be applicable for new technologies for which there is limited experience with their performance. Comparing calculated limit state probabilities for such technologies can help decision makers comprehend unfamiliar magnitudes of risk but is insufficient to establish levels of acceptable risk. A more fundamental understanding of the nature of risk perception is required. The willingness of people to incur risk seems to be strongly related to whether they incur the risk voluntarily or involuntarily. People tend to view risks associated with the built environment as involuntary in nature, and the level of acceptable risk is several orders of magnitude lower than what they would voluntarily accept, e.g. in riding in a small-engine aircraft or in mountainclimbing. The dread of consequences is also an important factor in risk perception; one event involving 1000 fatalities is viewed differently from a series of 1000 events, each involving one fatality.

The fact that risk analysis often provides a quantitative measure of safety has created a natural desire to validate probabilistic methods by comparing predicted to observed failure rates. Such comparisons seldom can be made at any but the most elemental level of structural component complexity. Even at such levels, the differences between predicted and observed failure rates are often substantial. There are a number of reasons for this lack of agreement. Suitable limit states for use in predicting failure rates may not be available for realistic complex systems. The first generation of probability-based design requirements reflect only the effects of stochastic variability; however, the majority of failures are due to human error, which may not be amenable to probabilistic modelling.

Finally, safety studies are invariably concerned with rare events and the need to make inferences based on small-sample statistics. A result such as that in Fig. 5.9 presents the decision maker with a dilemma. If the acceptable risk is presented as a single number, e.g. the probability of a degraded core incident must be less than 10^{-4} per year of operation, how is the analyst to be sure that the system is in conformance with the regulatory goal? What is the best point estimate of risk (current thinking leans towards the mean), and how does one justify its selection? What is the significance of such numbers in terms of operating experience, given the inadequate database and the sensitivity of the risk estimate to the distribution extremes? How can one be sure that the analysis of any complex system is complete and that all significant sources of uncertainty have been taken into account? It is questionable to compare probabilities calculated in a risk analysis to mortality statistics or other failure rates that are founded on a relatively large and stable statistical database.

Role of human error on risk assessment Reliability and risk analysis provide a mathematical framework for the analysis of uncertainty. To the extent that uncertainties can be modelled as stochastic variations in loads and strengths, these uncertainties are reflected in the limit state probability (or reliability index) that measures system safety. Modelling errors introduced by the use of approximate models of complex systems and limitations in the supporting database are also taken into account. However, failures rarely occur because of chance occurrences of unfavourably high design demands and low design capacities. Only 10 to 20 per cent of structural failures are traceable to stochastic variability in loads or strengths; the remaining 80 to 90 per cent are due mainly to errors.[15]

Errors occur in all phases of the building process: planning, design, construction and utilization. In the most general sense, one can think of error as the agent that causes things to go wrong. An error is an unintended departure from accepted practice, a fundamental mistake that should have been avoidable in standard engineering and construction practice. Errors are difficult to quantify, inasmuch as their source is human imperfection. There are errors of concept (stupidity, ignorance), errors in execution (carelessness, negligence) and errors of intention (irresponsibility). Such errors can occur even when competent organizations and qualified personnel are involved in design and construction and when accepted methods of quality assurance and control are employed.

Most risk and reliability analyses that have been developed to date have not considered failures due to error. The probabilistic models that have been used describe uncertainty (statistical regularity) under a set of pre-supposed standard conditions for design, construction, utilization and quality assurance. Minor deviations from the nominal values are considered as part of this uncertainty. However, human error effects generally cannot be related to the random deviations in the loads and strengths that current risk analyses take into account. An error cannot be represented simply as an extreme value of one of the design variables used in the reliability analysis. Rather, the error may correspond to a different event entirely, one that may change the applicable probabilistic models and the relevant limit state as well. Although there clearly is a need to include human error in risk and reliability analysis, the human element removes the solution to the error problem (at least partially) from the realm of classical reliability analysis with its foundations in statistics and probability theory. This point is addressed further in Chapters 8 and 9.

Mathematical models for analysing errors and their effects on the building process must be kept simple to be consistent with the current state of knowledge and available data. As with seismic PRA, the process of identifying scenarios of what might go wrong is more important than the calculated numerical risks. Let F denote the failure event of a structure or component and let E denote the event that an error occurs and is undetected. The probability of failure can be obtained as

$$P[F] = P[F|\bar{E}]P[\bar{E}] + P[F|E]P[E] \qquad (5.42)$$

in which $\bar{E}$ denotes the complement of E. The probability of event E in Eq. (5.42) can be analysed as

$$P[E] = P[D|O]P[O] \qquad (5.43)$$

in which $P[O]$ is the probability of occurrence of an error and $P[D|O]$ is the probability that the error goes undetected if it occurs.

Equations (5.42) and (5.43) contain the important notions of error occurrence, detection (and possible correction, depending on the circumstances) and impact. Safety can be managed by limiting the occurrence of errors (controlling $P[O]$ through an appropriate quality assurance plan, work force training, etc.), by detection of defects (controlling $P[D|O]$ through quality control), by minimizing the impact of undetected errors on system performance (controlling $P[F|E]$ through damage-tolerance design) or by a combination of these strategies.

The (conditional) probability $P[F|\bar{E}]$ is the 'classical' limit state probability described in detail in Sec. 5.2. The term $P[F|E]$ can also be evaluated by Eq. (5.15), but the occurrence of the error may change the form of the limit state function, and thus change the joint density function and the domain of integration. The evaluation of $P[E]$ requires the collection and analysis of data on human performance of common design, construction and operation tasks. All terms in Eq. (5.42) must be evaluated in order for $P(F)$ to be comparable to other societal risks.

5.6 RISK AND RELIABILITY COMMUNICATION

Risk is an inherent and unavoidable element of all human activities. The current system of codes and design procedures has evolved slowly over time and generally ensures acceptable safety and performance. However, the levels of risk yielded by the current system are unbalanced and indeterminate. Formal risk and reliability analyses offer a logical framework and quantitative methods for making safety-related decisions and an improved basis for formulating a consistent public policy towards safety.

When probabilistic risk and reliability analyses were first suggested as techniques for the rational assessment of safety, many specialists hoped that their use would enable safety analysis to become automated. Engineers were not long in discovering that this was a false hope. Instead of simply choosing a factor of safety to handle uncertainty, one now selected an appropriate set of distributions and statistics to model uncertainty, performed a set of relatively complex mathematical operations and obtained a P_f or β that could not be related to experience in a meaningful way. Not surprisingly, many engineers became frustrated with the prospect of using probabilistic methods as engineering decision tools. In hindsight, of course, it was unrealistic to expect that a mathematical algorithm could ever be substituted for professional judgement. Risk analysis will never eliminate the need to make decisions. Professional engineers whose main responsibility lies in drawing inferences and making decisions from technical data can take comfort from that fact.

Management of risk is the prime underlying motivation for using risk and reliability analysis. Risk analysis provides a framework for systematically considering what can go wrong with a complex engineered facility. This is one of its main advantages over the approach embodied in current codes and standards, in which the attention of the designer is focused on a limited collection of normative design-basis events. The idea of formulating hazard scenarios as part of safety evaluation is foreign to the current code environment, but is highly desirable in designing complex facilities to withstand the effects of extreme environmental or accidental events. Risk analysis encourages forethought and better allocation of efforts and scarce resources to control exposure to hazards. Properly used, it assists in identifying weak spots in the system design and, at the same time, reduces the possibility that costly efforts will be devoted to aspects that do not really matter insofar as safety is concerned.

Determinations of acceptable risk hinge as much on political as on technical issues. The idea of engineers being the sole arbiters of safety standards is less accepted nowadays, particularly where the technology involved is controversial. Informed involvement by the engineering community and by the public at large are required to ensure widespread support of regulatory policy and decisions affecting public health and safety. Natural phenomena, technology, economics and political forces interact to influence the level and the awareness of the public of risk. This interpretation is evolutionary in nature and is influenced by other than purely objective or scientific factors.

Public response to the earthquake hazard in the Western United States is a case in point. Although previous earthquakes in California have demonstrated the seismic vulnerability of unreinforced masonry construction, hundreds of masonry buildings were severely damaged in the San Francisco Bay area during the Loma Prieta earthquake of October 1989. This occurred because economic issues prevented new seismic-resistant design regulations, promulgated periodically to manage risk, from being applied retroactively to existing construction. The ongoing debate concerning nuclear power is another example of the complex interaction of technical, economic and political issues. Nuclear power is a technology which, by any objective risk measure, has performed well in North America, Western Europe and Japan. The elimination of nuclear power as an energy source would have a severe impact on the economies and standards of living in many modern industrial societies. Nonetheless, nuclear power is vigorously opposed by large, vocal segments of the public in these societies.

One of the most difficult aspects of risk and reliability management is in interpreting the measures of risk for the engineering community, not all of whom may be conversant with the technical methods used, and for the public at large, which generally is ignorant of such methods. Risk or reliability measures such as P_f or β compress a great deal of technical information into one number. Even experts are likely to disagree on the significance of these reliability measures for risk management decisions. It is not surprising that such numbers are misunderstood by the engineering community and are viewed with suspicion by the public. Effective risk communication targets the communication efforts to the intended audience and ensures that the risk analysis process is open to professional scrutiny.

Risk analysis does not create uncertainty, only a means for dealing with it. Above all, it provides a structured framework for thinking about how safety and reliability may be threatened by failures of engineered facilities to perform as anticipated in design. The benefits to be gained by implementing risk analysis include better allocation of resources for managing risks, an appreciation of the positive role that people play in reducing risks and an improved ability to recognize and respond to new hazards.

REFERENCES

1. Freudenthal, A. M.: The Safety of Structures, *Trans. ASCE*, vol. 112, pp. 125–180, 1947.
2. Freudenthal, A. M., J. Garrelts, and M. Shinozuka: The Analysis of Structural Safety, *J. Struct. Div., ASCE*, vol. 92, no. 1, pp. 267–325, 1966.
3. Ang, A. H.-S., and C. A. Cornell: Reliability Bases of Structural Safety and Design, *J. Struct Div., ASCE*, vol. 100, no. 9, pp. 1755–1769, 1974.
4. Melchers, R.: *Structural Reliability—Analysis and Prediction*, Ellis Horwood, Chichester, 1987.
5. Hasofer, A., and N. C. Lind: Exact and Invariant Second-Moment Code Format, *J. Engng Mech. Div., ASCE*, vol. 100, no. 1, pp. 111–121, 1974.
6. Shinozuka, M.: Basic Analysis of Structural Safety, *J. Struct. Engr, ASCE*, vol. 109, no. 3, pp. 721–740, 1983.
7. Ditlevsen, O. *Uncertainty Modeling with Applications to Multidimensional Civil Engineering Systems*, McGraw-Hill, New York, 1981.
8. Hohenbichler, M., S. Gollwitzer, W. Kruse, and R. Rackwitz: New Light on First- and Second-Order Reliability Methods, *Struct. Safety*, vol. 4, no. 4, pp. 267–284, 1987.
9. Rubenstein, R. Y.: *Simulation and the Monte Carlo Method*, John Wiley, New York, 1981.
10. Schueller, G. I., and R. Stix: A Critical Appraisal of Methods to Determine Failure Probabilities, *Struct. Safety*, vol. 4, no. 4, pp. 293–310, 1987.
11. Rackwitz, R., and B. Fiessler: Structural Reliability under Combined Load Sequences, *Computerized Structures*, vol. 9, pp. 489–494, 1978.

12. Galambos, T. V., B. Ellingwood, J. G. MacGregor, and C. R. Cornell: Probability-Based Load Criteria: Assessment of Current Design Practice, *J. Struct. Div.*, *ASCE*, vol. 108, no. 5, pp. 959–977, 1982.

13. Ellingwood, B., J. G. MacGregor, T. V. Galambos, and C. A. Cornell: Probability-Based Load Criteria: Load Factors and Load Combinations, *J. Struct. Div.*, *ASCE*, vol. 108, no. 5, pp. 978–977, 1982.

14. Ellingwood, B.: Validation Studies of Seismic PRAs, *Nucl. Eng. and Des.*, vol. 123, pp. 189–196, 1990.

15. Ellingwood, B.: Design and Construction Error Effects on Structural Reliability, *J. Struct. Engr*, *ASCE*, vol. 113, no. 2, pp. 409–422, 1987.

SIX

PROBABILISTIC SYSTEMS RELIABILITY

R. E. MELCHERS

6.1 INTRODUCTION

An engineering system, for example a nuclear power station, a sewerage treatment plant, water supply, transportation, in fact any industrial, electrical or mechanical system, has a number of components that may 'fail' in one or more ways and thereby possibly lead to failure of the total system. More generally it can be said that systems reliability is concerned with situations in which there is more than one limiting condition which needs to be considered to obtain a reliability estimate for the total system. In structural engineering, for example, the limiting conditions may be the failure of one or more members or, for a single member, the limiting conditions will be the different potential failure conditions (e.g. bending, shear, torsion, axial force and combinations thereof).

As in Chapter 5, the concept 'failure' needs to be defined properly before any detailed analysis can be carried out, and, as will be considered in Chapter 7, a criterion needs to be agreed upon for deciding whether 'failure' has actually occurred. For example, for a structure, failure may be (1) collapse, (2) excessive deformation, (3) loss of one or more members or (4) excessive local stress at one point, etc. For other systems, the context will usually indicate appropriate criteria. In redundant electrical or mechanical systems, for example, one commonly studied criterion is the 'failure' of m components out of the total of k components (e.g. Ref. 1). In this case, the components generally have binary characteristic functions—'fail' or 'no-fail'—and usually the failure rate is dependent only on the nature of the component itself. Generally such simple models of systems are not of great interest and will not be described herein. Concern will be with systems in which there is interaction between the components making up the system and between the components and the system itself, including external loading.

Some of the discussion to follow will be expressed in terms of structural engineering. However, it will be evident that this is not a restriction, since the concepts extend readily to, and have been applied to, other situations.

In attempting to assess systems reliability, it is important to know whether the system changes as it goes through whatever processes are necessary to lead to system 'failure' and whether those processes are best modelled probabilistically or deterministically. If the system changes, it is likely to be 'load-path dependent' and immediately much more complicated to analyse. Such cases will be discussed in a little more detail in Sec. 6.4; for the present, load-path independence will be assumed.

In the next section (6.2) the basic concepts for systems analysis will be introduced. In so doing component characteristics will be described, and event and fault tree notions introduced. In Sec 6.3 system idealizations are described, including 'series' and 'parallel' system idealizations. Calculation procedures are outlined in Sec. 6.4. Systems with several load processes are discussed in Sec. 6.5.

In the present chapter it is important to note that a rather particular and practically oriented probabilistic approach will be assumed to be valid. This approach permits probability statements derived from 'personal' estimates as well as from observation and relative frequency considerations. It is usually associated with 'subjective' or Bayesian labels and this is largely appropriate. In all cases it is important that the best available information be used. Furthermore, it follows that reliability statements resulting from using such information cannot, strictly, have relative frequency prediction content, although in certain situations they may be so used. A somewhat more detailed discussion is given by Melchers;[2] a readable but much more detailed discussion of the various views on the meaning of probability is available[3] and much more detailed discussions are given, for example, in Hasofer,[4] Lindley[5] and Matheron.[6]

6.2 SYSTEMS ANALYSIS

Understanding the System

To obtain an estimate of the reliability of a system, it is desirable that the deterministic behaviour of the system be understood and describable mathematically so that the appropriate relationships between the variables can be established. In particular the behaviour of the system and the ways in which it may 'fail' are of interest.

In many practical problems, however, the deterministic behaviour is not well understood. Rules of thumb may exist or there may be a large uncertainty associated with the existing procedures which 'describe' system behaviour. Despite such limited understanding, the system must be modelled for a reliability analysis, and often the only practical choice is simply to use the best available models, recognizing that there may be a very large uncertainty associated with the predictive power of any such a model. Ideally, that uncertainty should be quantifiable.

Once the model is established or adopted the probabilistic nature of each of the variables in the model needs to be known or estimated. To do so requires that all the uncertainties in the system are understood. Model uncertainty has already been mentioned and will be further described below. To help understand the system and the ways in which it may fail and to help identify the uncertainties, various techniques may be used. They have a variety of names, depending on the industry and area of application for which they were developed, e.g.

1. Hazard survey/hazard inventory
2. Conceptual design safety evaluation
3. 'Hazop'—hazard and operability study
4. Failure modes and effect analysis
5. Cause–consequence analysis

It is not necessary to review each of these in detail but merely to note that each technique aims at a critical review and analysis of the system under study. Each attempts to generate all imaginable possibilities for system failure and all relevant consequences and to identify the factors involved and their uncertainty. Generalizing, each may be thought of as a hazard scenario analysis, with the specific details depending on whether the system is a structure, a mechanical process or an operational procedure.

The actual generation of the potential hazards, the consequences and the related uncertainty factors prior to the design of a system is potentially a difficult process, since inhibited and constrained thinkings may well cause important hazards to be overlooked. Creative thinking techniques such as 'brain-storming' can be effective in this context.

Failure Mode Analysis—Event Trees

Not all aspects relevant to the analysis of a system may be immediately evident. Accordingly, an evolutionary development is often employed. One of the ways of 'unfolding' a hazard scenario is through 'event trees' (see Fig. 6.1). These are based on the notion of a succession of individual events leading to a system failure event. It is the identification of all possible sequences of events leading to system failure that is of interest.

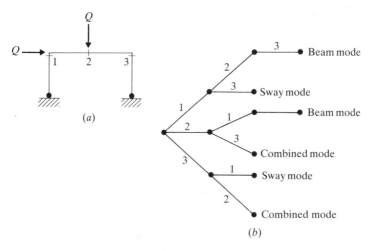

Figure 6.1 Event tree representation. (*a*) Simple rigid-frame structure showing potential plastic hinges. (*b*) Event tree representation of failure sequence by plastic hinge formation.

In an event tree, each complete 'branch' represents a sequence of events leading to failure of the system. For structural systems, each section along a sequence is a local component failure event, so that the complete path from 'intact' to 'failure' of the structural system represents a possible sequence of component failures equivalent to structural system failure. Many branches will not contain sufficient local component failure events to lead to structural system failure, and these branches may be ignored if interest is only in system failure. More generally, even sequences consisting of only some component failures may be of interest in the overall evaluation.

The mathematical relationship for each failure mode is obtained simply by considering the requirements for the occurrence of each event in a particular 'branch'. Thus in the *i*th branch, system failure will occur if each member or component of this branch fails

$$P(F_i) = P(F_{1i} \cap F_{2i} \cap \cdots \cap F_{ni}) \tag{6.1}$$

where F_{ji} is the event 'failure of the *j*th component in the *i*th failure mode'. Here n_i is the number of events in the *i*th branch (failure mode).

In expression (6.1) the intersection sign $\cap$ simply represents the statement 'and'; thus Eq. (6.1) means 'the probability of occurrence of failure events F_1 and F_2 and F_3, etc., for the *i*th branch (failure) mode'. The intersection sign is used so that conversion to multiplication can take place only if the events F_{ji} are independent of all other events in the branch. This is not the general case since components may be dependent through shared material strength or through sharing the same applied loading. For example, failure of member 3 in Fig. 6.1 may depend on failure of member

2. To allow for such dependency, conditional probability statements need to be written for Eq. (6.1) before it can be solved. The reader is referred to more advanced tests for the necessary details.

The mathematical relationship between individual branches or failure mode events F_i and the probability of system failure $P(F_S)$ is given by the union of all (m) possible modes of failure (branches):

$$P_f = P(F_S) = P(F_1 \cup F_2 \cup F_3 \cup \cdots \cup F_m) \qquad (6.2)$$

where F_i is the event 'failure in the ith mode or branch'.

In this expression the union signs $\cup$ may be read as 'or' so that Eq. (6.2) represents the probability of failure in mode 1 or mode 2 or etc. If the failure mode events in Eq. (6.2) are independent, the union signs may be replaced by addition (and this is often a crude upper bound). However, this is not the usual case.

It will be clear that the 'failure' events F_{ji} may occur in more than one branch or failure mode. As a result, the branches or failure modes are dependent, even if the events governing individual branch failure are not. It is this feature together with possible dependence of individual events F_{ij} that distinguishes system reliability evaluation considered herein (and based on structural systems reliability theory) from much of the earlier work on electrical and mechanical systems.

Failure Mode Analysis—Fault Trees

Whereas event trees consider the sequence of events leading to system failure, fault trees commence with the failure event (the 'top' event) and show the subevents contributing to that event. A typical fault tree representation for the rigid–plastic failure of a simple frame is shown in Fig. 6.2. The essential procedure is to take the 'top' event and to decompose it into contributing subevents, which are themselves decomposed in turn. The lowest subevents

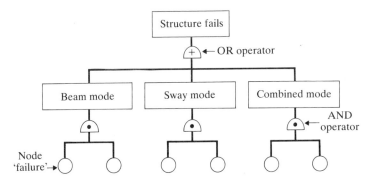

Figure 6.2 Fault tree representation.

usually consist of 'random' material failure, human error (operator, designer, checker, etc.), 'random' unforeseen natural event (wind, earthquake, etc.) or simply a limit to which information is available or beyond which the analyst considers it unnecessary to go.

Fault tree analysis relies heavily on being able to identify all important 'top' events—neglect of even one may lead to serious consequences for the accuracy of the risk analysis. As noted before, creative thinking techniques are important aids in establishing possible 'top' events. In new technologies some 'top' events will be established only after there has been an 'accident' at the system itself or at a similar system.

For systems in which it is known that the individual events are all independent of each other, strategies exist for identification of the 'minimal cut sets' or failure modes of the system. Algorithms to do this are available in the literature. Similarly, if probability statements can be made about the occurrence of each subevent, the probability of occurrence of the top event can be obtained relatively easily for independent subevents (e.g. Ref. 1). However, the situation is much more difficult if dependence must be considered. As noted already, such dependence may exist as a result of the nature of the system. For example, considering a structural system if a column fails but the structural system does not, there will be a redistribution of the way the load is carried by the system. This will affect the stress levels, in all or some of the other structural components, and hence their failure mechanisms. Failure of the next component is therefore dependent on failure of the first, and hence most events are conditional events. This has led to the notion of a 'modified' fault tree analysis for structural systems[7] but it should have application also to other systems with 'load'-type dependency.

Survival Mode Analysis

The ideas considered so far take a conventional approach, namely identification of ways in which the system can fail. It should be clear, intuitively, that if a failure mode is overlooked, there will be greater confidence in the system than is warranted, since the failure probability will be underestimated.

A completely different way of looking at the problem is to attempt to identify ways in which the system can survive or function. In this case, if a 'survival mode' is overlooked, the system reliability will be underestimated and the system failure probability will be overestimated. This approach is therefore a conservative one. It is most readily illustrated with a simple example.[2]

Consider again the simple 'plastic' portal frame shown in Fig. 6.1(a). The frame will survive (i.e. not collapse plastically) if at least one of the following combinations of plastic node events occurs (see Fig. 6.3):

1. Nodes 1, 2 and 3 survive (i.e. path ABEH)

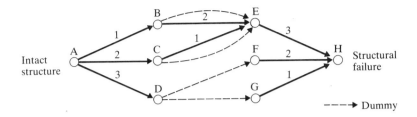

Figure 6.3 Survival mode representation.

2. Nodes 2, 1 and 3 survive (i.e. path ACEH)
3. Nodes 3 and 2 survive (i.e. path ADFH)
4. Nodes 3 and 1 survive (i.e. path ADGH)

Note that in the first two cases all nodes survive while in the third and fourth case one node (1 and 2, respectively) might actually fail without causing system failure.

Mathematically, the above statements may be written in terms of the probability of survival in the ith mode, as

$$P(S_i) = P(S_{1i} \cap S_{2i} \cap S_{3i} \cap \cdots \cap S_{li}) \tag{6.3}$$

where S_{ji} represents the event 'survival of the jth node in the ith survival mode'. The number l represents the number of nodes that make up the survival mode. Thus for event 1 above, Eq. (6.3) would read

$$P(S_{(i)}) = P[(AB) \cap (BE) \cap (EH)]$$

or equivalently

$$P(S_{(i)}) = P[\text{node}(1) \cap \text{node}(2) \cap \text{node}(3)]$$

Note that, in general, 'node' can be interpreted simply as a component of the system.

System survival requires survival in at least one survival mode, so that the probability of system survival is

$$p_s = P(S_s) = P(S_1 \cup S_2 \cup \cdots \cup S_k) \tag{6.4}$$

where S_s represents the event 'system survival' and the S_i are obtained from Eq. (6.3). Evidently, the probability of system failure is given by

$$P(F_s) = p_f = 1 - p_s = 1 - P(S_s) \tag{6.5}$$

The above approach, despite its appeal, has not been used widely in system reliability work. One of the difficulties is that the notion 'survival mode' appears to have less intuitive appeal than the 'failure mode' notion. For structural systems it is also not necessarily easily identified.

Basic Variables and Uncertainty

The equations presented so far are in terms of unions and intersections of events. To render these expressions operational requires that the events be describable in terms of the variables that govern them. Such variables are known as 'basic variables'. Each is described by a probability density function which models and expresses the expected value (mean) and the uncertainty (e.g. variance) associated with the value of the variable.

As noted in Chapter 5, the 'basic variables' may represent properties of the system (e.g. dimensions, strengths, capacities, etc.), applied loads (e.g. dead load, wind load, temperature variations, water pressure, etc.) or other factors. The latter may be used as multipliers or additive factors to allow for effects that are not necessarily well understood but about which some probabilistic information is available or can be obtained (e.g. mean, standard deviation). These factors can be used to represent all or some of the types of uncertainties that can arise in system reliability problems:

1. *Physical uncertainty* arises from limited understanding of the physical nature of a phenomenon or variable. It can usually be reduced by more detailed investigation, modelling and increased data collection (see also model uncertainty).
2. *Human factor uncertainty* arises from the uncertain effect of human involvement in projects. It is very important for realistic system reliability analysis that this matter be properly considered and adequately modelled. However, it is true to say that it is probably the least developed area of system reliability analysis.
3. *Physical modelling uncertainty* arises from the use of simplified models to represent system behaviour and/or physical phenomena.
4. *Statistical uncertainty* arises from the use of simplified probabilistic models (or description) of the uncertainties associated with a basic variable.
5. *Prediction uncertainty* arises from uncertainty in being able to predict a future state of affairs from existing information. This can be considered as another form of modelling uncertainty since some model for extrapolating into the future must be adopted to allow prediction to occur (even if the model is really quite implicit).
6. *Decision uncertainty* is that associated with deciding whether a phenomenon has actually occurred, for example deciding whether system failure has occurred. It may also be part of human factors uncertainty if the decision-making process is part of the system.

All of the above types of uncertainties can be grouped together and considered as uncertainty in the probabilistic modelling of the problem of interest. In all cases more detailed investigation and understanding could lead to better descriptions: the decision not to proceed with such work is a modelling decision and not one of inherent uncertainty. (In fact it is difficult to image a situation that is truly characterized by inherent uncertainty—see, for example, Ref. 6.)

6.3 SYSTEMS RELIABILITY FORMULATION AND IDEALIZATIONS

Two basic system idealizations can be identified. These have particular relevance in system reliability formulation and methods of failure probability computation. It will be convenient to formulate the system failure problem and then to consider the idealizations. Discussion of the computational possibilities will be deferred to Sec. 6.4.

Let $\mathbf{X}$ be a vector of basic random variables (loads, strength parameters, dimensions, etc.) (see Chapter 5) for which $f_{\mathbf{X}}(\ )$ is a known multivariate probability density function (p.d.f.). Also, let each failure mode F_i $(i = 1, \ldots, m)$ be represented by a so-called limit state equation $G_i(\mathbf{x}) = 0$ in basic variable space such that the domain $D: G_i < 0$ represents failure in the ith mode. Three such limit state equations are shown in Fig. 6.4 in the special case where $\mathbf{X}$ is two dimensional. The union of all these domains represents the region in which there is failure of the system according to Eq. (6.2). The contours of the 'hill' representing $f_{\mathbf{X}}(\ )$ are also shown.

The probability of failure is obtained from the probability expressed by $f_{\mathbf{X}}(\ )$ and which is within the total failure domain D, since at all points within

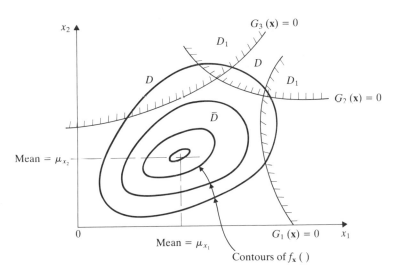

Figure 6.4 Basic structural reliability problem in two dimensions.

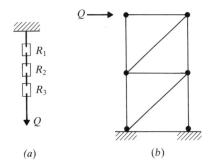

Figure 6.5 Series systems. (*a*) Chain as a series system. (*b*) Triangulated truss as a series system.

(*a*)   (*b*)

D at least one failure mode occurs. Thus the 'volume' under $f_X(\ )$ within D is the integral over the total shade-bounded zone in Fig. 6.4 given by

$$p_f = \int \cdots \int_{D \in X} f_X(x)\, dx \qquad (6.6)$$

The calculation required in Eq. (6.6) is generally not straightforward, but a simple physical interpretation can be given to the result. Imagine a chain of several links supporting a load as shown in Fig. 6.5(*a*). Failure of any one of the links will cause the load to fall, so that the 'structural system' fails—this is the interpretation of Eq. (6.2). Such a system is referred to as a 'weakest' link system or a 'series' system. It is an idealization for statically determinate structural systems (which 'fail' if one (or more) member fails) and for statically indeterminate structural systems governed by a maximum allowable stress criterion (i.e. the structural system is considered to have failed if anywhere within it some specified allowable stress is exceeded).

A further interpretation may be given. In Fig. 6.4 the zone $\bar{D}$, defined as the region *not* covered by D or D_1, represents survival of the system or the 'intersection' of the survival of each element in the chain, given by

$$\bigcap_{i=1}^{m} [G_i(x) > 0] \qquad (6.7)$$

Thus the probability of survival which corresponds to Eq. (6.3) is

$$p_s = \int \cdots \int_{\bar{D}} f_X(x)\, dx \qquad (6.8)$$

A physical interpretation can be given directly by considering again the structures shown in Fig. 6.5. For the structures to survive, each link in the chain must survive, and nowhere must the permissible stress be exceeded in the (statically indeterminate) structural system.

A different type of idealization is that of 'parallel' structural systems

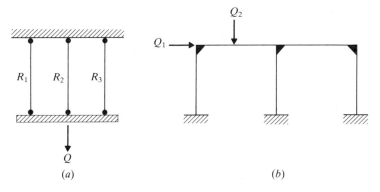

Figure 6.6 Parallel systems.

(see Fig. 6.6). In these, all critical elements must fail before the structural system fails. Thus all bars in Fig. 6.6(a) must yield to obtain the ultimate load, and in Fig. 6.6(b) all relevant plastic hinges must form for a particular collapse mode to occur. This may be expressed as failure of the system, given by Eq. (6.1), if F_i is defined as the event 'failure (e.g. yield) of the ith component'. Alternatively, if F_i is given by the limit state equation $G_i < 0$, the intersection of limit states of Eq. (6.1) is represented in Fig. 6.4 by the domain D_1, so that the probability of failure is

$$p_f = \int \cdots \int_{D_1} f_X(\mathbf{x})\,d\mathbf{x} \qquad (6.9)$$

The idealization of a structural system as a 'parallel' system works very well if the structural components are ideal rigid-plastic. Then conventional 'plastic' theory of structures can be applied directly to obtain expressions for limit state functions. For ideal elastic-brittle materials, failure of one element tends to lead to overloading and hence failure of other elements (progressive collapse) so that brittle systems are often assumed to fail with failure of the first member. For highly redundant systems, however, this is a rather conservative assumption. The situation is more complex for more realistic member behaviours.

6.4 COMPUTATIONAL APPROACHES

General

As in the reliability calculation for simple systems described in Chapter 5, there are essentially two types of approaches to the calculation of probability of failure or limit state violation: (1) methods in which the integration over the failure domain is carried out numerically, using either accepted techniques of numerical integration or Monte Carlo techniques, and (2) analytical methods in which simplifications are made to the probability density functions describing the random variables and so allowing the integration to be carried out. Various hybrid procedures can also be developed.

For the present it will be assumed that the system is such that the limit state functions are known and do not change during the system failure process. It will also be assumed that the loading is such that the 'time-independent' approach is valid. As noted in Chapter 5, this means that the loading has been so selected as to represent the maximum that will occur on the system during its expected lifetime. It is usually obtained by considering the maximum load that occurs in any one year and using an extreme value distribution to describe its probabilistic nature. The system is then assumed to be loaded only once by the extreme loading and the probability calculated is that of failure under the extreme loading event. Clearly this loading situation must be restricted to just one load or to one loading configuration in which all load components are completely (statistically) dependent.

In situations where more than one independent load acts on the structure, all loads must be considered in a 'load-combination' problem to produce the net effect as a single parameter equivalent load or structural action. However, there are limitations to the applicability of this approach (e.g. linear elastic structures). In general a 'time-dependent' reliability problem must be solved in which explicit consideration is given to each load. Some comments about the procedure for doing this will be made in Sec. 6.5, although a thorough treatment of this topic is beyond the scope of this chapter.

Numerical Methods

It is possible to use conventional methods of numerical integration to integrate the probability density $f_X(\ )$ over the failure domain D as given in Eq. (6.6). However, ordinary numerical integration of Eq. (6.6) becomes prohibitive in terms of computer time if X has more than about four or five components, as can occur in many realistic problems. The problem becomes worse when in addition there are several limit state equations to be evaluated for any given set of values of X. It is therefore necessary to look for more efficient numerical integration schemes.

One way in which the computation time can be reduced to a manageable amount is to turn to Monte Carlo techniques. In these, random selection is made of X values, selected from $f_X(\ )$, and the limit state equation(s) evaluated. If the system fails, under this deterministic evaluation, a counter is incremented. After a large number of samples, the total in the counter divided by the total number of samples estimates the failure probability. As will be readily evident, this scheme is not very efficient for very low probabilities of failure (e.g. 10^{-3}) as very many samples will be required (e.g. 10^4) to get only a few (e.g. 10) samples for which the system fails. Hence the accuracy will be low and the effort large. The problem is that most of the samples in the above scheme fall in regions in **X** space (see Fig. 6.4) near the means, and only very few in the failure domain. The key to progress is the use of importance sampling. This has already been described in Chapter 5.

It will be recalled that it consists of rewriting Eq. (6.6) in the form

$$J = \int \cdots \int I[\ ] \frac{f_X(\mathbf{x})}{h_V(\mathbf{x})} h_V(\mathbf{x})\, d\mathbf{x} \qquad (6.10)$$

where $h_V(\ )$ is now the p.d.f. from which samples are taken. By appropriate choice of this function, many more samples can be obtained that fall in the failure domain D and so increase the accuracy of the estimate for p_f for fewer samples. It also means that $h_V(\ )$ can be chosen to allow easy sampling to occur [since sampling from $f_X(\ )$ itself may be quite difficult].

For problems in systems reliability there are several limit state equations to be considered. This requires the use of a composite $h_V(\ )$ p.d.f., but the basic principles remain the same.

Various refinements of the basic strategy can be developed. Thus the samples can be clustered in groups and only one evaluation made for each cluster to determine if it is in the failure domain. This is particularly useful when the limit state functions are complex to evaluate. Usually the generation of the samples themselves is not a complex task. A further refinement is to use a search technique to help fix the sampling p.d.f. h_V and to use the evaluations of the limit state functions obtained during the search both for refining $h_V(\ )$ for sampling and for updating p_f. Several variants of this scheme have been proposed in the literature.

The disadvantage of importance sampling is that the regions of 'importance' must be identifiable without excessive computation being required. Unfortunately, this is not always possible. One particular case occurs when the limit state functions are implicit, such as might arise when a finite element analysis or a dynamic analysis is required for the structural analysis. If $h_V(\ )$ is not properly chosen, the estimate of failure probability can be worse than that obtained by a crude Monte Carlo approach!

Response surface techniques have been proposed to attempt to reduce the amount of computation required to evaluate the limit state equations. However, since the format for the response surface is not unique, this introduces a further area in which judgement is required for problem formulation. It also has the drawback that physical visualization is limited to three-dimensional surfaces.

A further possibility is that Eq. (6.6) might be reformulated in the (hyper)polar space. For reasonable forms of limit state equations this has the advantage that the region of most interest need not be identified *a priori*.

Further, importance sampling can be introduced in both the (hyper)circumferential and the radial directions if an appropriate understanding of the problem is available. Although the formulations for the above methods are relatively complex and will not be given here, the actual solution procedures are straightforward (e.g. Refs 8 and 9).

One of the major advantages of Monte Carlo methods is generality. For simpler methods of solution there are no restrictions on the form of $f_X(\ )$ nor on the properties of the limit state functions. Further, if all relevant limit state functions have been identified, Monte Carlo methods converge to the correct result as the number of samples approaches infinity. Bounds to convergence can be obtained using classical statistical techniques. However, it is not always clear how particular procedures ensure that all relevant limit state functions are in fact identified and hence considered. This means that, in general, convergence is conditional. More research is required in this area.

Regarding the computational efficiency of Monte Carlo methods, only general statements can be made. For a given uncertainty in the probability to be estimated, computation time increases roughly inversely with the probability, and linearly with the number of components of the basic variables. Unfortunately most of the estimates that have been given in the literature regarding the number of samples that must be employed to obtain reasonable results are of little value. Much depends on the degree to which the form of the problem can be exploited and on the precise nature of the sampling technique employed (see also Ref. 2).

Analytical and Bounding Methods

The first-order second-moment (FOSM) method outlined in Chapter 5 can be adapted also for system reliability estimation. As noted, it deals strictly with random variables represented only by their first and second moments (mean and variance). Except in the special case where $f_X(\ )$ is actually normally distributed, this means that the failure probability estimate (6.6) is approximated by adopting for $f_X(\ )$ a multidimensional normal distribution. This means that the calculated probability of failure may have more of a 'notional' or a 'relative' meaning (see also Refs 2 and 4).

FOSM is restricted to linear limit state functions and non-linear forms must first be linearized. As noted in Chapter 5, the point about which linearization is usually carried out is the 'design' or 'checking' point, corresponding closely, if not always precisely, to the point of maximum likelihood within the failure domain.

The failure domain for a two-dimensional standardized basic variable space y is shown in Fig. 6.7 as bounded by three limit state equations g_1, g_2 and g_3. Also shown are contours of $f_y(\ )$. Since the system failure probability p_f is given by the volume under $f_y(\ )$ bounded by the failure

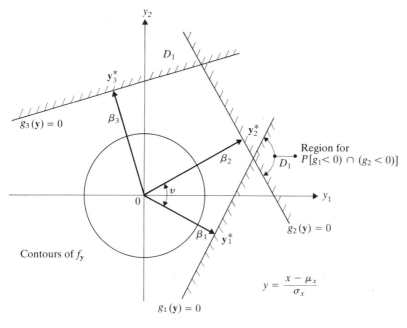

Figure 6.7 Linearization of limit states in standardized space.

domain D,

$$p_f = P[(g_1 < 0) \cup (g_2 < 0) \cup (g_3 < 0)] \qquad (6.11)$$

this probability can be bounded using some relatively simple results. A lower bound is obtained from the individual limit state which makes the greatest contribution to expression (6.11); in the case of Fig. 6.7 this is g_1. A crude upper bound can be obtained for small failure probabilities simply by adding the probability associated with each linear limit state function and ignoring any overlap. The estimate becomes worse as the failure probabilities increase. A more correct argument is that survival against failure in each failure mode is given by the product of survival in each (assumed independent!) failure mode. It follows easily that the bounds on p_f are

$$\max_{i=1}^{m} [P(F_i)] \leqslant P_f \leqslant 1 - \prod_{i=1}^{m} [1 - P(F_i)] \simeq \sum_{i=1}^{m} P(F_i) \qquad (6.12)$$

Experience shows that these bounds are sometimes rather far apart, particularly for systems with many limit state functions or when the limit state functions are (highly) correlated, such as when the same terms (for example loading terms) appear in more than one limit state equation.

Tighter bounds can be derived by making estimates of the joint failure probabilities enclosed by the overlapping failure regions shown in Fig. 6.7, and even better bounds can be obtained by considering higher-order intersection terms (see, for example, Refs 2 and 10).

When the limit state equations are non-linear, the FOSM method requires successive linearizations of each of the limit state equations to search for appropriate 'checking' or 'design' points. Similarly, when the basic variables are not described by normal distributions, the problem can be transformed to standard normal space by the use of the Rosenblatt transformation. This converts non-normal distributions to equivalent normal distributions and may be done in such a way that there is a good match in the region of greatest interest, that is at each checking point. However, this point is not known *a priori*, so that the solution procedure is again iterative. This approach to solving structural reliability problems is also known as the first-order reliability method. It can only seldom be performed analytically.

The FOSM method and its developments are, as noted, analytical methods operating on an approximation of the original problem. There are some restrictions to their application: (1) the random variables X must be continuous and (for most available algorithms) a transformation from x to the standard normal space y must exist and (2) the limit state functions must be explicit and (for many algorithms) continuous with continuous derivatives. In general, the method yields good accuracy for little computation time, although this will depend on the complexity of the evaluations of the limit state functions. Unlike the Monte Carlo methods, the computation time is not dependent significantly on the value of the probability to be evaluated.

Trends

It was remarked earlier that for systems having many limit state functions there are difficulties in bounding the probability being estimated. This is also a difficulty for complex systems having many failure sequences. The matter becomes acute when the limit state equations are not explicit and cannot be differentiated (easily or at all). This might arise where a finite element analysis or a dynamic analysis is required to determine a point on the limit state function. In fact, in such circumstances individual limit state equations can only seldom be obtained: all that will be known is that the system behaved in a satisfactory or unsatisfactory manner and the precise mechanism by which this occurred may not be apparent.

This type of problem is handled rather more easily using simulation methods, since no distinction need be made between different limit state functions and when they apply, provided the satisfactory/unsatisfactory decision can be made. Hence there has been a trend to look at the system in total as if it is described by only one (perhaps non-linear and discontinuous)

Figure 6.8 Stochastic process.

limit state function. However, such an approach cannot be considered wholly adequate in general, since for some problems the precise sequence of component failure can be important.

Load Path Dependence

In general the capacity of a system will depend on the order in which the various loads are applied to it. In structural engineering there are important exceptions: ideally elastic structures governed by a maximum stress criterion (e.g. brittle structures) or perfectly ideal plastic structures. For real structures, however, and for most other systems, the way the capacity is reached is a complex process, depending possibly on the history of the various load systems to which the system has been exposed. Since most loads are of a stochastic nature, there are very many realizations possible for any particular load type (see also Fig. 6.8). When more than one stochastic load acts on a system, the possible combination of loading realizations is clearly large. In general, some of these combinations of realizations are more likely to occur than others. When realizations of loading are plotted in load space, it will be found that the load paths do not, in general, follow well-defined patterns.

In conventional structural design and analysis, for example, there is little direct concern with this issue. It is usually considered sufficient to develop a load scenario for which there is reasonable confidence that it represents one or more extreme load combinations. For shakedown analysis this extends to a loading cycle with properties conservatively approximating those that might be expected in practice. However, in general there is no attempt to simulate the actual time variation of loading.

It should be noted that it is sometimes forgotten that the models and techniques used by convention are accepted because they allow structures to be designed and that the structures so designed survive and behave well. This does not mean, however, that the models closely represent reality, as is required in a reliability analysis (see also Ref. 11).

6.5 SYSTEM RELIABILITY AND LOAD PROCESSES

Stochastic Loading

As noted already, loads acting on systems may be modelled as stochastic processes (see Fig. 6.8). Models for such processes may include continuous Gaussian processes or various discrete or mixed processes (see Fig. 6.9). The reliability of a system under such loading may be represented by the realizations of system capacity or strength R and applied loading effect $S(t)$, as shown in Fig. 6.10. It was noted earlier that in much conventional (structural) reliability theory the stochastic nature of the loading processes is ignored (see Sec. 6.4). More generally, problems with more than one loading system need to be considered using stochastic process theory.

The Outcrossing Rate

The essential ideas associated with the use of stochastic process theory for the calculation of a (structural) failure probability rely on the concept of the outcrossing rate. For illustration, consider a simple structural system problem with only two loads acting. Let each be modelled by a (continuous) stochastic process X_i and consider just one realization of these two processes. This joint realization is shown in Fig. 6.11. Also shown are realizations of the structural strengths plotted in the load space ($\mathbf{X}$). The probability of

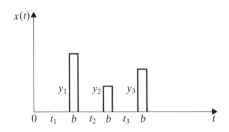

Figure 6.9 Realization of Poisson spike processes.

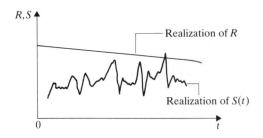

Figure 6.10 Typical realizations of load effect $S(t)$ and resistance $R(t)$.

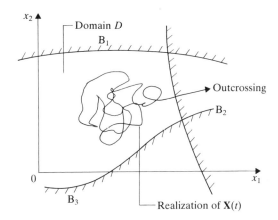

Figure 6.11 Two-dimensional outcrossing from domain D.

failure for the system is now the probability that the system fails at time zero (i.e. when the loads are first applied), plus the probability of the (vector) load process leaving the safe domain D at some later time. If the load process is stationary, that is the description of its probability properties do not change with time, and provided the probability of outcrossing is low, the failure probability for the closed time interval $[0, t]$ may be approximated by the so-called 'first-passage probability', which may be written, in simplified form, as

$$p_f(t) \leqslant p_f(0) + [1 - p_f(0)] \nu t \qquad (6.13)$$

where $p_f(0)$ is the probability of failure at time $t = 0$ and ν is the mean 'outcrossing rate'.

For a given domain boundary the outcrossing rate for a stochastic vector process $(\mathbf{X})$ depends on the rate at which the 'pulses' of the load components X_i 'renew' or reapply themselves as well as the average size of the pulse (see Fig. 6.12 in the one dimensional case). Analytic expressions for the outcrossing rate are only available for a limited number of stochastic process types and then only for simple domain boundaries (see, for example, Refs 2 and 10).

Most real reliability problems are characterized also by the uncertainty of the structural strength (or other capacity measure). This means that the domain boundaries shown in Fig. 6.11 above are not, in general, discretely defined. Hence solution of $p_f(t)$ for given domain boundaries is only part of the problem. If now $f_\mathbf{R}(\ )$ describes the uncertainty associated with structural strength, the structural system failure probability becomes

$$p_f(t) = \int_{-\infty}^{+\infty} p_f(t \mid \mathbf{x}) f_\mathbf{R}(\mathbf{x}) \, \mathrm{d}\mathbf{x} \qquad (6.14)$$

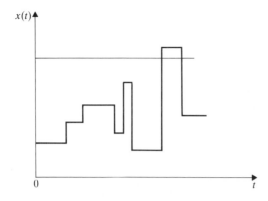

$x(t)$

0 t

Figure 6.12 Realization of Poisson square-wave process.

where $p_f(t|x)$ is the conditional failure probability given that the resistance (vector) $R = x$. It is given by Eq. (6.13). The evaluation of Eq. (6.14) has only recently been addressed in a serious fashion. Essentially two approaches are being explored; a modification of first-order second-moment ideas (e.g. Ref. 12) and a Monte Carlo technique using hyperpolar sampling in the space of the original processes (e.g. Ref. 13). Details of these methods are beyond the scope of this short review; at this stage it is not possible to give a sensible comparison of the relative effectiveness and efficiency of these methods. However, it is likely that this will be similar to that obtained for time-invariant probability calculation techniques.

6.6 CONCLUSION

The present chapter has considered the determination of the basic approaches and techniques for the determination of system reliability. The various uncertainties to be considered in a reliability assessment were reviewed and the analysis of the system was considered in terms of event and fault trees.

It was shown that systems may be idealized as series or parallel systems or complex combinations of these. The reliability calculations depend to some extent on these idealizations, at least for the approximate but analytic first-order second-moment method and its developments. In these methods in particular, various bounding theorems are important to allow practical application.

The intelligent application of Monte Carlo simulation was also considered. In particular, importance sampling was outlined and an indication given of sampling in the (hyper)polar space. Both of these approaches are considered to be particularly attractive for problems for which the limit state evaluations are complex.

Systems in which the order of loading governs behaviour and hence the probability of failure form a particularly difficult class. Some discussion of possible approaches to this type of problem was given.

When more than one load process or load system acts on a system, it may be necessary to invoke stochastic process theory. The basic ideas behind this were outlined and an indication given of the application of FOSM and Monte Carlo techniques.

REFERENCES

1. Henley, E. J., and H. Kumamoto: *Reliability Engineering and Risk Assessment*, Prentice-Hall, Englewood Cliffs, N.J., 1981.
2. Melchers, R. E.: *Structural Reliability Analysis and Prediction*, Ellis Horwood/Wiley, Chichester, 1987.
3. Barnett, V. D.: *Comparative Statistical Influence*, Wiley, Chichester, 1973.
4. Hasofer, A. M.: Objective Probabilities for Unique Objects, in *Risk, Structural Engineering and Human Error*, M. Grigoriu (ed.), University of Waterloo Press, Waterloo, Ontario, pp. 1–16, 1984.
5. Lindley, D. V.: *Bayesian Statistics: A Review*, Society of Industrial and Applied Mathematics, 1972.
6. Matheron, G.: *Estimating and Choosing*, Springer-Verlag, Berlin, 1989.
7. Hadipriono, F. C., and H. S. Toh: Modified Fault Tree Analysis for Structural Safety, *Civil Engineering Systems*, vol. 6, no. 4, pp. 190–199, 1989.
8. Ditlevsen, O., R. E. Melchers, and H. Gluver: General Probability Integration by Directional Simulation, Report 392, DCAMM, Technical University of Denmark, 1989.
9. Melchers, R. E.: Radial Importance Sampling for Structural Reliability, *J. Struct. Engng*, ASCE, vol. 116, no. 1, pp. 189–203, 1990.
10. Madsen, H. O., S. Krenk, and N. C. Lind: *Methods of Structural Safety*, Prentice-Hall, Englewood Cliffs, N.J., 1986.
11. Ditlevsen, O., and P. Bjerager: *Methods of Structural Systems Reliability, Structural Safety*, vol. 3, pp. 195–229, 1986.
12. Wen, Y. K., and H. C. Chen: System Reliability Under Time Varying Loads I, *J. Engng Mech.*, ASCE, vol. 115, no. 4, pp. 808–823, 1989.
13. Melchers, R. E.: Load Space Formulation for Time-Dependent Structural Reliability, *J. Engng Mech.*, ASCE, to appear 1992.
14. Thoft-Christensen, P., and Y. Murotsu: *Application of Structural Systems Reliability Theory*, Springer-Verlag, Berlin, 1986.

SEVEN

ACCEPTABLE RISK

S. G. REID

7.1 INTRODUCTION

Life is full of uncertainties, and the associated risks are an accepted part of our everyday lives. Indeed, Benjamin Franklin (letters, 1789) remarked that 'in this world nothing can be said to be certain except death and taxes', and it is clear that even those certainties are not without risk. The acceptance of some risk is therefore a part of 'common sense', as is the rejection of unacceptable risks. However, the general principles of risk acceptance are extremely complex, and the determination of the acceptability of particular risks is not a simple matter. Clearly some risks are 'accepted' unknowingly, some known risks are accepted because it is believed that they cannot be practicably avoided or reduced, and some known reducible risks are accepted in the sense that they are tolerated because of perceived benefits.

Most common risks can be dealt with satisfactorily using simple common-sense rules based on heuristics, but decisions involving other risks must be analysed and assessed from first principles. Unfortunately the appropriate principles for risk assessment procedures are difficult to identify, and there is no simple way to ensure that a decision based on risk assessment is 'correct'. This can lead to a lack of confidence in decisions concerning risks, both on the part of the decision makers and on the part of those affected by the decisions.

Clearly engineered facilities have their own risks, including risks to life and limb, risks of unserviceability, environmental risks and financial risks. Some of these risks can be practically eliminated (e.g. through dependable design procedures or safe work practices and operating procedures), but some risk is inevitable. However, the risks associated with engineered facilities are generally regulated to provide acceptable risk levels for the protection of the general public, the work force and the owners of the facilities (and also practising engineers). Regulations have been introduced to deal with a multitude of hazards, and consequently the volume of regulations is enormous (and it could be argued that this constitutes a hazard, in itself). Even for normal buildings, the regulations are voluminous and they deal with such diverse matters as the safety and serviceability of load-bearing structures; fire safety; the safety of mechanical service equipment (including escalators and elevators); the safety of electrical wiring, fittings and equipment; the strength and safety of architectural glazing; and occupational health and safety, including requirements for plumbing, ventilation and air-conditioning (to provide acceptable air quality with regard to hazards such as Legionnaire's disease) and controls on the use of hazardous materials such as asbestos.

Existing regulations generally prescribe procedures for the design, construction and operation of engineered facilities which are judged (by the regulatory authority) to be acceptable on the basis of past experience. Over the years, the engineering profession has had great success in setting technical standards that have been accepted by the community, and the profession has taken responsibility for ensuring that the standards continue to be refined to take advantage of technical advances. Engineering scientists have concentrated mainly on the refinement of models describing the behaviour of physical systems, but increasing attention is now being paid to the development of explicit criteria for assessing engineering safety and acceptable risks.

Early approaches to engineering safety were based on deterministic concepts, according to which safety was assured by making safe assumptions about the behaviour of physical systems and using appropriate safety factors based on engineering judgement. Current approaches to engineering safety are generally based on probabilistic concepts, according to which safety is defined in terms of acceptable probabilities of failure. Sophisticated techniques of probabilistic risk analysis have now been developed to estimate the probabilities of engineering failures, but a sound general basis for assessing the acceptability of the estimated risks has not yet been established. The question that remains to be answered is 'How safe is safe enough?'

In the field of structural engineering, the development of probabilistic methods for the analysis of structural safety has led to the development of reliability-based structural design codes. These codes are usually limit state design codes with partial safety factors to account for the variability of loads and resistances. The specified values of the partial safety factors have been chosen to provide consistent reliabilities related to target values of the calculated (nominal) probabilities of failure (often expressed in terms of safety indices). In most cases target reliabilities have been chosen to maintain the structural reliabilities implicitly associated with previous codes. Accordingly, it has not been necessary to establish explicit criteria for determining acceptable risk levels for normal structures. However, the currently accepted levels of structural safety and serviceability are not necessarily the most appropriate, and different risk levels are accepted for other related hazards such as fires.

The need to establish explicit risk acceptance criteria for structures is a matter of concern mainly to engineering philosophers, designers of unusual structures (such as offshore structures) and regulatory authorities. Designers of unusual structures are interested in risk acceptance criteria because they cannot rely on past experience, and regulatory authorities are becoming interested as they see a need to develop fundamental risk-based building performance criteria relevant to all aspects of building regulation (including structural safety, fire safety, etc.). However, the need to establish risk assessment criteria for normal structures is not a matter of concern to the general public, and the community remains confident in the structural design standards established by the engineering profession.

On the other hand, the absence of established risk acceptance criteria has led to crises of confidence in the regulation of controversial large-scale technologies such as those involving nuclear power, liquified gas fuels or toxic chemicals. Engineers and technologists have responded by developing methods of probabilistic risk assessment including risk analysis, risk evaluation and risk management, based on the principles of system analysis and statistical decision theory. If used correctly, the methods of probabilistic risk assessment can provide useful insights into quantitative aspects of technological risks. However, the methods of probabilistic risk assessment have failed to achieve their original purpose which was to avoid controversy in the regulation of hazardous technologies by establishing rational and incontestable technological criteria for determining acceptable technological risks. Instead, the technology of risk assessment is controversial, in itself, and it has not solved the fundamental philosophical problems of risk management and societal risk acceptance. Accordingly, there is still a lack of confidence in the regulation of hazardous technologies, and there is now a need to establish an acceptable basis for the use of probabilistic risk assessments in the management and regulation of engineering safety.

Clearly the regulatory authorities would like to have simple dependable methods of risk assessment and clearly defined risk acceptance criteria so that risks can be satisfactorily controlled from a societal point of view, without undue regulatory complications. Similarly engineers and technologists would like to have simple dependable methods of risk assessment so that the 'correct' technical decisions can be made, and they would like to have clearly defined risk acceptance criteria so that they can clearly demonstrate compliance with regulatory requirements. The general public would also like to see regulatory processes based on dependable methods of risk assessment and clearly defined risk acceptance criteria, to improve public accountability and to restore confidence in the regulation of hazardous technologies.

From an engineering or technological point of view, quantitative methods of risk assessment and quantitative risk acceptance criteria might appear to be both necessary and sufficient for the purposes of risk assessment and regulation. However, the determination of acceptable risk levels depends fundamentally and inescapably on value judgements which cannot be standardized or quantified. Therefore, from a societal point of view, quantitative methods must be contained and controlled within decision-making processes that can be depended upon to take account of societal values. Furthermore, acceptable risks are not predetermined variables in such decision-making processes: they are the product of the decision processes. Thus acceptable risks are the product of acceptable decision processes, just as acceptable governments are the product of acceptable political processes. If a decision is the result of an acceptable decision process, then it is not necessary to agree with the decision to find it acceptable. This is an accepted principle in conflict resolution ranging from industrial arbitration to umpiring in competitive sports.

Risk acceptance criteria and practical risk-based decision-making processes are discussed below, with particular reference to the methods of probabilistic risk assessment. The nature of risk and the techniques of probabilistic risk assessment are discussed in detail elsewhere in this volume, but the general background and principles relevant to risk acceptance are reviewed briefly for the sake of completeness and to set the scene according to the world view of the author. The characteristics and limitations of the methods of probabilistic risk assessment are reviewed with regard to the appropriate role of the methods in the development of risk-based criteria for engineering safety. General principles are proposed for assessing the acceptability of risks and a procedure is described for practical risk-based decision making to regulate technological risks.

7.2 RISK ASSESSMENT

The term 'risk' means different things to different people, and it is not possible to give a precise and concise definition that conveys the full meaning and the connotations of risk. In general terms, risk refers to the danger associated with processes with uncertain outcomes. The nature of risks is extremely complex, and the perception (and acceptability) of risks is affected by many factors concerning the nature of the hazards, the exposure to risks, the possible consequences of undesirable outcomes and the benefits associated with the risks. Some of the important factors are noted in Table 7.1.

Risk assessment is a field of common interest to social scientsis, physical scientists, statisticians, engineers, economists, technologists and others.

Table 7.1 Risk characteristics

Hazard characteristics:
Natural/man-made
Avoidable/unavoidable
Controllable/uncontrollable
Local/global
Continuous/periodic
Familiar/unfamiliar
Old/new
Known/unknown
Certain/uncertain
Predictable/unpredictable
Changing/unchanging
Stable (self-limiting)/unstable

Exposure characteristics:
Voluntary/involuntary
Compensated/uncompensated
Occupational/non-occupational
Continuous/periodic/discrete
Controllable/uncontrollable
Equitable/inequitable

Characteristics of possible consequences:
Likely/unlikely
Minor/major/disastrous/catastrophic
Personal/group/communal/societal
National/international/global
Known/unknown
Normal/dreadful
Familiar/unfamiliar
Permanent/temporary
Controllable/uncontrollable
Reversible/irreversible
Immediate/cumulative/delayed
Equitable/inequitable

Characteristics of associated benefits:
Known/unknown
Certain/uncertain
Essential/non-essential
Equitable/inequitable

However, a general unifying theory of risk assessment has not been developed. Thus risk assessment is a multidisciplinary conglomerate; it is not a distinct discipline. Accordingly work in the field of risk assessment is characterized by a lack of agreement on fundamental principles, and much of the work is goal oriented and based on expedient and untested assumptions. Reviewers have noted these characteristics and generally concluded that risk assessment is an immature science.

However, it is the writer's view that the field of risk assessment includes a social science of risk assessment and a distinct technology of quantitative (probabilistic) risk assessment. The work of the social scientists concerns the fundamental nature of risks, the development of realistic models of risk assessment based on heuristics and the role of the risk assessment technology in societal decision making. The work of the technologists concerns the development of quantitative procedures to expedite risk management (and regulation). The technology of probabilistic risk assessment is not based on the (social) science of risk assessment. Hence the technology is immature and the results are not dependable.

The literature on risk assessment is extensive and rapidly expanding. The literature reflects the diverse and fragmented nature of work in the field and is mainly concerned with the details of particular applications of the risk assessment technology. Literature on the general principles of risk assessment represents various schools of thought, often associated with particular institutions.

Reasonably balanced presentations of work on risk assessment may be found in some Committee Reports and edited collections of papers, including those of Kates[1] and the National Research Council[2] which present concise, perceptive and reasonably comprehensive reviews of general principles. The Royal Society[3] also presents a reasonably comprehensive review of general principles, but the conclusions reflect a technological bias. Other books worth reading include those of Fischhoff et al.[4] for a perceptive philosophical review of risk acceptance problems, Shrader-Frechette[5] for a discussion of philosophical problems of risk assessment and Sassone and Schaffer[6] for a comprehensive and critical review of the related methods of cost–benefit analysis.

The famous WASH-1400 report on nuclear reactor safety[7] should also be mentioned, because it describes an important archetypal case study of probabilistic risk assessment. WASH-1400 concerns the analysis (description) of risks, and the acceptability of the risks is discussed in related reports.

7.3 THE TECHNOLOGY OF PROBABILISTIC RISK ASSESSMENT

The technology of probabilistic risk assessment is based on the presumption that risks can be represented in terms of probabilities and expected 'costs' of possible outcomes of risk-producing processes. Accordingly, the many non-quantifiable factors relevant to intuitive (heuristic) risk assessment are ignored. Techniques for probabilistic risk assessment (the overall process) include techniques for risk analysis, risk evaluation and risk management. Probabilistic risk analysis yields estimates of the probabilities of undesirable outcomes associated with hypothetical modes of failure. The estimated probabilities of failure are used as the basis for risk evaluation, using techniques involving risk comparisons, (including comparisons with 'acceptable risk' levels), the cost-effectiveness of risk reduction and cost–risk–benefit analyses. Corresponding risk management techniques involve risk acceptance, risk reduction and risk optimization based on statistical decision theory. The techniques of probabilistic risk analysis and risk evaluation are briefly reviewed below with regard to the general principles, characteristics and limitations of the techniques, rather than the technical details.

Probabilistic Risk Analysis

The technology of probabilistic risk analysis is based on the techniques of systems analysis and reliability engineering. The techniques have been developed for the analysis of complex systems composed of large numbers of discrete components which perform (or fail to perform) specific functions. Accordingly, probabilistic risk analysis involves:

1. The identification of risk-generating hazards (natural and man-made)
2. The identification of system components
3. The analysis of the functional relationships between the system components
4. The identification of potential system-failure modes (or sequences)
5. The estimation of the probability (or rate) of occurrence of a system failure, for each failure mode and
6. The analysis of the consequences of system failures

The identification of all significant risk-producing hazards (e.g. tornadoes, hurricanes, lightning, explosion, human error, sabotage, etc.) is essential for a realistic risk analysis. The identification of significant hazards (failure-initiating events) is commonly aided by the use of check-lists prepared for specific industries (e.g. the aviation, chemical and nuclear industries). However, the identification of all significant hazards cannot be assured, and the reliability of hazard identification for any system can be assessed only on the basis of long-term experience with the performance of similar systems.

The identification of system components and the analysis of their functional relationships requires an intimate knowledge of a particular system, but various general methods have been developed to identify and analyse sequences of component failures that would lead to a system failure. Common methods of analysis include event tree analysis and fault tree analysis.

An event tree represents possible sequences of events involving the success or failure of discrete system components (or subsystems) which are intended to perform specific functions. An event tree grows from an initiating event and it branches wherever a system component acting in a chain of events might either succeed or fail in the performance of its intended function. Event trees are used to derive estimates of the probabilities of occurrence of failure sequences, based on estimated probabilities of occurrence of failure-initiating events and estimated reliabilities of system components (or subsystems).

A fault tree represents the combinations and sequences of events (subsystem failures) that could cause a particular system failure. A fault tree is traced back from a particular system failure event (referred to as the top event) and spreads down through lower-level events until it reaches the basic failure events (i.e. the basic causes of the system failure, including human errors). Thus a fault tree has a root-like structure. The branching structure of a fault tree is defined by logic gates located at branch intersections. The logic gates (e.g. AND gates and OR gates) define the causal relationships between lower-level events and higher-level events. Fault trees are used to derive estimates of the probabilities of occurrence of the top events from estimates of the probabilities of occurrence of the basic events. Thus fault trees can be used to obtain estimates of subsystem reliabilities required for event tree analysis of failure sequences.

Event trees and fault trees are based on logic, but the results of event tree and fault tree (and similar) analyses are not necessarily dependable. The process of constructing event trees and fault trees (synthesis) is error prone, and problems arise in the analysis of the trees. Problems with event tree and fault tree analyses include: the use of uncertain estimates of basic failure probabilities; the propagation of errors in probability estimates; the treatment of common cause failures (i.e. multiple failure events with a common cause); and the imposition of limits on problem size (for numerical tractability). In principle, the problems of numerical analysis can be resolved, but the dependability of the results depends fundamentally on the dependability of the assumptions and numerical estimates included in the analysis. In general, the accuracy (and hence the dependability) of numerical estimates can be assessed, but the dependability of assumptions (in the synthesis of the event trees and fault trees) cannot be verified except on the basis of extensive practical experience with the operation of physical systems similar in all significant respects to the system being analysed.

Furthermore, the completeness and dependability of event trees and fault trees can not be ensured by their detailed development. In the reactor safety study WASH 1400,[7] event trees encompassed approximately 130 000 potential accident sequences and fault trees were constructed down to the basic component level (e.g. relays, wires, wire contacts, gaskets, etc.) to determine the basic causes of system failures. A representative fault tree included about 300 basic component failure causes, 700 higher faults (intermediate between basic cause and system failure), 1000 fault relations (logic gates) and 30 000 combinations of basic component failures that would result in system failure. Nevertheless, the event trees and fault trees were not complete, and their dependability is questionable—especially in view of the experience of nuclear reactor accidents which have involved unforeseen accident sequences (e.g. at Three Mile Island and Chernobyl).

To complete a probabilistic risk analysis, the consequences of failure are analysed for each mode of failure or accident sequence. The consequences are generally analysed with regard to simple quantitative measures of expected costs, such as probabilities of death for individuals and expected numbers of deaths for communities. However, such simple quantitative measures are generally not dependable indicators of the real consequences of failure.

Probabilistic Risk Evaluation

Probabilistic risk evaluation involves evluation of the results of probabilistic risk analyses with regard to postulated risk acceptance criteria. Methods of probabilistic risk evaluation are generally based on risk comparisons, the cost-effectiveness of risk reduction and/or cost–risk–benefit analyses.

Risk Comparisons

The risk comparison approach to risk evaluation involves comparisons with the risk levels associated with a range of hazards for which risk statistics are available. Typical estimates of risks of death associated with various hazards are shown in Table 7.2. Only a few of the risk levels indicated are directly related to engineering safety, but the other risk levels provide a basis for comparisons. The risks of death due to engineered facilities are generally small (numerically) by comparison with ambient risk levels.

It is often assumed that the risk comparison approach to risk evaluation can be extended to include comparisons with 'acceptable risk' levels. Accordingly it is assumed that acceptable (and unacceptable) risk levels can be determined from the risk statistics for existing (accepted) risks. To account for the wide range of observed risk levels for various activities, different levels of acceptable risk have been suggested for voluntary and involuntary activities and for individual and societal risks.

The distinction between acceptable risks for voluntary and involuntary activities was popularized by Starr[10] who examined the relationship between the risk of death and the economic benefit (measured in terms of direct costs and income) for several technologies and activities. On the basis of his analysis Starr formulated three hypotheses which are sometimes referred to as 'laws of acceptable risk': (1) the public is willing to accept voluntary risks roughly 1000 times greater than involuntary imposed risks, (2) the statistical death rate from disease appears to be a psychological yardstick for establishing the level of acceptability of other risks and (3) the acceptability of risk appears to be crudely proportional to the third power of the benefits (real or imagined).

Table 7.2 Risk statistics for people exposed to various hazards

Typical risks: probability of early deaths per person per calendar year

Cause	Risk ($\times 10^{-6}$ p.a.)
Building hazards	
Structural failure (UK)[8]	0.14
Architectural glazing (Australia)	3
Building fires	
Australia	4
UK	15
USA	> 20
Natural hazards (US)[7]	
Hurricanes (1901–1972)	0.4
Tornadoes (1953–1971)	0.4
Lightning (1969)	0.5
Earthquakes (California)[9]	2
General accidents (US, 1969)[7]	
Railway travel	4
Electrocution	6
Air travel	9
Water transport	9
Poisoning	20
Drowning	30
Fires and burns	40
Falls	90
Road accidents	300
Occupations (UK)[3]	
Clothing manufacturing	5
Vehicle manufacturing	15
Chemical and allied industries	85
Shipbuilding and marine engineering	105
Agriculture	110
Construction industries	150
Railways	180
Coal mining	210
Quarrying	295
Mining (non-coal)	750
Offshore oil and gas (1967–1976)	1 650
Deep-sea fishing (1959–1968)	2 800
Sports[3]	
Cave exploration (US, 1970–1978)	45
Glider flying (US, 1970–1978)	400
Scuba diving (US, 1970–1978)	420
Power boat racing (US, 1970–1978)	800
Hang gliding (UK, 1977–1979)	1 500
Parachuting (US, 1978)	1 900
All causes (UK, 1977)[9]	
Whole population	12 000
Woman aged 30	600
Man aged 30	1 000
Woman aged 60	10 000
Man aged 60	20 000

However, it should be noted that Starr's conclusions were challenged and rejected by many researchers. Consequently, in a later paper by Starr, Rudman and Whipple[11] quantification of risk–benefit relationships was avoided, and it was noted that in assuming 'voluntary' risks:

> ... the controlling parameter appears to be the individual's perception of his own ability to manage the risk-creating situation ... [while] ... the individual exposed to an involuntary risk is fearful of the consequences, makes risk aversion his goal, and therefore demands a level for such involuntary risk exposure as much as one thousand times less than would be acceptable on a voluntary basis.

This interpretation of the voluntary/involuntary distinction is more consistent with the interpretations of other researchers who have concluded that the apparent aversion to involuntary risk can be better explained by the higher potential for catastrophe and inequity that often accompany that type of risk and the importance of dependable controls. Hence a distinction based on the degree of control has been proposed as a generalization of the voluntary/involuntary distinction. Furthermore, it is generally agreed that an important determinant of acceptable risk is the acceptability of the process that generated the risk.[4]

Nevertheless, for the purposes of probabilistic risk assessment, it is still

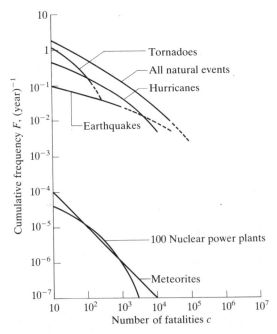

Figure 7.1 Frequency–consequence curves for risks to US population.

often assumed (on the basis of expendiency) that an involuntary risk to an individual is negligible (i.e. unconditionally acceptable) if it is similar to the risk due to natural hazards (approximately 10^{-6} p.a.) and it is excessive (i.e. unconditionally unacceptable) if it is similar to the risk due to disease (approximately 10^{-3} p.a. for a 30 year old). Thus it is assumed that acceptability depends on the particular circumstances (associated benefits, etc.) only for intermediate risks (10^{-6} to 10^{-3} p.a.).

To account for the societal impact of multiple deaths caused by a single event, risks involving multiple fatalities have been compared using frequency–consequence curves such as those shown in Fig. 7.1.[7] Furthermore, it has been suggested that levels of societal risk are acceptable if the relevant frequency–consequence curves lie below certain limiting lines (Farmer curves) parallel to the line for meteorites in Fig. 7.1. However, it should be noted that frequency–consequence curves are deceptive, and the total risk limits implied by Farmer curves are critically dependent on the magnitude of the worst possible event.[12] Also it should be noted that Farmer curves imply no special aversion to accidents causing large numbers of deaths. This is inconsistent with public attitudes which show an especially strong aversion to risks associated with multiple fatalities and catastrophes. Various researchers have attempted to describe this aversion by equating N lives lost simultaneously to N^m lives lost individually ($m > 1$).

Cost-Effectiveness

Whereas the risk comparison approach to risk evaluation is based on the assumption that the acceptability of a risk depends primarily on the estimated level of the risk, the cost-effectiveness approach to risk evaluation is based on the assumption that the acceptability of a risk depends primarily on the cost to reduce the risk. For life-threatening risks, the cost-effectiveness of risk reduction is related to the marginal cost of saving a life. Comparisons can be made between the marginal costs of saving lives for various life-saving procedures, assuming the various costs and lives saved are comparable. Such comparisons reveal that procedures used to save particular lives (e.g. search and rescue procedures) generally have higher marginal costs than procedures used to save statistical lives (e.g. road safety procedures), but there are variations of several orders of magnitude in the apparent marginal costs. Evidently private and public expenditure on safety is not strongly dependent on the cost-effectiveness of risk reduction (as assessed by the methods of probabilistic risk assessment).

Cost–Risk–Benefit Analyses

For the purposes of cost–risk–benefit analyses, it is assumed that all costs, risk and benefits (including those based on aesthetic and moral values) can be expressed in terms of monetary values. The evaluation of economic costs and benefits is relatively straightforward (ignoring considerations of justice, equity, social welfare, environmental impact, etc.), but the evaluation of risks is difficult because it is necessary to assign a monetary value to life.

Attempts to assign a value to life are generally based on the evaluation of societal and personal values (revealed preferences, implied preferences and expressed preferences) or economic values (human capital). It is generally assumed that life can be assigned a value that is independent of the nature of the risk environment, and only the expected costs and benefits are considered.

The analysis of revealed preferences is based on the assumption that preferences (values) can be revealed by the analysis of accepted cost–risk–benefit trade-offs. Accordingly an apparent value of life can be assessed on the basis of statistical cost, risk and benefit data for any activity involving risk. The analysis of implied preferences is based on the assumption that legal decisions are based implicitly on the societal value of life. Accordingly the implied value of life may be inferred from legal rulings concerning compensation for the loss of life. Expressed preferences are determined directly by asking people to express their preferences concerning cost–risk–benefit trade-offs for hypothetical (quantified) costs, risks and benefits. The expressed preferences are analysed to obtain apparent valuations of life.

According to economic models, life is treated as an economic commodity or resource. Economic measures of the societal value of life include; discounted expected future earnings (gross productivity), discounted expected future earnings less consumption (net productivity) and discounted losses imposed on others due to the death of an individual. A similar measure of the personal value of life is the discounted expected future consumption.

A considerable amount of work has been carried out on procedures for valuing lives. However, the analysis of preferences yields inconsistent results, and economic models yield unrealistic and ridiculous results (e.g. discounted net productivity would indicate that the lives of the young and elderly are worthless). Furthermore, all the procedures are fundamentally flawed from a philosophical point of view, because they are based on a principle of quantitative reductionism.[5]

7.4 CRITICAL APPRAISAL OF PROBABILISTIC RISK ASSESSMENT

The techniques of probabilistic risk assessment (including risk analysis, risk evaluation and risk management) are based on quantitative (probabilistic) measures of hypothetical risks. Some of the techniques for calculating the hypothetical quantities in probabilistic risk assessments are elegant and sophisticated, and they give an impression of authority and precision.

However, there are fundamental problems with probabilistic risk assessment, and the results are not necessarily realistic, dependable or even meaningful.

The fundamental problem with quantitative risk assessment is that risks cannot be characterized solely in terms of quantitative parameters. In reality, the nature of risks is extremely complex, and the perception (and acceptability) of risks is affected by many non-quantifiable factors. Clearly, probabilistic risk assessment concerns only a few of the many factors relevant to realistic and dependable risk assessments. Therefore, probabilistic risk assessments are incomplete and not necessarily dependable.

Nevertheless, proponents of probabilistic risk assessment argue that it provides essential information for informed decision making. Furthermore, they claim that it provides uniquely 'rational' results, based on the separation of objective and subjective components. Accordingly, the process of risk assessment (including analysis, evaluation and management) is viewed as an objective process, and the characteristics of objectivity and subjectivity are assigned to the parameters of the probabilistic risk assessment model. It is presumed that the objective parameters include probabilities, direct financial benefits and direct financial costs, and the subjective parameters include personal and societal evaluations of intangible benefits and costs.

However, the claims of objectivity are simplistic and unrealistic. In reality, most apparently objective parameters are subjective to some degree. For example, the very probabilities upon which probabilistic risk assessment is based are subjective (Bayesian) probabilities, not objective (frequentist) probabilities. Hence experts commonly disagree on the estimation of supposedly objective values, and they also tend to underestimate the uncertainty in their own estimates.

Furthermore, it is unrealistic to presume that the fundamental processes of risk assessment are objective. Probabilistic risk analyses are based on analytical models that reflect the predilections of the analysts (emphasizing or ignoring various factors so that the analyses give the 'right' answers), and the techniques of probabilistic risk evaluation and risk management are based on a technological paradigm that lacks philosophical objectivity.[5]

It should be recognized that subjectivity, *per se*, is not objectionable. However, the disguised subjectivity of probabilistic risk assessments is potentially dangerous and open to abuse if it is not recognized.

Criticisms of probabilistic risk assessments concern not only the completeness and dependability of the results but also the effects of probabilistic risk assessments on the decision-making processes of risk management. Critics argue that probabilistic risk assessments focus attention on the factors that can be quantified, thereby diverting attention away from critically important considerations such as the controllability of the risk-producing processes (and associated social changes) and the distributions of costs, risks and benefits (with regard to equity).

From a pragmatic point of view, the usefulness of probabilistic risk assessments can be assessed from their impact on the management of technological risks. The record shows that probabilistic risk assessments have been used mainly to confirm and justify predetermined conclusions, and they have failed to resolve differences of opinion concerning acceptable risks. Thus the numerical results of probabilistic risk assessments are not necessarily useful. However, the process of probabilistic risk assessment can be useful as a catalyst for making explicit assessments of risks (accounting for non-quantifiable factors) within a larger review process. The nature of the review process is all important with regard to the dependability of the decisions.

7.5 THE ROLE OF PROBABILISTIC RISK ASSESSMENTS IN THE REGULATION OF ENGINEERING SAFETY

It would be convenient if regulatory authorities could specify acceptable risk levels for risk-based performance requirements (or a basis for their determination) and designers could demonstrate compliance on the basis of probabilistic risk assessments. However, acceptable risk levels are difficult to define (they cannot be determined analytically for they depend on value judgements) and probabilistic risk assessments are not sufficiently dependable to allow designs based on their independent use by designers (unlike, for example, the accepted methods of structural analysis, which are dependable if not accurate).

In view of the limitations of probabilistic risk assessments, the following conclusions are presented concerning the role of probabilistic risk assessments in the assessment and regulation of engineering safety:

1. Acceptable risk levels cannot be dependably predicted by the methods of probabilistic risk assessment alone.
2. The methods of probabilistic risk assessment are suitable for the investigation of hypothetical results for research purposes. Hypothetical results should not be used for design purposes, unless they are fully supported by relevant and dependable empirical evidence.
3. In most cases, the methods of probabilistic risk assessment are not sufficiently dependable for use in design, because the process of probabilistic risk analysis is based on simplistic models of complex behaviour and the processes of risk evaluation and risk management are based on contrived and undependable measures of risk.
4. In particular cases, probabilistic risk analyses might be suitable for code writing or design purposes, provided: (a) the nominal risks estimated by the methods of probabilistic risk analysis are not sensitive to reasonable variations of the assumptions upon which the hypothetical risk model is based and (b) the relationship between nominal risks and real risks can

be dependably predicted. It should be noted that nominal risks can vary depending on the methods of analysis, and nominal risks can be significantly different from the real (statistical) risks. Therefore acceptable nominal risks can not be defined independently of the particular methods of risk analysis.

7.6 REALISTIC RISK ACCEPTANCE CRITERIA

Risk acceptance depends fundamentally on complex value judgements, and therefore explicit risk acceptance criteria must allow for explicit value judgements taking account of all relevant qualitative and quantitative characteristics of risks (Table 7.1). Furthermore, acceptable risks can be determined only through acceptable processes; they are not independent variables or physical constants in the processes of risk acceptance.

In accordance with intuitive or heuristic decision making, the acceptability of risks appears to be determined mainly with regard to the *need* for risk exposure, *control* of the risk and *fairness*. For a risk to be acceptable there must be a real need to be exposed to the risk, there must be dependable controls over the risk-producing process and there must be a fair and equitable distribution of risks, costs and benefits.

On the other hand, quantitative risk-acceptance criteria are concerned primarily with *uniformity* (or *consistency*) of standards and *efficiency*. According to the methods of probabilistic risk assessment, consistency and efficiency are assessed with regard to risk comparisons, marginal costs of risk reduction or economic measures of combined costs, risks and benefits.

Clearly there are significant differences between intuitive risk acceptance criteria and quantitative criteria. Quantitative criteria cannot realistically account for the full range of risk characteristics included in intuitive or heuristic decision making, and the criteria of probabilistic risk assessment are not generally consistent with intuitive results.

The risk comparison approach to risk assessment is based on the assumption that risks are acceptable if they are relatively small (according to probability measures). However, this approach ignores the qualitative characteristics of risks and ignores the intuitively important principles of need, control and fairness. From an intuitive point of view, risks are not necessarily acceptable when they are small and quantitative risk comparisons are valid only if the risks are comparable with regard to all relevant risk characteristics.

The cost-effectiveness approach to risk assessment is based on the principle that the optimal distribution of expenditure on risk reduction is achieved when the available funds are distributed to the option (or options) with the lowest (equal) marginal costs. However, from an intuitive point of view, this is valid only if: the risks are truly comparable with regard to all risk characteristics (not simply with regard to quantitative measures); the costs are also truly comparable with regard to personal and societal values; and the safety expenditure can be realistically transferred between the options for risk reduction. In reality the above conditions are seldom satisfied.

Furthermore, although the cost-effectiveness approach avoids problems involved with the evaluation of lives and deaths, it implies that all deaths are equally unacceptable (which is not the same as assuming that all lives are of equal value). Again this is counter-intuitive, for most people perceive various degrees of unacceptability depending on the particular circumstances of death. For example, the death of a drunk smoker who sets fire to a mattress is not as unacceptable as the death of an innocent child killed in the same fire. Such distinctions are generally lost in the cost-effectiveness approach to risk acceptance.

Risk acceptance criteria based on cost–risk–benefit analyses suffer from all the limitations of the cost-effectiveness criteria, plus limitations due to the quantitative reductionism required to place a monetary value on human life. Critics of such quantitative reductionism argue that it ignores important differences of kind, so that it is like comparing apples with oranges. Proponents argue that it is an everyday necessity to compare dissimilar things such as apples and oranges. However, the critical point is not that such comparisons must be made, but that they must be made in a way that accounts for the differences.

The differences between intuitive risk acceptance criteria and quantitative criteria are generally attributed to a lack of rationality in the criteria. Proponents of quantitative criteria claim that such criteria are intrinsically rational and that the intuitive criteria are irrational because they are based on risk perception rather than quantitative analysis. On the other hand, critics of quantitative risk assessment question the rationality of reliance on quantitative criteria that ignore many characteristics relevant to intuitive risk perception and heuristic decision-making.

In fact, the presumed rationality of quantitative risk acceptance criteria is of the nature of an untested hypothesis. To test the rationality of quantitative risk acceptance criteria as a scientific principle, it is necessary to define rationality and to devise a testable hypothesis. A reasonable definition is that risk acceptance criteria are rational (from the point of view of a decision maker) if, and only if, they yield the result that the decision maker would choose, given all available information (including the result of the quantitative risk assessment). Using this definition, it is possible to test the hypothesis that quantitative risk acceptance criteria are rational, and it is easy to show that the hypothesis must be rejected. However, it can also be shown that it is rational to include quantitative risk assessments in the decision process.

In view of the above, rational risk acceptance must be based fundamentally on intuitive risk acceptance criteria, taking account of probabilistic risk assessments. Realistic criteria must also account for social and political realities. This is not convenient from the point of view of engineering design and regulation, but realistic risk acceptance criteria can be developed efficiently on the basis of the Pareto principle, equity and dependability. According to the Pareto principle, a proposal should be accepted if it would yield benefits without imposing any adverse effects on anyone. The conditions for Pareto improvements can be relaxed to include improvements such that no individual suffers a net adverse effect and also potential Pareto improvements involving compensating payments. Any proposal that could not yield (potential) Pareto improvements should be rejected, unless it could be justified on the basis of improved equity with regard to the distribution of costs, risks and benefits. Furthermore, realistic risk acceptance criteria must be dependable in the sense of minimizing the possible costs of wrong decisions. For decisions involving the acceptability of technical systems, wrong decisions could involve either: accepting an unsatisfactory system or rejecting one that is satisfactory. In general, the consequences of accepting an unsatisfactory system are much worse than the consequences of rejecting (i.e. postponing acceptance of) a satisfactory system. Therefore dependable risk acceptance criteria are essentially those that dependably control the risk of accepting an unsatisfactory system.

Realistic and dependable principles for risk-based decision making and for assessing the acceptability of risks are given below:

1. The level of acceptable risk is not a constant. It depends on many factors, including the controllability of the risk, and the distribution of the associated costs and benefits.
2. Acceptable risk levels should be assessed on the basis of current (accepted) risk levels, with regard to potential Pareto improvements and potential improvements in equity. In general, it is not acceptable to increase current risk levels.
3. Risk levels should be assessed with regard to explicit assessments of all relevant qualitative and quantitative risk characteristics.
4. If practicable, quantitative risk parameters should be estimated by probabilistic risk analysis and the dependability of the estimates should be assessed.
5. If risk levels cannot be dependably estimated by probabilistic risk analysis, they should be estimated on the basis of empirical evidence (e.g. from prototype testing), and the dependability of the estimates should be assessed. Risk levels should not be estimated on the basis of extrapolation beyond the limits of empirical data unless there is dependable evidence of the dependability of the extrapolation.
6. If risk levels cannot be dependably estimated on the basis of probabilistic

risk analysis or empirical evidence, then the risk levels shall be deemed to be unacceptable.

7. If dependable estimates of all relevant quantitative risk parameters are available, then the acceptability of the risks should be assessed with regard to explicit assessments of all relevant qualitative and quantitative characteristics (costs, risks and benefits) of the system. Acceptability should not be assessed on the basis of single-valued measures of risk such as those contrived according to the methods of probabilistic risk evaluation.

Clearly 'engineering judgement' must continue to play an important role in determining the acceptability of engineering risks. Probabilistic risk assessments cannot take the place of engineering judgement, but they can improve it by providing relevant information.

The application of the principles noted above could be assisted by developing detailed procedures for particular applications. A procedure for the application of the principles of risk-based decision making is outlined below.

7.7 A PROCEDURE FOR RISK-BASED DECISION MAKING

The following procedure is recommended for making decisions concerning the control of existing risks or the introduction of new risks. The procedure could be used by code committees concerned with the formulation of code requirements, the assessment of proposals not covered by code requirements and the assessment of requests for relaxing or waiving code requirements. In particular, guidance is given concerning the use and interpretation of probabilistic risk assessments.

It has been noted that risk-based decision making is inherently complex and difficult because it involves fundamental value judgements. The recommended procedure does not relieve the user of the responsibility (and the right) to make the difficult decisions based on such judgements.

The recommended procedure for risk-based decision making consists of the following steps:

1. Carry out a preliminary analysis to determine the general nature of the decision problem and to identify relevant decision characteristics (of a general nature) and appropriate reference system(s).
2. Make a preliminary assessment of acceptability and determine whether further detailed analysis is required.

3. If a detailed decision analysis is required, identify the particular qualitative and quantitative decision factors that should be evaluated. In particular, select appropriate probabilistic risk parameters.
4. Estimate probabilistic risk parameters by probabilistic risk analysis and review the estimates to assess their relevance and dependability.
5. Carry out a detailed assessment of acceptability, based on explicit assessments of all relevant factors.

Preliminary Analysis

The first step in the decision process to determine the acceptability of a technical proposal is to define the decision problem in terms of its general characteristics. Thus it is necessary to assess the scope of the problem, to identify relevant decision factors of a general nature (both qualitative and quantitative) and to assess the importance of each decision factor.

In decisions concerning the acceptability of technical proposals, the relevant decision factors concern not only the intended (technical) effects but also the unintended (technical and non-technical) side effects. In many cases the intended technical effects may be obvious and the side effects may be negligible. However, in some cases (e.g. involving potentially hazardous technologies) the intended technical effects may be complex and the possible side effects may be wide ranging and critically important.

It is important to identify general decision factors and to assess their importance in qualitative terms before detailed quantitative analyses are considered. Accordingly, a clear view of the whole problem can be obtained, and the results of detailed analyses can then be placed in perspective. If detailed analyses are entered prematurely, there is a danger that the analyst might not see the forest for the trees.

To assist in the identification and qualitative assessment of general decision factors, Table 7.3 may be used. (See also Table 7.1 for a list of important risk characteristics.) The usefulness of the results will depend on the imagination and judgement of the user. Care should be taken to avoid dismissing or overlooking any factor that might be important.

The relevant decision factors define the dimensions of the decision problem, and the importance of the factors determines their weighting in the decision process. It may be possible to reduce the dimensions (and complexity) of the decision problem by choosing a suitable reference system for comparisons. For example, the assessment of a proposed fire protection system might be simplified by choosing a comparable reference system such as an existing sprinkler system. In choosing a reference system, consideration should be given to the acceptability of the reference system itself, with regard to changing standards and anticipated technical developments.

Table 7.3 Qualitative and quantitative decision factors —identification and assessment of importance

	Importance		
Decision factor	High	Medium	Low
Qualitative factors:			
Environmental impact†			
Physical environment			
Social environment			
Ethical and moral factors‡			
Legal and political factors§			
Security¶			
Quality of life and life-style††			
Psychological factors††,‡‡			
Other§§			
Quantitative factors:			
Costs of goods and services¶¶			
Economic effects†††			
Macroeconomic effects			
Microeconomic effects			
Injuries and deaths			
Health statistics‡‡‡			
Environmental impact§§§			
Physical environment			
Social environment			
Other§§			

† Related to the qualitative nature of the environment, including the potential for disaster (no matter how unlikely); especially important with regard to new technologies.

‡ Including equity considerations and moral responsibilities.

§ Including formal rights and responsibilities of individuals, groups and the State.

¶ Including accountability and safeguards against abuse (e.g. sabotage).

†† Related to the general (not only physical) health of the community.

‡‡ Including perceptions, fears and expectations.

§§ Including specified performance requirements.

¶¶ Including initial, maintenance and life-cycle costs.

††† Related to investment, production, employment, social welfare and health systems, etc., including economic costs and distribution effects related to equity.

‡‡‡ Including incidence of illness, life expectancy, etc. (cf. economic measures such as costs of health services, productivity losses, etc.).

§§§ Related to quantifiable parameters (e.g. travel times, pollution levels, etc.).

Preliminary Assessment of Acceptability

Once the general decision factors have been identified and the importance of each factor has been qualitatively assessed (e.g. in accordance with Table 7.3), then a preliminary assessment of the acceptability of a technical proposal should be carried out to determine whether:

- the proposal should be accepted without further analysis,
- the proposal should be rejected without further analysis or
- the proposal should be given further detailed analysis.

This preliminary assessment can be made in accordance with the process shown in Fig. 7.2, based on the principles of equity (concerning equitable distributions of costs, risks and benefits) and the Pareto principle. Any proposal that could not yield (potential) Pareto improvements should be rejected, unless it could be justified on the basis of improved equity. The preliminary assessment of the acceptability of a proposal should be carried out with regard to the general characteristics of the proposal (Table 7.3) rather than particular technical details.

Detailed Analysis

If necessary, a detailed analysis of a proposed system should be carried out to identify and assess the particular characteristics of the system that are relevant to its acceptability and to identify and resolve (if possible) any conflict over matters of principle.

To identify matters of principle that need to be resolved, the qualitative assessment of general decision factors should be reviewed. If there are conflicting viewpoints related to any of the qualitative factors of Table 7.3, then a method for dealing with the conflict should be determined. In some cases it might be necessary to obtain rulings from recognized authorities with appropriate jurisdiction (e.g. concerning legal matters). It should be noted that conflict due to differences between value systems (conflicting paradigms) cannot be resolved by 'rational' analysis. If conflict over matters of principle cannot be resolved (e.g. between environmentalists and economic 'rationalists'), then further detailed analysis is not likely to yield useful results.

If general principles can be established to deal with the qualitative decision factors, then the quantitative decision factors from Table 7.3 should be reviewed to determine the particular quantifiable characteristics that should be assessed. It is very important to distinguish between the things that should be quantified and the things that can be quantified. If the things that should be quantified can not be quantified, then further analysis is not likely to be useful.

Ideally, relevant quantitative performance parameters should be specified

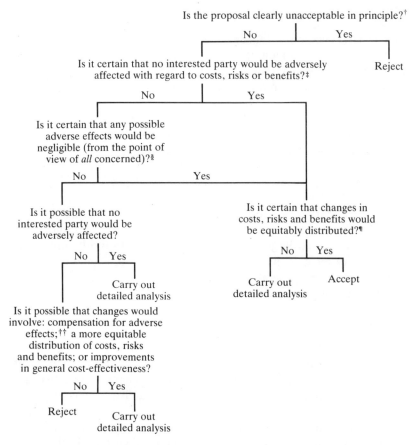

† A proposal would be clearly unacceptable in principle if it were illegal, contravened a binding agreement, involved the use of banned substances (e.g. asbestos), etc.

‡ An interested party is any party (contemporary or future) whose interests should be protected by the regulatory authorities (excluding commercial interests). This is with regard to not only majority interests but also minority interests. Caution must be exercised in predicting the effects of new technological processes.

§ The cumulative effect of individually negligible effects might be significant.

¶ An existing (accepted) risk might become inequitable (unacceptable) if that risk is maintained in order to reduce costs or yield benefits for persons not exposed to the risk.

†† Increased risks might, for example, be compensated by significant cost savings for the party at risk.

Figure 7.2 Preliminary assessment of acceptability.

in predetermined performance requirements. However, it is necessary to identify the particular quantitative parameters that are necessary and sufficient (together with the qualitative factors) for a dependable assessment of the acceptability of the proposed system. The selection of appropriate parameters requires judgement, and care should be taken to avoid unreasonable biases (unintentional or intentional) in the selection of quantitative parameters.

In general, relevant quantitative parameters concern costs, risks and benefits. These parameters must be evaluated with regard to a particular population (e.g. local, national or global), and the distribution of costs, risks and benefits within that population should also be assessed. It should be noted that many monetary 'costs' are transfer payments and are therefore representative of distribution effects rather than total effects (i.e. one man's loss might be another man's gain).

In general, risks are characterized by a range of possible outcomes and associated probabilities (or expected frequencies) of occurrence. The full range of possible outcomes should always be assessed, particularly with regard to the worst possible outcome. For complex systems, the methods of systems analysis should be employed to assess the range of possible outcomes. If necessary, the probabilities of the various outcomes should then be assessed, using methods of probabilistic risk analysis, It should be noted that the assessment of probabilities might not be necessary if all the possible outcomes are acceptable or if the worst possible outcome is totally unacceptable (no matter how unlikely it might be).

Careful consideration should be given to the definition of probabilistic risk parameters to ensure that they can provide useful and dependable information for the purposes of risk-based decision making. In some cases it might be necessary to assess several probabilistic parameters of a particular risk. For example, it might be necessary to consider risks of death with regard to: the mortality rates for the total population, the individuals most at risk, risk averters, etc.; the mortality rate due to delayed effects; reduced life expectancies; conditional probabilities of death following particular events; the probabilities of catastrophic events (involving the loss of many lives); etc. In general it would be useful to estimate the full probability distribution functions of the relevant parameters (e.g. mortality rates), but probabilistic risk assessments generally yield estimates of expected values only.

It should be noted that it is necessary to obtain *dependable* estimates of all relevant variables. Dependability is not synonymous with accuracy (although accurate information is certainly dependable). Dependable information is information that provides a dependable basis for decision making, to minimize the costs of wrong decisions (as discussed in Sec. 7.6). Normally, dependable information is that which effectively minimizes the risk of accepting an unsatisfactory system.

In order to obtain dependable results from a detailed analysis, the analytical procedure should include a critical review. The aim of the review should not be to confirm the analytical results: the aim should be to find fault with the analytical procedure and assumptions (implicit and explicit).

In many cases, critical reviews can be most effectively carried out by parties seeking to protect opposing interests (commercial, environmental, etc.), and such parties should be invited to comment on analyses and to present their cases in a process of public review, whenever practicable.

Assessing the Dependability of Probabilistic Risk Assessments

In general, the methods of probabilistic risk evaluation and the corresponding methods of risk management are not sufficiently dependable for practical decision making. However, the methods of probabilistic risk analysis can be useful if the (un)dependability of the results is assessed and taken into account. Ideally the dependability of any type of probabilistic risk analysis should be assessed by comparing the predicted (model) risks with actual (observed) risks for real systems. However, this is possible only if there is a dependable historical record for assessing the actual risks (including those associated with extremely rare, and possibly catastrophic, events).

Clearly the dependability of a probabilistic risk analysis of a novel system cannot be assessed directly from past experience. For such an analysis, the dependability should be assessed with regard to the dependability of the component elements of the analysis and the importance of the component elements in the decision process. A component is critically important if possible variations of that component could influence the final decision and a component is non-critical if possible variations could not influence the decision. Accordingly, the dependability of a probabilistic risk analysis can be assessed with regard to the dependability and criticality of its component elements, in accordance with Table 7.4. If any of the elements of a risk analysis is critically undependable ($U*C = 1$), then the resultant risk analysis is undependable; otherwise the analysis is dependable. It should be noted that an element is undependable until proven otherwise (beyond all reasonable doubt) and similarly an element should be dependably assessed as critical until proven otherwise.

The assessment of dependability is essentially a matter of judgement, and therefore assessments of dependability will vary from person to person. Assessments may be obtained from risk analysis experts, but it has been shown that experts tend to underestimate the uncertainty in their own fields of expertise. Independent (disinterested) assessments are therefore required. These assessments can be obtained by asking: 'Is this a reasonable basis for decision making, bearing in mind the consequences of making the wrong decision?'

Detailed Assessment of Acceptability

A detailed assessment of the acceptability of a proposed technical system should be carried out on the basis of detailed analyses of all relevant

Table 7.4 Undependability and criticality of component elements of a risk analysis

Component of analysis	Undependability indicator U† 0 = dependable 1 = undependable	Criticality indicator C 0 = non-critical 1 = critical	Critical undependability indicator ($U*C$)
Hazard identification‡			
System model			
Physical system§			
Human performance¶			
Failure mode identification††			
Probability estimates‡‡			
Inherent randomness			
Uncertainty			
Consequence model §§			
Physical impact			
Social impact			

† The dependability of any analytical model (and the underlying assumptions) can be assessed only by extensive comparisons of the predicted (model) behaviour and the actual (observed) behaviour of real systems. Furthermore, the dependability of a model can be established only for the types of system observed and the range of operating conditions encountered. Accordingly, rigorous prototype testing might be required to establish the dependability of a novel system.

‡ Check-lists can be useful for hazard identification. Check-lists of general hazards for conventional systems should be included in regulations concerning general performance requirements. For novel systems it is necessary to identify other existing (previously negligible) hazards to which the proposed system might be susceptible and any new hazards (e.g. technological hazards) which might be introduced by the system itself.

§ In general, it is possible to develop realistic and dependable models of physical systems, based on the observed behaviour of similar systems. However, the dependability of physical system models declines if the models are used to predict behaviour outside the range of observed behaviour.

¶ In general it is extremely difficult (if not practically impossible) to develop realistic models of human performance. Simple (transparent) models might be more dependable than complex (obscure) models. Nevertheless, models of human performance should take account (implicitly or explicitly) not only of specific performance requirements but also of the general 'climatological' factors (industrial climate, financial climate, political climate, etc.).

†† Failure mode identification involves the identification of all possible failure states and the identification of all possible 'accident sequences' leading to those failure states. Failure mode identification for complex or novel systems might require rigorous prototype testing.

‡‡ Estimates of probabilities (or component reliabilities) generally include allowances for inherent randomness (statistical variations) and uncertainty (imperfect knowledge). Inherent randomness can be dependably assessed using statistical methods. Uncertainty is more difficult to assess, but dependable (if not accurate) assessments can generally be made.

§§ The consequence model should include all consequences related to the quantitative risk parameters selected previously. Hypothetical consequence models (cf. empirical models) are generally undependable. In particular, it should be noted that the consequences of any process that might change the natural balance of the environment (e.g. a hazardous technological process) cannot be dependably predicted.

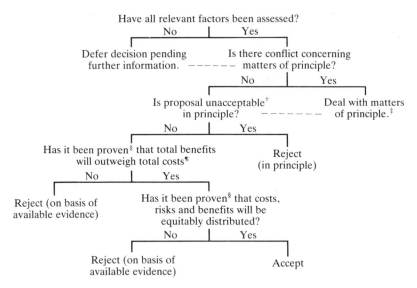

† A proposal would be unacceptable if: risks could exceed existing limits ('acceptable' risks); possible consequences (potential catastrophes) would be absolutely unacceptable; political or social requirements would not be met; etc.

‡ It might be necessary to obtain rulings from appropriate authorities and/or to include public participation in the decision-making process.

§ The case for acceptance must be *proven* beyond all reasonable doubt, based on *dependable* evidence.

¶ Decisions should not be based on single-valued (monetary) measures such as those contrived according to the methods of probabilistic risk assessment. Decisions should be based on explicit and dependable assessments of all relevant factors. Due weighting should be given to the costs of rare catastrophic events (not just the expected costs). Assessments of costs and benefits should include possible effects on future developments.

Figure 7.3 Detailed assessment of acceptability.

qualitative factors and quantitative parameters (Table 7.3). The acceptability of risks should be determined in accordance with the principles of risk-based decision making described previously in Sec. 7.6. A procedure for the detailed assessment of the acceptability of a proposal is outlined in Fig. 7.3.

7.8 CONCLUSION

There is no simple answer to the question 'How safe is safe enough?'. The answer depends fundamentally on complex value judgements. These judgements transcend analysis, and therefore general criteria for risk acceptance cannot be defined analytically or quantitatively. In reality, acceptable risks can be derived only from acceptable processes of risk management, based on value judgements appropriate to the circumstances. Acceptable risk levels are not predetermined factors in such risk management processes.

Nevertheless, methods of probabilistic risk assessment (including not only risk analysis but also risk evaluation) have been proposed to expedite the processes of risk management and to circumvent value judgements. These methods are based on the mathematics of statistical decision theory, concerning the estimated probabilities and expected costs of hypothetical events. The essential feature of these methods is that they are quantitative. This is both a strength and a weakness. It is a strength because it guarantees that an analyst can produce a (mathematically) feasible solution to any risk assessment problem, using standard techniques of numerical analysis, and it is a weakness because it guarantees a solution to the wrong problem, for any real problem involves non-quantifiable value judgements.

It can, of course, be shown that if costs are defined in such a way that they represent negative utilities (preferences), then the maximization of an expected utility is the only mathematically rational basis for decision making, because it leads to the solution that must be preferred above all others. However, this argument is based on the presumption that preferences can be defined in terms of general mathematical expressions, and it is a circular argument that preferences must be derived from utility functions that must be derived from preferences. Clearly, hypothetical utility functions must be formulated in accordance with actual preferences and not *vice versa*. In reality, preferences can be dependably determined only by directly weighing up the pros and cons using that most powerful of decision tools, human intelligence. The appropriate role of probabilistic risk assessment is to analyse some of the pros and cons (while noting the limitations of the methods of analysis).

Although general criteria for risk acceptance cannot be explicitly defined in simple terms, general principles for determining realistic risk acceptance criteria have been described with regard to the need for risk exposure, control of the risk and fairness. For a risk to be acceptable there must be a real need for risk exposure, the risk producing processes must be dependably controlled and there must be a fair and equitable distribution of costs, risks and benefits. Accordingly, realistic risk acceptance criteria can be developed on the basis of the Pareto principle, equity and dependability. Any risk generator that will not yield Pareto improvements should be rejected, unless it can be justified on the basis of potential Pareto improvements and more equitable distributions of costs, risks and benefits. Furthermore, realistic risk acceptance criteria must be dependable in the sense of minimizing the potential costs of wrong decision.

Realistic principles for risk-based decision making have been described with regard to the methods of probabilistic risk assessment. According to these principles, acceptable risk levels depend on the circumstances and they should be evaluated with regard to explicit dependable assessments of all relevant factors (qualitative and quantitative). Acceptability should not be assessed on the basis of single-valued measures of risk, such as those contrived according to the methods of probabilistic risk evaluation.

For particular classes of risk-management problems, the general principles for risk assessment may lead to quantitative limits for acceptable risks. However, for any particular problem, the quantitative limits will be dependent on the methods of risk analysis and the processes of risk management.

In the future, the methods of probabilistic risk assessment will be more widely applied than they are today and more sophisticated techniques will be developed. Improved techniques of probabilistic risk assessment will support—not supplant—engineering judgement and public debate in the assessment of engineering risks and the determination of acceptable standards.

REFERENCES

1. Kates, R. W.: *Risk Assessment of Environmental Hazard*, Scientific Committee on Problems of the Environment (SCOPE) report 8, Wiley, Chichester, 1978.
2. National Research Council (NRC): Risk and Decision Making: Perspectives and Research, *Report of the Committee on Risk and Decision Making*, Assembly of Behavioural and Social Sciences, NRC, National Academy Press, Washington, D.C., 1982.
3. The Royal Society: *Risk Assessment*, Report of a Royal Society Study Group, The Royal Society, London, January 1983.
4. Fischhoff, B., S. Lichtenstein, P. Slovic, S. L. Derby, and R. L. Keeney: *Acceptable Risk*, Cambridge University Press, Cambridge, 1981.
5. Shrader-Frechette, K. S.: *Risk Analysis and Scientific Method*, D. Reidel, Holland, 1985.
6. Sassone, P., and W. Schaffer: *Cost–Benefit Analysis: A Handbook*, Academic Press, London, 1978.
7. United States Atomic Energy Commission/Nuclear Regulatory Commission: Reactor Safety Study: An Assessment of Accident Risks in United States Commercial Nuclear Power Plants, *Report WASH-1400 (NUREG 75/014)*, N. C. Rasmussen (Chairman), National Technical Information Service, US Department of Commerce, Springfield, Va., 1975.
8. CIRIA: *Rationalisation of Safety and Serviceability Factors in Structural Codes*, report 63, Construction Industry Research and Information Association, London, July 1977.
9. Kletz, T. A.: Hazard Analysis—A Review of Criteria, *Reliability Engng*, vol. 3, pp. 325–338, 1982.
10. Starr, C.: Social Benefit versus Technological Risk, *Science*, no. 165, pp. 1232–1238, 1969.
11. Starr, C., R. Rudman, and C. Whipple: Philosophical Basis for Risk Analysis, *Annual Rev. of Energy*, vol. 1, pp. 629–662, 1976.
12. Reid, S. G.: Frequency–Cost Curves and Derivative Risk Profiles, *Risk Anal.*, vol 7, no. 2, pp. 261–267, 1987.

EIGHT

THE PSYCHOLOGY OF RISK

N. F. PIDGEON

8.1 INTRODUCTION

While the aim of engineering is the production of technological artefacts, it is important to recognize that engineering, engineers and their products do not exist in a social vacuum. Every engineered artefact is in some way utilized by, and in its own turn shapes, modern society and the people in it. While engineering technology has made life both safer and more efficient in many ways, our increased control over the physical and social environment has raised fundamental questions of safety and social acceptability. Many of the hazards that we face today from technological systems are qualitatively different from those faced even one hundred years ago. In particular, a key feature of modern-day hazards is that the impact of breakdowns in safety in systems (such as nuclear and chemical plants, nuclear weapon command and control systems, and mass transportation systems) may be difficult to contain at a local level, leading to the possibility for cross-national or even global consequences. It should therefore come as no surprise to learn that many people in society have grown concerned with the risks that they have to face from such technological systems. It is this concern that has, to a large degree, provided the background to studies of how people deal with risks, a topic that has become an important one to applied psychologists over the past twenty years.

The importance of the psychology of risk to the topic of engineering safety cannot be underestimated, and is bound up with the key question of what constitutes *acceptable risk* (Chapter 7). The question of acceptable risk is a complex issue, involving not just technical assessments of 'facts' but ultimately the values society puts upon such things as progress, the distribution of the costs and benefits from a technology and the consequences of breakdowns in safety such as lives lost, morbidity and economic disruption. In engineering practice one manifestation of the difficulties of dealing with such values comes when acceptable limits are to be set for Codes of Practice. Indeed, Codes of Practice can be viewed as institutionalized mechanisms for setting acceptable risk levels, whether in a traditional 'rule-of-thumb' sense, where uncertainty criteria are implicit, or in the more recent forms which take probabilistic uncertainty explicitly into account. It is clear, however, that the question of acceptable risk involves not only the producer but also the user (in the general sense of society at large) of technological systems and products. How the user construes risk and safety will underpin any acceptability debate, and in the limit serious accidents might make a particular technology seem too hazardous for society to accept at all. For example, it might be argued that this was one unintended consequence of both the Three Mile Island and the Chernobyl disasters for the Western nuclear industries.

The psychology of risk is not a homogeneous topic. Issues that have been studied include both experts' and laypeople's processing of probabilities and utilities, with a particular focus upon the ways in which these might deviate from more formal, normative approaches for characterizing uncertainty and value; the perception by laypeople of the risks from specific technological systems; and the communication of risk information between 'experts' and members of the public. In this chapter, this research is reviewed briefly. In Sec. 8.2 the early conceptions of probability are discussed and psychological studies thereof are reviewed. Initially it was believed that individual processing of probability and utility could be described in terms of the normative models of mathematics and economics. In Sec. 8.3 more recent work on people's processing of probabilistic information, and in particular on cognitive heuristics and biases, is reviewed. This research has identified a number of serious limitations to intuitive probability judgement. In Secs 8.4 and 8.5 the topics of risk perception and communication, respectively, are discussed. In Sec. 8.6 the findings of this work are related to the formal risk assessment model. In this section some of the difficulties that human error poses for the practice of risk assessment with complex technological systems are also noted.

8.2 PSYCHOLOGICAL PROBABILITY

A central concern throughout this volume is the topic of uncertainty. In engineering and statistical treatments of reliability theory the basic philosophical question of what precisely uncertainty might be is often taken as unproblematic, with various versions of probability typically being utilized. Of course, one of the lessons of the current book is that probability is too narrow a concept of uncertainty if we are to deal adequately with the ill-structured problems posed by many technological hazards. However, in order to trace current work on the psychology of risk we need to start with the concept of probability.

Lay beliefs about probability are multifaceted and reflect the confusion in the literature regarding the precise nature of uncertainty. To ask the question 'What is uncertainty?' of a group of students in any discipline is likely to elicit a range of responses associated, primarily, with conceptions of probability; for example, uncertainty is something to do with games of chance—it is a frequency, a personal degree of belief, a likelihood and it is just plain luck! All of these ideas are derived from the chequered history of the probability concept, and in order to understand the evolution of psychological experiments on risk we need to explore the distinctions between the differing 'types' of probability. At least three principal definitions of probability can be found, and these provide the background to our discussion of psychological studies. The three types are termed *classical, frequency* and *subjective* probability, respectively.[1]

The concept of mathematical probability first dates from early studies of the age-old art of gambling. The sixteenth century Italian mathematician Cardano is credited with introducing the classical definition of probability, that is the ratio of favourable outcomes in a game of chance to the total number of possible equally likely outcomes. Such a definition views probability as a property of concrete physical entities. Thus, the probability of throwing two sixes with two dice is obtained by dividing the number of ways in which two sixes can be obtained (one) by the total number of possible outcomes (thirty-six). Assuming that all outcomes are equally likely with an unbiased dice, the probability is therefore $1/36$. In practical terms such a definition is, of course, limited, since it restricts consideration only to situations where outcomes are indeed equally likely. Situations where outcomes are not equally likely (e.g. biased dice) cannot be addressed if we rely upon such a definition to operationalize uncertainty. More seriously, the classical definition is in many respects circular, since the term 'equally likely' clearly means, if it is to mean anything at all, equally probable.

Relative frequency probability arose in the work of mathematicians such as Poisson and Venn in the nineteenth century, primarily as the result of the need to address some of the problems associated with the classical approach. By the relative frequency account probability is defined to be the limiting value of the number of favourable to total outcomes over an infinite series of identical trials. By providing an empirical basis for probability assessment, the relative frequency approach renders problems such as that of biased dice mathematically tractable; that is if you want to know the probability of two sixes, just observe how many occur over a long series of throws of the same pair of dice. Classical statistical theory (upon which much of reliability theory is based) relies almost exclusively upon such a conception of probability, and such a concept is undoubtedly very valuable where well-defined, highly repeatable events generate long-run data on random processes. The relative frequency definition of probability has much in keeping with the empiricist tradition and is held by its proponents to be the only 'objectively' valid basis for treating uncertainty. Accordingly, relative frequency is sometimes referred to as 'objective probability'.

The third type of probability is that of subjective or personal probability and is the most important from a psychological perspective. In contrast to the frequentist approach, subjective probability, most closely identified with the Bayesian school of statistics, emphasizes the notion of probability as a personal *degree of confidence* or *degree of belief* in the occurrence of an event. Here probability is viewed as a behavioural rather than an empirical concept, that is resulting from an individual's state of knowledge *about* the world rather than being an objective property *of* the world. Hence, the subjective probability of any event can legitimately vary across individuals as a function of their own knowledge of that event. More powerfully, and unlike the frequentist definition that relies upon long-run arguments, subjective probability in principle allows us to cope with particularistic, non-repeatable events. An example would be the probability that Argentina will gain sovereignty over the Malvinas (Falkland Islands) before the year 2010.

While subjective probability is an intuitively plausible psychological concept, its mathematical treatment, and in particular the question of its measurement, remains a controversial issue within statistics. Formal treatment of this problem was first attempted independently in the 1930s by Frank Plumpton Ramsay and Bruno De Finetti. Both axiomatized a numerical measure of subjective probability by introducing the idea that its measurement can proceed from an analysis of an individual's preferences among bets. Both also commented upon the notions of *coherence* and *consistency*. For an individual's subjective probabilities to be represented numerically in such a way that they conform to the probability calculus, his/her preferences among bets (and hence by implication his/her subjective probabilities) must be both coherent and consistent. Coherence requires that an individual be rational to the extent that the relationships between his/her subjective probabilities do not allow the construction of a bet that is preferred but entails a certain loss. For example, if, for any particular individual, $P(E)$ is not found to be equal to its complement $1 - P$ (not E) then a so-called 'Dutch Book' can be constructed, conditional upon the event E. Here a set of gambles can be constructed, which are preferred by this individual, but where he/she is bound to lose money whatever happens. Consistency, on the other hand, requires that an individual's preferences be logically non-contradictory; for example, they must be transitive. These requirements can be expressed in terms of a number of common-sense axioms to which the individual's preferences must adhere. The most generally accepted axiom system, unifying the theories of personal probability and value (or utility), is provided by Savage.[2] This system forms the basis of both Bayes' theorem for probabilistic belief revision and the subjective expected utility (SEU) model of decision making. A coherent individual is therefore one who is rational in the sense that his/her preferences conform to the Savage axioms, and as a consequence to the Bayesian model or to the maximization of the subjective expected utility (defined as the product of the subjective worth of consequences to a decision maker and the subjective probability of attaining such consequences). It is important to note here that the theory of subjective probability, while holding a *prima facie* psychological significance, is essentially a *normative* theory; that is it is a system that provides one particular definition of how rational judgement and choice *should* be arrived at. It does not necessarily provide a framework that accurately describes how individuals *do* in fact process uncertainties.

The Bayesian school of probability held a number of important implications for psychologists. Most importantly it provided the framework around which experiments could be performed to see if individuals attempt to maximize SEU or to update their personal probabilities in line with Bayes' theorem. Experiments during the 1960s tended to confirm the view that individuals were indeed generally coherent when faced with simple probability pay-off gambling decisions. In addition, one important finding was the so-called *conservative Bayesian* effect. Using the 'bookbag and pokerchip' paradigm, individuals were found to revise their personal probabilities only partially in line with the predictions of the Bayesian model. The normative theory of subjective probability requires that when an individual is presented with information that is diagnostic with respect to the truth of two or more mutually exclusive hypotheses, the individual should revise his/her opinion in accordance with Bayes' theorem. The typical bookbag and pokerchip task is conducted as follows. Individuals are initially shown two or more bookbags, or alternatively urns, each containing a number of pokerchips of a specified composition. For example, 70 red and 30 white chips in one bag and 30 red and 70 white in a second. The experimenter then selects one of these bags at random without showing the individual which it is. At this point it is assumed that the typical individual will have a subjective belief of 0.5 for each of the mutually exclusive hypotheses: H_1, the bag selected contains a majority of red chips and H_2, the bag selected contains a majority of white. Successive draws of chips are then made from the selected bag, without replacement. After witnessing each draw, individuals are required to give their posterior probability estimates for the competing hypotheses H_1 and H_2. The typical finding, labelled by the psychologists Ward Edwards and Larry Phillips as *conservatism*, is that subjects' estimates on each successive draw will be less extreme (although in the correct direction) than the normative result calculated with Bayes' theorem. This basic phenomenon was found to be remarkably robust, with variations such as changes in composition of the chips in the bag, the number of draws, or the response mode failing to alter the fundamental pattern of results.

8.3 HEURISTICS AND BIASES

Experiments with gambles and bookbags came to an end, however, in the early 1970s. Crucial to their demise was the view that individuals, rather than being imperfect SEU maximizers or intuitive near-Bayesians, might in fact not be Bayesian at all! Although this fresh look at the psychology of judgement and decision making took place in the early 1970s, an influential theoretical work in this respect was that of the psychologist Herbert Simon. He suggested[3] in 1955 that:

> Because of the psychological limits of the organism (particularly with respect to computational and predictive ability) actual human rationality striving can at best be an extremely crude and simplified approximation to the kind of global rationality which is implied, for example, by game theoretic models (p. 102).

Simon's argument is a simple one. He points out that the intrinsic calculational complexity demanded of an individual by normative models such as SEU or Bayes' theorem is incompatible, under all but the most trivial of circumstances, with the limited cognitive resources of the human mind. Simon rejected, as a practical *description* of the intuitive judge and decision maker, the theory of the 'economic individual' who is always rational in the sense that he or she maximizes SEU when taking decisions or adheres to Bayes' theorem when updating personal probabilities. As an alternative, Simon suggested that actual choice behaviour can be more parsimoniously described in terms of the *principle of bounded rationality*. By this Simon means that the individual, in order to cope with the complexities of the choice environment, constructs a simplified cognitive representation of the world that facilitates via the use of simple choice rules, or heuristics, functional decisions within the context of that representation. One such simplified decision rule suggested by Simon was the *satisficing principle*; that is rather than seek to maximize SEU across all available options (often a potentially very large set), a choice can be made of the *first* option that is found to satisfy a fixed set of criteria. The general notion underlying Simon's argument was the suggestion that any realistic model of rational judgement and choice must be sensitive to the constraints set both by the decision problem and the psychological resources available to the individual. With respect to the latter, particularly important limitations are our lack of intuitive calculational power and the limits on the number of discrete items that can be held in working memory and hence be available for conscious processing at any one time (a maximum of between seven and ten items).

Simon's pioneering theoretical work was to be resurrected twenty years later by the cognitive psychologists Tversky and Kahneman.[4,5] They suggested that the individual, because of modest computational abilities, will employ a range of simplifying judgemental strategies, or *heuristics*, in order to reduce or limit cognitive strain when assessing subjective probabilities. Tversky and Kahneman suggest that the use of such simplifying strategies will often lead to efficient and optimal responses, but under some circumstances will result in severe and systematic error or *bias*.

The work of Tversky and Kahneman has become influential both in psychology theory and in a number of applied contexts. An example of one cognitive strategy for judging probability suggested by Tversky and Kahneman is the *availability heuristic*. They suggest that a decision maker will judge the subjective likelihood of an event A in part as a function of the ease of recall, or availability, of similar instances from memory. For example, if I wish to take a taxi from my university department to another part of the city, I could ring in advance for a reservation. Alternatively, given that I work in a busy city centre, I might take a chance of being able to flag down a taxi as I go outside. Clearly, if I wish to judge the likelihood of success for the latter course of action, I require some estimate of the frequency of taxis in the road outside my department. According to the availability explanation, I form such a judgement by attempting to recall as many instances as possible of taxis in the road outside. If I can recall many such instances then it is probably a reasonable course to save on the telephone call. Clearly, such a strategy will often provide subjective probability estimates that correspond closely to the 'objective' frequency of the occurrence of taxis outside my department in working hours. In this respect judgemental heuristics often do serve us efficiently and well. However, Tversky and Kahneman point out that ease of recall, as a basis for estimates of subjective probability, may also depend upon factors other than statistical frequency. Examples of such factors include imaginability (do I recall only black cabs and not minicabs?), vividness of coding in memory (do I strongly recall witnessing one particular cab involved in an accident in the road last year?) or recency of coding (I recall seeing a taxi on my journey in this morning, but can I remember other mornings?).

As will become clear in the next section, work on availability, and heuristics and biases in general, is important for understanding some aspects of risk perception.

8.4 RISK PERCEPTION

The notion of risk perception arose as a direct result of the initial work on cognitive illusions and biases in judgement and decision-making. In psychology, the concept of perception has traditionally been characterized as a subjective, personal, representation of some concrete and agreed reality or stimulus. Such a representation cannot be a direct reflection of reality, but rather it is an approximation to that reality, reflecting both aspects of the stimulus and the personal characteristics of the individual. In very general terms the perceptual system is useful, often veridical, and typically reliable. However, it is nevertheless sometimes flawed. For example, we take for granted the workings of our own visual system, but many complex physiological and cognitive processes intervene between the receipt of a retinal image and its interpretation in terms of a three-dimensional representation. To name but one, the input to the brain from the eyes consists of two slightly different two-dimensional retinal images. The brain relies upon a number of subtle cues (for example texture, edge contiguity and the slight disparity between the images in the left and right eyes) to generate an overall three-dimensional representation. Although a highly efficient system has evolved for depth perception, which is highly accurate under most circumstances, the ease with which eye and brain can be tricked by the well-known visual illusions demonstrates that this system is not an infallible one.

By analogy, the notion that much of our thinking about risks might be driven by deep-seated psychological processes that might lead to 'illusory risk perceptions' is an appealing one. Following the work of Tversky and Kahneman on errors and biases, psychological risk perception research saw a dramatic increase in the mid-1970s. As with much applied science, this was not simply a curiosity-led phenomenon, but was in part driven by a general social agenda, albeit implicitly. The first wave of public environmental awareness, particularly in the United States in the late 1960s, focused a significant minority of the population in opposition to certain new technologies, such as nuclear power. Advocates of such technologies, confident at that time in the belief that such systems were inherently safe, wished to pose the question of why public perceptions of the 'true' risks were (to them) exaggerated.

As discussed in the previous section, the recent psychological research within the judgement and decision-making paradigm has shown that people sometimes do not cope well with probabilistic tasks, utilizing a range of simplifying heuristics such as availability in order to make intuitive judgements of probabilities. Clearly, such studies have mostly been conducted in the psychological laboratory, using relatively artificial experimental paradigms, and often with college students as subjects. While there are good reasons to believe that the theoretical findings of laboratory research can indeed be transferred to more naturalistic settings and different subject populations, much of the recent risk perception work has sought to elicit people's judgements of a range of realistic hazardous activities with which they might be expected to have some familiarity. Such studies of risk perceptions, using realistic events, initially appeared to confirm the view that individuals might not be fully normative (in the Bayesian sense) in their appraisal of risk.

However, and somewhat surprisingly, it also appears to be the case that individuals often hold a relatively sophisticated view of risk, involving important qualitative factors that are missing in formal reliability theory and risk assessment techniques.

Discussing the first wave of risk perception research, Fischhoff et al.[6] comment that:

> At first blush, assessing the public's risk perceptions would seem to be very straightforward. Just ask questions like: What is the probability of a nuclear core meltdown? or How many people die annually from asbestos-related diseases? or How does wearing a seat belt affect your probability of living through the year? The response can be compared with the best available technical estimates, and deviations can be interpreted as evidence of the respondents' ignorance (p. 28).

However, the elicitation of risk judgements is not as simple as it might at first seem. The political or opinion poll, capable of influencing people's responses through the way in which the questions are framed, is familiar to all of us. Such effects are also present in psychological judgement studies. A classic finding, concerning the way in which judgements can be influenced by the framing of the question, is derived from work on eyewitness testimony. In the typical experiment subjects are first shown a film of an accident between two automobiles and then asked to recall aspects of the event. Asking the question 'At what speed do you think car A was travelling when it smashed into car B?' will elicit a higher average speed estimate from subjects than will the question 'At what speed do you think car A was travelling when it hit car B?'. Such framing effects also need to be countered when asking questions about risk. This is not to imply, however, that individuals are infinitely malleable in their responses to psychological or other questions. Rather, the form in which the question is framed is a key part of the conditions of testing, which will influence (explicitly or implicitly) a respondent and which therefore must be carefully considered when appraising the findings of such research.

When problems with question framing are accounted for, a robust finding from both laboratory and field studies is that individuals in Western societies (both expert *and* lay) tend to rank the chances of dying from particular hazards very much in line with the available statistical estimates. For example, Fischhoff et al.[6] report that people accurately judge that motor vehicle accidents claim more deaths per annum in the United States than do floods or tornadoes. Where systematic discrepancies between intuitive and statistical estimates do occur it is in dealing with extreme values; that is people tend to overestimate the chances of dying from very low probability events (e.g. botulism) and underestimate those of very high probability ones (e.g. cancer). One possible explanation of this systematic effect with high and low frequency events is people's use of the availability heuristic. As discussed earlier, laboratory studies have demonstrated that individuals will, under some circumstances, judge the likelihood or frequency of an event A in part as a function of the ease of recall, or availability, of similar instances from memory. Long-term memory is a relatively sophisticated apparatus, and we can make the relatively mild assumption here that people build up a store of knowledge about hazards in much the same way as they do for other more mundane events, that is through life experiences and through exposure to information sources such as friends, literature and the mass media. When asked to give intuitive judgements of risks, people might subsequently employ the availability heuristic to generate an answer. Most of the time such a strategy will lead to reasonable answers. However, on some occasions it may lead to departures from the statistical estimates. It has been argued that today one of the key influences over what is initially stored, and therefore ultimately available in memory, will be information from the media. Sensational (over)reporting in the media of occurrences of relatively rare accidents such as fatal lightning strikes may serve to increase the availability of such events. Conversely, relatively 'mundane' causes of death, such as most single automobile accidents or common influenza, rarely make the news. This might lead to people overestimating the likelihood of rare but reported sensational events and underestimating the more mundane unreported ones.

A second important empirical finding of risk perception research concerns the relationship between personal control over a hazardous activity and risk acceptability. This issue was first discussed extensively by Starr in his classic paper.[7] Many people will accept, and happily engage in, relatively risky activities which they believe they have some degree of personal control over; for example smoking, mountain climbing or motorcycling. Conversely, activities that we feel that we have no personal control over, such as flying, or which are perceived to have been imposed upon us by others (for some people nuclear and chemical plants) may be seen as less acceptable, regardless of the estimated likelihood of harm. The apocryphal case of the smoking hang-glider pilot who nevertheless refuses to fly on British Airways might be cited as evidence of gross irrationality (or at the least an inconsistency) in thinking about risks! This is, however, to miss a more sophisticated interpretation—that lay conceptions of risks, and in particular the ways in which they influence and provide a framework for acceptability judgements, are in some respects more complex and rich than that provided by the statistics of risk assessment. For example, the belief that personal control over a hazardous activity brings some increased invulnerability to personal harm is, of course, a two-edged sword. Where an individual is highly skilled this may indeed be the case. On the other hand, and unlike the popular vision of driving, we can not *all* be better than average drivers! Similarly, at the level of society, if our culture places great value upon personal freedom, it might be entirely reasonable under some circumstances to trade off an increased likelihood of harm against personal control over the environment.

Interestingly, one emphasis within the current volume is upon the importance of complementing risk prediction with *risk management* for the safe control of ongoing hazardous processes. One consequence of such a view is that there is normative value in retaining flexibility and freedom of action when dealing with certain classes of large-scale hazard. This is particularly so when dealing with open-world situations where ambiguity, uncertainty and ignorance about possible future worlds are high.[8]

Although the risk estimates of laypeople and experts, such as risk assessment professionals, *both* tend to correlate with statistical estimates of the likelihood of harm, there are a number of notable exceptions. In early psychometric studies it was found that some activities, such as nuclear power generation, were judged by laypeople to be very risky compared to the low-risk estimates provided by experts. Other studies have required individuals to rate a range of hazardous activities in terms of a set of qualitative factors thought to be relevant to risk judgements and risk acceptability. Such studies demonstrate that the lay characterization of risk is underpinned by relatively complex qualitative factors.[9] In particular, people's judgements of hazardous activities are sensitive not only to statistical frequency (where it is possible to estimate this) but also to factors such as the familiarity of an activity (or, conversely, its 'unknownness'), its catastrophic potential (in terms of power to harm, in the worst possible case, a large number of people), its anxiety potential (or dread), as well as its personal controllability. The activity of nuclear power generation occupies a rather unique position with respect to this constellation of factors. A reactor accident is seen as being relatively unfamiliar, as personally uncontrollable, with the potential for catastrophe and as extremely anxiety provoking. Conversely, the risks from an activity such as cycling are seen as familiar, subject to personal control, with a low potential for catastrophe and not anxiety producing. One conclusion is that lay judgements of the riskiness of nuclear power are related to both statistical considerations and to this qualitative set of factors.[10] Expert (e.g. risk assessors') judgements appear to be less influenced by the qualitative factors. However, it is worth recognizing here that with very low probability events, where long-run data are unavailable and where complex sociotechnical systems are involved, expert risk assessment becomes much more a matter of individual judgement than of empirical fact. This is illustrated by the observation that risk experts do not always agree on what is an appropriate estimate, and reflects one of the significant degrees of freedom underlying risk assessment models. Under such circumstances arbitrating between expert and lay characterizations of risk is much more a matter of faith than it might at first seem! This is a point to which the discussion will return in Sec. 8.6

The psychometric studies of risk perception are valuable demonstrations, although they have been criticized upon a number of grounds. In particular, the psychometric approach tends to neglect the social (see Chapter 9) and political contexts within which beliefs about risks are formed and risk decisions are made. For example, Eiser and Van der Pligt[11] found that attitudes towards the costs and benefits of nuclear power were embedded in much wider social and political values. They surveyed groups of pro-nuclear and anti-nuclear individuals at the end of the 1970s, asking them to indicate the values that they felt would 'contribute most to an improvement in the overall quality of life'. Eiser and Van der Pligt comment that:

> The pro-nuclear group stressed the importance of 'advances in science and technology', 'industrial modernisation', 'security of employment' and 'conservation of the natural environment'. The anti-nuclear respondents put even more emphasis on the last factor and stressed the importance of 'decreased emphasis on materialistic values', 'reduction in scale of industrial, commercial and governmental units' and 'improved social welfare' (p. 161).

The study of Eiser and Van der Pligt serves to illustrate the important fact that the beliefs underlying risk perceptions cannot be divorced from the more general world views that individuals hold in their daily lives. It also implies that individuals with judgements that differ from expert assessments of risks are not of necessity irrational; rather, we should accept that lay conceptions of risk are much wider, and qualitatively different, than is implied by the economic model underlying traditional risk assessment practice. A converse implication of the risk perception work, which is explored in the next section, is that people's appraisals of risk will be sensitive to particular types of information.

8.5 RISK COMMUNICATION

During the 1980s, psychological studies of people's conceptions of risk changed emphasis. Interest in the topic of risk perception waned and the focus of many current studies is upon risk *communication* (e.g. Ref. 12). Apart from the interest of academic psychologists, a number of different agendas might be met by applied risk communication research. On the one hand, professional and corporate bodies charged with operating hazardous technologies often wish to devise information programmes that will modify in some way the unreasonable views (as they see it) of opponents of their technologies. It is interesting to note here that such an agenda starts from the (not uncontroversial) assumption that a particular activity is safe, that the public have exaggerated the risks and that the communication of information about safety is therefore required. One subsidiary goal here is to devise preemptive strategies for routine information provision. A second is devising messages to cope with the aftermath of any serious accident or incident. At a corporate level one significant unforseen consequence of the accidents at Three Mile Island and Chernobyl has been the 'public relations' fallout, expressed in a lack of confidence in the nuclear industry world-wide (see also Chapter 14).

There is, however, a second reason for conducting risk communication research. A number of agencies, particularly specialist government departments such as weather or disaster bureaux, are concerned with the preparation of plans for well-defined but uncertain emergency events. Typically such agencies are charged with both the identification of likely hazards and the issuing of warnings for the public. One important concern of such agencies is that when a real emergency does occur the public may ignore warnings or mitigation instructions, leading to a failure to take appropriate protective action. Interestingly, the frame of reference for such agencies is the opposite to that of the groups charged with controlling hazardous technologies. Emergency planning agencies make the assumption that they hold accurate information about the potential onset of a dangerous condition (such as an impending flood or tornado) and that their function in times of crisis is to motivate the public to take protective behaviour. This is, in effect, starting from an assumption that there is danger and that the public, having undervalued the true risks, will not perceive and respond to such danger appropriately. The emphasis here is therefore upon the ways in which prior planning can equip the public to respond to the right warnings in the 'appropriate' ways.

Although risk communication is a relatively new topic, research into persuasive communication in general has a long history in social psychology. Typical findings are that the success of any communication depends upon the characteristics of the sender, of the message and of the receiver. For risk communication research, a clear conclusion to be drawn from this work is that if the message is not appropriately matched to the frame of reference of the audience then the communication may fail (or even prove counter-productive). For example, if a target audience is concerned with the lack of personal control over a chemical plant next door, a simple message focusing upon statistical risk assessments may fail to allay concern. Similarly, statements such as 'a year living within a one-mile radius of a chemical facility is equivalent to crossing the road once' may fail to have impact if the recipients of this message do not view the two activities as being *qualitatively* comparable; for example with respect to the qualitative risk characteristics outlined in the previous section. Hence, such a message may fail if a recipient is concerned with his/her lack of personal control over large-scale chemical processing or its catastrophic potential.

A second important consideration is that risk communication is not merely driven by risk communicators. It is important to recognize that individuals are active seekers, generators and processors of information about hazards. Hence, research has also focused upon the conditions under which individuals will seek to gain new knowledge about hazards. With respect to information-seeking behaviour, several models of individual behaviour have been proposed. Cvetkovich and Earle[13] note three hypotheses that might be used to explain when individuals will seek out new information about risks. The first of these is the *utility hypothesis*. Here individuals are assumed to be rational expected utility maximizers, and so seek out information about a hazard that has a high chance of large losses (with possibly low personal benefits). The second is the *psychological response hypothesis* and derives from the psychometric findings outlined in the previous section. By this account people are motivated to seek information about a hazard when that activity is associated with high levels of undesirable qualitative characteristics, e.g. unfamiliarity, anxiety potential and lack of personal control. A third model of information-seeking behaviour is known as the *trust hypothesis*. Here it is assumed that people seek information about hazards if they feel that they cannot place trust in society's agents (e.g. politicians, government regulators, together with public and private corporations) to control a hazard adequately on their behalf or to provide complete and accurate information about it.

8.6 THE TECHNICAL RISK PARADIGM AND HUMAN ERROR

Throughout the discussion so far, the notion of a risk *perception* has been taken to imply some form of subjective representation of an independent concrete reality. It is worth examining this view in some detail. This view is based, as noted earlier, upon the visual perception analogy which implies the existence of a concrete stimulus independent of the observer. In theory at least, the overall accuracy of the visual system can be calibrated against characteristics of the external stimulus. There are now, of course, many philosophical doubts over this rather simplistic position, implying as it does that observer and observed can be unambiguously separated (see also Chapter 1). However, the concept of a perceived risk is used in a similar way to that of a perceived stimulus in visual psychology; that is it implies, implicitly or explicitly, that a concrete risk, against which the accuracy of individuals' intuitive assessments can be calibrated, does indeed unambiguously exist. As many of the chapters in this volume illustrate, our current understanding of the multifaceted nature of uncertainty suggests that this is not such a straightforward assumption to make as was once thought. For example, if risk perception is to be measured against some actual 'objective' risk, we might start by asking: 'What is risk?'. This is not a trivial question and it raises some deep philosophical questions.

A simple account of risk is that it has something to do with the combination of both the uncertainty and the negative consequences associated with a future, anticipated, hazardous event. Taking the relatively restricted probabilistic view of uncertainty, we might therefore define risk as being the conjunction of probability and (negative) utility. However, it is important to recognize that many definitions of risk exist across the statistical, engineering and social science literatures.[9] By the Bayesian account, the rational individual will indeed seek to minimize the product of subjective probability and (dis)utility. This is in effect what traditional risk assessment seeks to accomplish, with its divide-and-conquer strategy of analysis. However, this is not an uncontroversial position, and several problems exist with such a definition. Although the probability *calculus* is relatively undisputed, it is less clear how to justify the use of one type of probability over the other in many situations or how to combine different types (e.g. the adjustment of a subjectively assessed prior estimate by a well-corroborated frequency estimate). Other difficulties include the inability of the Bayesian model to deal with open-world uncertainties, and the related problems of dealing probabilistically with human and organizational errors (see also Chapter 9 in this volume). Such considerations force us to recognize that the assessment of risk will always be *conditional* upon a set of modelling assumptions.[14]

Deficiencies with the technical risk paradigm and its reliance upon quantitative predictive methods are clearly highlighted when we consider the role of human agency in the generation of accidents. The core agenda for safety assessment in hazardous systems has been framed by the response of the engineering community to the problem of acceptable risk. This effort has focused upon the development of formal methods for the *prior* specification of the limits to reliability. Such methods, including probabilistic risk assessment, are based upon the principles of modern decision theory, and one central requirement here is that the analyst is expected to be capable of arriving at some form of unambiguous problem structure, in a so-called 'small-world' representation.[2] In the case of probabilistic risk assessment this requirement is translated into the need for prior specification of an exhaustive and realistic set of failure scenarios for the hazardous activity. However, analysis of accidents in technological systems suggests that this requirement may not be easily met except for the most trivial and well understood of systems.

It is becoming increasingly clear that it is restrictive to talk of failures in large-scale hazardous systems purely in technical terms. Individuals, their organizations and groups, and ultimately their cultures, are all implicated in the design, construction, operation, use and decommissioning of such systems. Consequently, it is not surprising to find a number of investigators pointing to the role of human agency in the generation of disasters. In popular accounts of disasters, such agency is often described as 'human error'. Such a notion is important in Western societies, where we have a long-standing habit of allocating blame on an individual basis. There is also a sense in which *all* error can be said to be human error. However, this is a rather loose usage of the term, and it is important that attempts to find an identifiable culprit do not obscure the more subtle background causes of failures. The latter are typically complex, multiple and rooted in the social and organizational properties of the overall sociotechnical system associated with a hazardous technology (see also Chapter 9 in this volume). One particular implication of such a view is that we should not treat human error as a single undifferentiated phenomenon. Rather, it should be seen as part of a family of problems of behaviour that might have their origins in inadequacies at the level of managerial activities, institutionalized information systems and social arrangements for the conduct of work, as well as the actions of identifiable individuals. This sets us some serious challenges, for in order to conduct risk assessment we need to deal systematically with the human and organizational preconditions to failures.

For a restricted set of individual forms of human error the techniques of risk assessment may well be appropriate. For example, a distinction can be made between slips and lapses, on the one hand, and mistakes, on the other. Slips and lapses are essentially failures to achieve an intended and appropriate plan. An example would be a failure of omission such as occurs when it is (properly) intended to secure a ladder to some scaffolding, but through oversight or distraction the individual responsible forgets to do this. Such failings, often associated with maintenance activities, can be modelled in a frequency sense if a clear definition of correct practice is available and if sufficient operating experience and accurate error reporting are available. Mistakes, on the other hand, involve the correct execution of an inappropriate plan. For example, we might complete the securing of the ladder, but to the wrong (and perhaps dangerous) section of scaffolding. Slips, lapses and mistakes are discussed in the traditional human factors literature, and some attempt has been made to calculate statistical frequencies for these with a view to modifying overall risk assessments.

Since the accidents at Three Mile Island and Chernobyl, two further categories of human error have prompted concern and some research; these are cognitive decision errors and procedural violations, respectively. Interest in cognitive decision errors focuses upon system operators who are charged with the control of highly complex systems whose precise failure modes may be unpredictable (in advance) and very difficult to diagnose accurately under the real-time constraints of an actual emergency. One significant characteristic of highly complex systems, such as process plant or modern aircraft, is that routine operation of the systems under normal conditions may not facilitate learning of the skills needed for dealing with the system states likely to be present during an emergency. Furthermore, two critical and often conflicting dangers are likely to exist for operators in any emergency. Firstly, they may be faced with incomplete information, as would occur when they do not have the appropriate (or are relying upon faulty) sensors to highlight critical plant states. Secondly, operators of complex systems may be faced with information overload during an emergency; too many alarms may be set off and there may not be enough time to identify clearly root causes or to deal with the rapid onset of events. This was an important factor at Three Mile Island, where the reactor operators, faced with both inadequate instrumentation and multiple alarms at an early stage in the transient, misdiagnosed the condition of the plant, leading them to take decisions that made the situation worse. It is an interesting question as to whether this should be attributed to 'operator error' or to poor training and plant design.

A second example of cognitive decision error concerns the crash of a British Midlands Boeing 737 twin-engined jet in the United Kingdom at Kegworth, Leicestershire, in January 1989. Here the two pilots were faced with a partial single-engine failure shortly after takeoff. For a number of reasons the pilots diagnosed a failure in the inappropriate engine. This led them to shut down the wrong (good) engine. Although such twin-engined aircraft are designed to fly and land adequately, in an emergency, on only one engine, the British Midlands aircraft crashed when the truly faulty engine failed completely during the approach to emergency landing. It was, at this point, too late to restart the good engine. The accident investigation concluded that the cockpit display had provided the pilots with correct information on the state of both engines, and a simplistic analysis of the events might point to pilot error as the sole cause. However, the background factors to the misdiagnosis and the subsequent failure of the crew to notice the mistake included: a novel and possibly confusing engine instrumentation layout, which may have been misread under stress; the lack of a third flight officer dedicated to the monitoring of engine instruments; the flight crew's inability to directly observe the engines, coupled with a lack of communication between cabin crew and the flight deck (cabin staff had correctly observed which of the engines was emitting flames). As is characteristic of many such sociotechnical failures, the reasons for the error of judgement, which ultimately served to undermine the technical redundancy inherent in the twin-engine design philosophy, reside more in subtle aspects of the human/technology interface than in the actions of any single individual.

Procedural violations by operators, such as the deliberate neglect of set safety procedures or the bypass of safety systems, are present in all areas of human activity. However, it is only recently that they have gained close attention in the context of technological hazards and human factors practice.[15] In particular, the accident at Chernobyl focused attention on this issue, since the event was in part the result of the deliberate shutting down of safety systems. This had been done in order to conduct an experiment on the reactor, ironically with the end goal of providing data for improving reactor safety! The reasons why individuals resort to intentional violations of safety rules and systems are various and complex, and not always merely driven by personal idiosyncrasy. More likely, features of the design interface between the technology and the humans involved will generate pressures for violations. For example, the design of (or lack of resources available to the operators of) a complex system may create conflicts, under operational pressures, between certain procedures, leading to the neglect of some over others. This was one of the underlying causes of the sinking with tragic loss of life of *The Herald of Free Enterprise* ferry off Zeebrugge.

The simple conclusion to be drawn from the recent work on human errors is not encouraging either for the future safe operation of complex systems or the application of formal, quantitative methods of risk assessment. While errors such as slips and lapses might be, albeit with some difficulty, handled within the technical risk paradigm, it is less clear how mistakes, cognitive errors and violations are to be modelled. As technologies become more complex the latter classes of error might be expected to become more common. Such a consideration forces us to realize the need for comprehensive *risk management* programmes to operate in parallel with risk prediction efforts. Living with the possibility that risk prediction will always be incomplete (at least with respect to human behaviour) requires that we continue to monitor the consequences of risk decisions long after they have been made, with a view to making control adjustments as and where necessary. A practical dictum to follow here might be 'what looks acceptable today may not look so tomorrow'.

8.7 CONCLUSION

In this chapter recent psychological studies of risk perception and communication have been reviewed, together with the theoretical work on the psychology of human error. Clearly, this presents only one social science perspective on risk and hazards, and another can be offered by taking an explicit sociological level of analysis (Chapter 9) of both the question of risk acceptability and the analysis of accident causation. It is, however, interesting to note that the concept of risk communication is often conceptualized in terms of a one-way process, between a communicator and some form of uninformed audience, usually 'the public'. Communicators of risks tend to rely upon the technological risk paradigm, discussed at length elsewhere in this book, as the baseline measure of what the 'true' risks are. One conclusion that might be drawn from this is that public sensitivities to certain hazards are solely the result of emotions or of biased cognitive processes, to be corrected by appropriate information campaigns. It is clear, however, from the parallel discussion of human error presented here that the technological risk paradigm will have great difficulty in arriving at an undisputed evaluation of risk under many circumstances. This raises an intriguing possibility—that risk communication might be conceptualized as a *two-way* process between lay people and experts. The psychological studies reported, in contrast to those within the engineering paradigm, show that individuals are sensitive to quite complex qualitative aspects of hazards. Perhaps, therefore, our handling of risk in society, and in particular the strategies adopted for risk management, should also be more qualitative in approach, reflecting some of the concerns of laypeople with aspects of hazardous systems such as controllability and familiarity. Certainly, this would seem an important prerequisite if technology is to remain both adequately managed and acceptable to broad sections of our society.

REFERENCES

1. Barnett, V.: *Comparative Statistical Inference*, Wiley, Chichester, 1973.
2. Savage, L. J.: *The Foundations of Statistics*, Wiley, New York, 1954.
3. Simon, H. A.: A Behavioral Model of Rational Choice, *Q. J. Econ.*, vol. 69, pp. 99–118, 1955.
4. Tversky, A., and D. Kahneman: Judgement under Uncertainty; Heuristics and Biases, *Science*, vol. 185, pp. 1124–1131, 1974.
5. Kahneman, D., P. Slovic, and A. Tversky (eds): *Judgement under Uncertainty*, Cambridge University Press, Cambridge, 1982.
6. Fischhoff, B., S. Lichtenstein, P. Slovic, S. L. Derby, and R. L. Keeney: *Acceptable Risk*, Cambridge University Press, Cambridge, 1981.
7. Starr, C.: Social Benefit Versus Technological Risk, *Science*, vol. 165, pp. 1232–1238, 1969.
8. Smithson, M.: *Ignorance and Uncertainty*, Springer-Verlag, Berlin, 1989.
9. Vleck, C., and P. J. Stallen: Rational and Personal Aspects of Risk, *Acta Psychologica*, vol. 45, pp. 273–300, 1980.
10. Slovic, P.: Perception of Risk, *Science*, vol. 236, pp. 280–285, 1987.
11. Eiser, J. R., and J. Van der Pligt: *Attitudes and Decisions*, Routledge, London, 1988.
12. Gow, H. B. F. and H. Otway: *Communicating with the Public about Major Accident Hazards*, Elsevier Applied Science, London, 1990.
13. Cvetkovich, G., and T. C. Earl: Judgement and Hazard Adaptation: A Longitudinal Study of Responses to the Risks of Water Contamination, *Acta Psychologica*, vol. 68, pp. 343–353, 1988.
14. Pidgeon, N., B. A. Turner, and D. I. Blockley: Hazard Assessment in Structural Engineering, in *Reliability and Risk Analysis in Civil Engineering*, Vol. 1, *Proceedings of ICASP-5*, N. Lind (ed.), Institute for Risk Research, University of Waterloo, Canada, 1987.
15. Holloway, N. J.: 'SURVIVE': A Safety Analysis Method for a Survey of Rule Violation Incentives and Effects, in *Safety and Reliability in the 90s: Will Past Experience or Prediction Meet Our Needs?*, M. H. Walter and R. F. Cox (eds), Elsevier Applied Science, London, 1990.

NINE

THE SOCIOLOGY OF SAFETY

B. A. TURNER

9.1 INTRODUCTION

Engineering is a human enterprise. All technical activities are purposeful and the goals to which they are directed can only be human ones—in general, goals concerning the arrangement and shaping of the material world for our use and convenience. As well as supplying the objectives towards which such engineering activities are steered, human beings also design, construct, operate, maintain and dispose of engineering installations. The success or failure of an engineering project is thus dependent upon the way in which they carry out these crucial tasks.

To the sociological eye, engineering systems are always *sociotechnical systems*, made up of a technical system embedded within a social system. To understand why an engineering project might fail, on the one hand, or might safely perform to specification, on the other, the recognition that the technical aspects of a project are always intertwined with social and human factors is important. After large-scale accidents, more than two-thirds of the recommendations typically made by public inquiries refer to social and administrative matters: to the need to communicate better, to clarify administrative responsibilities, to improve supervision and monitoring, to search for more satisfactory procedures and to develop anticipatory research. As we shall see below, we cannot predict in detail the form of major engineering failures, but we *can* expect that after such incidents there will be a strong emphasis upon reviewing and correcting the social as well as the technical aspects of a failed sociotechnical engineering system.

Someone—and it may be the engineer if no one else is willing—has to take care of such social and administrative matters to enable an engineering installation or construction to continue to function satisfactorily. In the absence of such care, engineering projects will repeatedly fail for non-technical rather than for technical reasons. Engineers have a vested interest in seeing that their projects are not subverted by the way in which they are constructed, operated or maintained, and to support this interest they may have to attend to the human factors relevant to a particular project, if only to assure themselves that appropriate administrative personnel and procedures are in place.

Looking more closely at the typical engineering process (Fig. 9.1), the sociotechnical systems involved may be separated into three overlapping and interconnected types: *in-house systems, installation systems* and *end-user systems*:

1. *In-house systems* are the organizational, professional and technical settings in which the design engineer or the engineering planner works in order to devise and specify a new engineering system. Typically the activities in such settings will be concerned with the everyday professional practice of the design engineer. Questions about the clarity of the brief being tackled, the adequacy of the design and environmental information available, the appropriateness of the engineering models and standards being used, the accuracy of design calculations made and the procedures for checking and reviewing the quality of the design process are relevant to this practice. To understand the background of such systems it is important to enquire about matters such as the level and recency of professional training, arrangements for updating such training, the work-load, the level of back-up staff and resources and the patterns of communication and organization prevalent in the design offices or engineering practices concerned.

   It is also pertinent to consider the scope that engineers have in their practice for learning from previous errors. Engineering design often proceeds by trial and error or by looking for ways of counteracting trouble

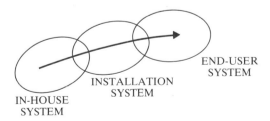

Figure 9.1 Sociotechnical subsystems making up a typical engineering system.

that has been previously experienced.[1] In handling such matters, and also in the related activities of finding compromises between function and cost or between conflicting functions, many of the skills used are unspoken ones, rarely articulated, questioned or justified, and the improvements in the safety of engineering practice may require a closer and a more explicit look at some of these tacit practices and their appropriateness.[2]

2. *Installation systems* are those organizational and technical arrangements concerned with the manufacture of components and with the assembly or the construction of a project. In civil engineering, this system would include the on-site organizations, their personnel, administration and support and their technical activities, as well as the various manufacturers of materials and components used in the construction of a building. Such installation systems are always project based, with the mission of completing a project according to a prior design. On completion of the project, personnel, equipment and administration can be redeployed to new works. Civil engineering installation systems have their own distinctive qualities which derive from this mobile pattern of grouping and regrouping, often with the recruitment of subcontractors or casual workers.

3. *End-user systems* are those concerned with the use, operation and maintenance of the project, and also those responsible for its demolition or its disposal at the end of its useful life. For the majority of engineering undertakings these end-user systems are most difficult to identify and to provide for adequately. The length of time during which a building or other artefact might be in use and the multiplicity of groups, organizations and individuals who might have contact with it during its working life increase the uncertainties. Most engineers have little control over the way in which their clients make use of their product, and even if they attempt to exercise control through negotiations with the original client, this arrangement is unlikely to extend to subsequent owners or users, especially if there is a change from the original use. On the other hand, it should be noted that numerous system failures have been caused in part by oversimple assumptions by designers and planners about the nature of the end-user system.[3]

An engineer concerned with the safe design and operation of a project has, therefore, to ensure that due account is taken of the social as well as the technical aspects of design, construction and use. A good designer is aware of the properties of the components which he/she wishes to use—attentive to their implications for the system as a whole and also to their limitations. In an engineering project which is understood as a sociotechnical system, this means that the engineer has to make some assessment of the properties and the limitations of *social* as well as technical components. Of course, the properties of the social elements in a system are often more complex, more indeterminate, more fuzzy and more difficult to specify comprehensively than those of the technical elements. While this apparent imprecision may be unpalatable to some engineers, social elements, as we have seen, are important to the success of engineering projects, so that the competent engineer does need to recognize them and to take account of them in professional practice.

9.2 SAFETY OR RISK?

It is common to talk of the issues of hazard, danger and project failure as matters of 'risk', and in a number of countries there are now requirements that 'risk assessments' be carried out before major new industrial construction projects can be approved. The term risk itself, however, is not an entirely helpful one: it is, of course, a crucial idea in the insurance business, but the rationality used to calculate insurance premiums is only rarely reflected in the way in which people actually behave. Also, it is by no means easy to deal formally with the risks that are inherent in a given technical arrangement or installation. The documented difficulties of such technical risk assessment (see, for example, Refs 4 and 5) are added to when we examine risk management and safety control from a sociotechnical perspective. Since formal risk assessments of a system can never provide more than a partial view of the hazards,[4] decisions about risk will almost certainly be in error. In most real-life, open-world situations, the information needed to make a good-quality assessment of risk is typically not available. It is therefore important to ensure that risk prediction is always complemented by strategies for the ongoing control of safety.[6,7]

Within engineering design, reliable information may exist about the likelihood of failure of specific, commonly used components under certain conditions—those components that have been frequently used and also often rigorously and repeatedly tested. However, information about the likelihood of failure of combinations of such components, or of larger, more unique subsystems, not to mention the total system itself, is much less commonly available. Also, while we now know much about the way in which individual people assess and deal with risks (see Chapter 8 in this volume), it is also important to recognize that the perception of risk and hazard is not a private or an individual matter.

Individual variations notwithstanding, the dangers that we emphasize and the dangers that we ignore are in large part already selected out for us by the groups and the society to which we belong.[8] Rather than being an independent factor that can be assessed and precisely specified, most of the dangers that we face are to a great degree interdependent with, or are generated by, the activities of our own groups and our own society. Those who live by hunting and fishing need to contend with the dangers of the environments into which they place themselves, as well as with the potential hazards of self-inflicted injuries from guns, spears, arrows or trawl nets. Military societies transform death and danger by making their confrontation a part of the destiny of the warrior who should prefer to die bravely and gloriously rather than to survive as a coward. Our own endorsement of a way of life that uses cars and aeroplanes, electricity, plastics, high-rise office buildings and the other trappings of contemporary industrial society brings with it an associated set of risks of traffic accidents, pollution, collision and collapse on a grander scale than has previously ever been possible. We provoke the hazards whose risks we then have to learn to cope with.

Nor is it the case that risks are equally distributed within modern societies: whether we consider general death rates, occupational death rates, the danger from accidents in the home, inability to work as a result of chronic illness, or a range of indicators of general health, it is overwhelmingly clear that it is more 'dangerous' to be poor, since figures for all such factors increase as we move down the socioeconomic scale—'the poor risk more'. It is also a complication that the risks that we can most accurately assess in advance are the ones that are well known and well structured. Since, as we shall see below, most major system failures arise as a result of ill-structured combinations of factors, whose dimensions become apparent only with hindsight, it is clear that such events cannot be well captured by means of highly exact anticipatory risk assessments.

A final caution to be expressed about the idea of risk relates to the way in which attention given to a numerical assessment of risk, which, it is claimed, can be calculated in an impersonal and a detached manner, detracts from or covers over the issues of moral judgement and blame which crop up whenever things start to go wrong. In the design stage of a new project, a risk assessment figure may have the appearance of a precisely and accurately calculated certainty, but in the unfortunate event of a failure in which people are killed or injured—or even one in which they merely lose money—this apparently impersonal risk assessment number has to be interpreted as one element in the multiple issues of guilt, blame and responsibility. On matters of danger and safety and their social implications, we can never take a neutral attitude.

Thus, although it is often valuable to discuss issues of safety, danger and hazard in terms of risk, such discussions do tend to place a lot of stress upon risk as something faced by an individual who needs to make a decision. This pushes into the background the way in which our involvement with, and our reactions to, risk and danger are strongly influenced by the way we live in our complex, organized society. The sociotechnical systems devised and produced by engineers form part of this highly structured society and assessments of their safety or lack of safety will inevitably be made against the backdrop of shared morals, beliefs, values and practices. In one way or another, the collective processes of the society will specify what is regarded as important and to be defended, what may readily be disregarded and how responsibilities and blame are to be allocated. For many purposes, therefore, rather than discussing risk, it may be more helpful to try to understand issues of hazard and safety by examining the properties of breakdown or adequacy in sociotechnical systems.

9.3 BREAKDOWN AND LEARNING

Much can be learned about sociotechnical engineering systems by examining what happens when they fail and whether the failure is a benign or a catastrophic one. If it is possible to set on one side the adverse consequences associated with it, the condition of system breakdown is an ideal state for promoting system learning. Studies of engineering failures[3,9] show that there are regularities in the manner in which complex systems fail, and an understanding of these regularities can be used to improve engineering safety design.

Perrow[9] has suggested that some contemporary technical installations are so complex and so closely meshed that accidents are inherent in their design: such systems generate what he calls 'normal accidents'. Systems of this kind display both a high degree of complexity and a very tight degree of coupling. The features that characterize high complexity and tight coupling are summarized in Table 9.1.

Table 9.1 Perrow's characteristics of high complexity and tight coupling

Dimension 1. High or low complexity
High complexity is associated with:
- Tight spacing of equipment
- Very close production steps
- A multiplicity of common mode connections of components
- A limited possibility of isolating failed components
- Limited awareness of interdependencies because of personnel specialization
- Limited substitution of supplies and materials
- Unfamiliar and unintended feedback loops
- Many control parameters with potential interaction
- Indirect or inferential information sources
- Limited understanding of social processes

Dimension 2. Tight or loose coupling
Tight coupling is associated with:
- Unacceptability of delays in processing
- Invariant sequences of operation
- Only one method to meet the goal
- Little slack possible in supplies, equipment or personnel
- Buffers and redundancies deliberately designed into the system
- Limited substitution of supplies, equipment and personnel also anticipated in the design

Source: Charles Perrow, *Normal Accidents: Living with High-Risk Technologies,* Copyright © 1984 by Basic Books. Reprinted by permission of Basic Books, a division of Harper Collins Publishers Inc.

Perrow argues that most manufacturing production, while it demonstrates a degree of tight coupling, is of relatively low complexity, so that failures at one point in the system have relatively few unintended consequences for the rest of the system. The civil aviation and the railway systems are of high complexity, but the physical separation of individual units—aircraft or trains—means that failures, however catastrophic, are relatively self-contained. This, together with the very high profile accorded to public transport systems, provides both the opportunity and the stimulus to learn from failures and errors, so that the lessons learned can be built into other units in the system. A failure in a particular type of aircraft will lead to the grounding of others of that type until suitable modifications can be devised and implemented.

The most dangerous sociotechnical arrangements according to Perrow— those that show both high complexity *and* tight coupling—are advanced chemical and nuclear installations. Here the degree of complexity of the systems and the difficulty of isolating sections of them from each other mean that the plant has properties that cannot be fully understood in advance by those working on its in-house design. In consequence, when they do occur errors cannot necessarily be contained.

In practice the concepts of 'complexity' and 'tight coupling' have turned out to be difficult to use analytically and it seems likely that they are not as independent of each other as Perrow's initial accounts suggested. Moreover, Perrow does not specify clearly whether his comments have more force when applied to technical systems alone or whether similar effects are produced by both social and technical complexity and interdependence. However, his analysis does enable us to learn about some aspects of systems failures by drawing our attention to the safety implications of the growing complexity and interdependence of many of today's most advanced industrial installations. Such properties only become fully apparent to those within the end-user system when something goes wrong, and even then the system will often behave in a counter-intuitive way which makes it difficult to control.[9,10] The strong implication of Perrow's analysis is that, in the extreme, the only way of avoiding serious but 'normal' accidents in some complex and tightly coupled systems may be to refrain from constructing them.

In my own research I have taken a rather different developmental approach to system failures and to the problems of learning from them.[3] On the basis of an initial study of disasters in Britain over an eleven-year period, I identified a pattern which suggests that large-scale accidents have many causes rather than a single cause and that their preconditions build up over a period of time, rather than springing into existence instantaneously. The model points to the way in which crises and disasters develop in a covert and unnoticed fashion during an 'incubation period', the typical sequence of events being set out in Table 9.2. From an initial situation when the circumstances of the project in question are 'notionally normal', the

**Table 9.2 Development sequence
of systems failures**

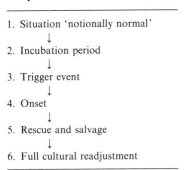

1. Situation 'notionally normal'
   ↓
2. Incubation period
   ↓
3. Trigger event
   ↓
4. Onset
   ↓
5. Rescue and salvage
   ↓
6. Full cultural readjustment

incubation period starts to develop at the point at which circumstances start to deviate, covertly, from that which is believed to be the case. This state of affairs continues to develop until it is terminated by a 'trigger event' which combines the predisposing factors into a single occurrence, usually an unanticipated discharge of energy of some kind, which provokes the onset of a system failure. Typically there then follows an immediate period of rescue and salvage, followed later by some form of adjustment, often a public inquiry, which identifies the reasons for the failure and for their hidden character, and attempts to stop similar incidents recurring in the future.

In retrospect, events within the incubation period can be reconstructed as an event sequence diagram, a tree-like causal structure of contributory incidents with the trigger event and the onset of the failure at its focus. Events that contribute to system failure may be from the in-house system, the installation system or the end-user system, or, more commonly, from all three sources. Event sequence diagrams exhibiting this kind of structure can be used to summarize the events associated with a failure and to relate inquiry findings and lessons learned to the causal pattern identified.[11] At the moment, work is under way[12] to summarize and capture the information from numerous case studies of structural failure, using event sequence diagrams of differing levels of generality, and to use this material to construct an intelligent knowledge base which will be used within in-house systems to assist structural engineering designers in their work. The general kinds of predisposing features which typically associate and interact together in various combinations during the incubation period to produce large-scale accidents or disasters are set out in Table 9.3.

Up to the point at which the trigger incident allows the failure to be realized, this kind of pattern is a 'disaster waiting to happen'. For this reason, it offers us a way of examining and taking advantage of both near-miss events and minor, unanticipated failures. Near-misses are unforeseen events which

Table 9.3 Turner's model of preconditions of disaster

Predisposing features typically found during an incubation period are:
- Organizational rigidities of perception and belief
- Decoy phenomena which distract attention from genuine hazards
- A range of many types of *information* and *communication difficulties* associated with the ill-structured problem which eventually generates the accident. Such ambiguities, noise and confusion are frequently complicated by unexpected elements injected into the situation by 'strangers' who are unfamiliar with the system, most frequently members of the public, and by additional surprises arising from unanticipated aspects of the 'site' or of the technical system involved
- Failure to comply with existing safety regulations
- A variety of modes of minimizing or disregarding emergent danger, especially in the final stages of the incubation period

---

offer a clue to the existence of a developing 'incubation period'. Potentially they can be used to bring to an end an incubation period while avoiding a catastrophic outcome, but they can only do so if they are registered and acted upon. Near-miss events of all kinds offer themselves as valuable opportunities for discovery which should be assiduously reviewed.

The importance of treating near-misses and accidents as learning opportunities is also one of the central conclusions reached by a group of American investigators who have looked in particular at the problems of 'high reliability organizations'.[13] The common characteristics of such organizations, which ranged from US Navy aircraft carriers to the national electricity distribution system, was their ability to create and to maintain an open learning system, a system in which accidents were regarded as opportunities for learning rather than as occasions for attributing blame, and in which near-misses were treated as matters for serious discussion and review. These observations, taken together with the earlier discussion of systems failures, suggest that it would be useful for engineers not only to look initially at their own in-house systems but also at the installation systems and at the end-user systems for their projects in order to assess whether these systems are capable of learning from error. It is worth noting that the constraints of the fear of legal action and of damage to professional reputations within the civil engineering industry, especially in those countries where it is organized in a multiplicity of relatively small professional practices, ensure that, collectively, the in-house systems of the industry do *not* operate like a high-reliability organization. Attempts, for example, to set up anonymous reporting systems for failures and near-misses, analogous to those operated by airline pilots, have so far foundered, and there seems to be a premium on secrecy rather than openness.

In planning a system, design engineers often seek to protect certain core technical aspects of their scheme by limiting the extent to which they need to be actively concerned with the social or human characteristics of the end-user system. Using technological means to bar from the system those people who are not specially trained or specially informed about it removes the need to protect the inner workings of the system from them. Thus, railway tracks and construction sites are fenced off to exclude all but trained personnel; electric motor units are permanently sealed; computer systems have hierarchies of access to exclude the casual user from key areas of the system; and so on. However, those *strangers* (see Table 9.3) who are being excluded constitute a very large and diverse class of people, whose behaviour cannot always be adequately anticipated in advance. Problems can be created on a construction site, for example, if it has not been recognized that the installation system may have to interact with: sales representatives; trade union officials; family and friends of employees; down-and-outs and squatters; members of the emergency services; and so on. Quite apart from the fact that limited access systems are themselves sociotechnical systems, which in turn may have their own flaws, the activation of hazards within the installation system by such 'strangers' to the system is an uncertain element which may provide one contributory factor in an incubatory buildup to failure.

Any physical assembly possesses a multiplicity of technical properties, not all of which will have been anticipated in the framework within which the assembly was designed. We may use the term *site* (see Table 9.3) to refer to this condition which often provokes unexpected failures 'on site'. Any particular object may be present in a system because of only one of its properties, but it unavoidably brings with it all of its other features. Thus, while a thermostat can be represented in a circuit diagram as an electrical systems component, it also has inevitable physical attributes. 'On site', it is possible to stop a thermostat from working in a way that is wholly unpredictable from the circuit diagram—by kicking it!

The term 'site' thus alerts us to the incidence of surprises that arise from unanticipated properties of the technical system involved. Even when safety features are designed into a system, these features themselves have multiple properties that complicate their function. Emergency exits, for example, can also offer opportunities for unauthorized entry, so that repeatedly in public buildings and especially in places of entertainment we find that doors have been blocked or padlocked to prevent them being used as entrances, without a full realization of the implications of this blockage for their use as exits in a fire or other emergency.

More generally, this pattern makes us realize that no activity or construction can be either wholly safe or wholly dangerous, for all human plans, projects and actions entail both risk and safety. Risk and safety are interdependent and co-available. In designing or operating a sociotechnical system, therefore, the engineer cannot expect to *eliminate* danger or failure: the task is to balance the possible favourable outcomes of a given arrangement against its possible adverse consequences. Professional judgements about this balance of safety, however, will be deficient if they fail to cover the social as well as the technical aspects of the project in question.

9.4 SAFETY CULTURE

A more comprehensive way of looking at hazard and danger in all three of the sociotechnical systems we have identified—in-house, installation and end-user—is to enquire how *safe* they are as organized systems. No organization, of course, can be wholly safe, but recent inquiries do suggest that some organizational practices can shift the balance of likely outcomes towards improved safety.[14] The 'high-reliability' organizations we have already referred to strive to promote a free flow of information, and also seek to encourage their employees to take responsibility for using that information as a resource for enhancing safety, rather than seeing it as a punitive basis for organizational control. To encourage people to behave in such an open and responsible way in their work, all aspects of the organization in which they are employed must reinforce that behaviour. This means that reward and promotion systems, job allocation and control systems, performance and responsibility systems and practices of communication, power and authority all need to be adjusted to strengthen the open learning patterns that will enhance safety.

In settings such as the explosives industry, which have long experience of highly dangerous processes, some of the organizational patterns developed include consciousness-raising programmes to enhance concern about safety; rigorous rule enforcement; invited inspection of the plant by outside experts; rapid-response mechanisms to allow employees to deal with irregularities; special provisions to preserve information about process steps if there should be an explosion: and the careful monitoring and screening of visitors and personnel. A final stage in hazard reduction has been achieved through product conception, as the industry has designed explosives that become active only when mixed at the point of use.

Such precedents can be built upon by specifying more generally some of the features of a safe organization. We may propose that a safe organization is one that promotes a caring attitude on the part of both its individual employees and the organization as a whole—caring about the positive and the adverse consequences of individual actions and of the actions of the enterprise. Care embraces both a concern for the material outcomes of actions and a solicitude for their effects upon people. This implies that, as well as recognizing the responsibilities of individuals, we need to consider organizations as entities responsible for the morality of their outcomes, an approach that has recently been reflected in the new prominence, in the United

Kingdom, of the crime of corporate manslaughter in connection with the capsize of the car ferry *The Herald of Free Enterprise.*

Safe operations imply the early recognition and the early control of variations from normal practice which might generate hazards for people or disruption for things. Caring thus needs to be built into normal activities, to allow monitoring and correction and especially self-monitoring and self-correction. Where possible, steps should be taken to localize the consequences of any variations that may disturb orderly, safe activities. The requirement for self-monitoring and self-correction implies the exercise of responsibility by both workers and professionals. This does not mean that there should be no rules about safe behaviour, for good rules, well-planned and monitored, are crucial for safety. What should be avoided, however, is the construction of rules that are to be followed mechanically and especially the creation of situations in which people have to work in spite of the rules in order to carry out work safely.

It is useful to try to identify for a particular technology or set of operations the tasks that are absolutely essential for safe working. Once identified, the questions of how these tasks should be specified and how they might be shared out among different jobs and work roles can be addressed. This is not a step that should be taken too hastily: if a workable arrangement is to be found it is better to live with some uncertainty rather than to close off options too soon.

Since the individual and corporate learning that promotes safety depends upon an open flow of information, communication links and boundaries within the systems concerned should not be drawn in ways that impede the *sharing* of information, knowledge and learning about hazards and about safe operations. People in work organizations are usually grouped according to the technology that they have in common (for example a typing pool or a switchboard); according to common territory (all staff on the fifth floor); or according to shared time allocations (all of the temporary staff deal with the seasonal overload). The implications of these alternative groupings and their boundaries should be considered from the point of view of the communications which are desirable for care and safety.

Information should, in the first place, be available where it is needed for action. Thus an appropriate information system from a safety point of view should supply a work team with the feedback to allow them to control variances that might emerge from their work and that are likely to generate adverse effects for the installations or the people they are working with. This kind of feedback uses information as a basis for action, as distinct from the use of information either for recording purposes or for control in power games.

In a safe organization, the roles that people occupy in their work must be recognized as complex, for even if someone is only carrying out a very simple task, they will also be expected to care—that is to think about and to pay attention to the possible undesirable consequences of their actions for plant or for other people, whether these are fellow employees or outsiders. For this reason, it may be desirable to enlarge rather than to subdivide further the most simple and the most specialized tasks. This suggests that a job that is safe and provides safety for others is also one that will contribute towards the quality of working life. Support and recognition, variety and a defined personal area of decision making should thus go along with safe working, as should being able to relate what one does to the wider context of one's present and future life outside the work-place. Moreover, the establishment of a safe organization of this kind cannot be thought of as a once-and-for-all activity, and the safety performance of the organization and of its internal arrangement need to be subjected to regular evaluation and review.

Underpinning all of these observations is the recently recognized importance for safe operation of developing an appropriate *safety culture* within systems and organizations. The term 'culture' is widely used in social science, and in the present context it is useful to understand it as referring to the collection of beliefs, norms, attitudes and expectations shared collectively by members of a society, organization or group. These joint outlooks define the identity of the group and also enable the members of that group to make a common sense of the world around them. The more specialized 'safety culture' is thus the set of people's shared beliefs, norms, attitudes and expectations within a given organization or sociotechnical system that relates to minimizing the exposure of employees, managers, customers, suppliers and members of the public to dangerous conditions.

Safety culture was first referred to by the OECD Nuclear Agency in their analysis of the implications of the Chernobyl radioactivity release for Western nuclear industries. The term was then used fairly narrowly to refer to operator qualifications, to operator control and to aspects of the working environment and the administrative system which were directly related to safe operation. The present discussion assumes that there are aspects of culture relevant to safety beyond what the OECD report refers to as *individual* attitudes to safety and danger, attitudes which they thought could not be regulated. Shared attitudes and beliefs are of crucial importance in determining how people in work settings regard the implementation of safety precautions and the enforcement of safety rules.[14]

It is true in one sense that individual attitudes cannot be regulated in a precise manner, but much management writing over the past ten years has been predicated upon the assumption that managers *can* influence the shared attitudes of their employees by operating upon the culture of their companies. Following the discussions about organizational culture we might suggest the following requirements for the promotion of a good safety culture.

At a senior management level, there needs to be a strong emphasis upon safety as part of a broad strategy of risk control, in which a high priority for safety matters is balanced against other needs for low costs, high production or high quality. Coupled with this would be a realistic view of the short-term and long-term hazards entailed by the organization's activities. It is desirable to foster a climate that offers a positive response to criticisms, comments and feedback arising from the lower levels of an organization, or from outside it, with such inputs being reviewed for insights into operational matters rather than being rejected out of hand as foolish interruptions from the ill informed.

A good safety culture would promote the operation of appropriate, realistic and workable rules relating to hazards and to the control of potentially damaging energy sources. These rules need to be supported and endorsed throughout the organization, for concern with safety needs to be 'representative' of those in the system not punitively imposed by one group on another. Personnel need to be well trained and appropriately educated. They need to have an appreciation of the possible sources of dangerous disruption to their normal work and of the possible consequences of unsafe acts, and to be aware of unusual conditions of their equipment and of unusual actions by both members of the organization and by 'strangers' coming from outside.[3]

In sum, four very general characteristics may be advanced as the starting points for a good safety culture within a sociotechnical system: these are the establishment of a caring organizational response to the consequences of actions and policies; a commitment to this response at all levels, especially the most senior, together with an avoidance of over-rigid attitudes to safety; provision of feedback from incidents within the system to practitioners; and the establishment of comprehensive and generally endorsed rules and norms for handling safety problems, supported in a flexible and a non-punitive manner. All of these features need to be reinforced by the generation of appropriate shared beliefs and expectations about safe and caring behaviour.

The incentive to take so much time and effort to set up and maintain safe organizational systems is provided, of course, by the rising costs of failing to operate safely. The costs of failure, in insurance premiums, in liability, in reputation or image, and in adverse effects upon sales are steadily rising. Governments, the professions and the public are all stepping up the standards of safety that they require, responding to their improved understanding of the way in which risks are generated, to their higher levels of education and to their expectations of a higher, more hazard-free standard of living.

9.5 CONCLUSION

A sociological understanding of the activities associated with safe engineering practice must begin by placing the technical activities of the engineer in the context of a wider view of behaviour in a number of interlinked sociotechnical systems. This means paying attention to social roles, to status hierarchies and power structures, to information flows and to culturally shared beliefs about appropriate safety behaviour, together with the sanctions that sustain these beliefs.

Such issues may seem to be remote from many of the traditional concerns of the engineering profession. However, issues of safety are rapidly being given more priority on both national and international management agendas, in response to the increasing severity for companies of the adverse consequences for finance, sales and reputation which follow upon failure. The responsibilities and obligations of professional engineers with regard to safety are also being increasingly tightly specified. In the face of these pressures, it seems likely that the ambit of the professional engineer will have to be extended to cover the kinds of broad-brush concerns with safety that have been outlined above.

Discussions of the kinds of hazards that engineers have to cope with in their professional work can be aided to some degree by risk assessments, which have value in sketching out some likely potential dangers from new installations. However, such assessments need to be supplemented by a more systems-oriented understanding of the properties of technical systems, of the social systems within which they are always embedded and of the manner in which these sociotechnical systems are likely to fail.

It is important to the engineer who now has to become more closely engaged with the social elements of such sociotechnical systems to realize that, while these elements display regularities that can be studied, codified and understood, they can never be considered in a completely objective or neutral way. Moreover, all of our technical world is also permeated with social significance, so that even technical issues cannot be discussed or referred to without judgements and evaluations being made.

In professional life, the social features of in-house, installation and end-user sociotechnical systems will be of key interest to an engineer concerned with safety. To avoid disastrous engineering failures, it is important to assess whether such systems operate safely and to ask whether they demonstrate the enthusiasm for open learning from error and the caring attitudes that characterize organizations that will perform well in terms of reliability and safety. Only by taking account of such issues will engineers be able to guard against those human factors that may induce future project failures.

REFERENCES

1. Whyte, R. R. (ed.): *Engineering Progress Through Trouble: Case Histories Drawn from the Proceedings of the Institution of Mechanical Engineers*, Institution of Mechanical Engineers, London, 1975.

2. Polanyi, M.: *Personal Knowledge: Towards a Post-Critical Philosophy*, Routledge and Kegan Paul, London, 1958.
3. Turner, B. A.: *Man-made Disasters*, Wykeham Press, London, 1978.
4. Blockley, D. I.: *The Nature of Structural Design and Safety*, Ellis Horwood, Chichester, 1980.
5. Fischhoff, B., S. Lichtenstein, P. Slovic, S. L. Derby, and R. L. Keeney: *Acceptable Risk*, Cambridge University Press, Cambridge, 1981.
6. Pidgeon, N. F., B. A. Turner, B. Toft, and D. I. Blockley: Hazard Management and Safety Culture, paper presented to the International Workshop on Emergency Planning, Middlesex Polytechnic, 4–6 October, 1989.
7. Collingridge, D.: *The Social Control of Technology*, Frances Pinter, London, 1980.
8. Douglas, M., and A. Wildavsky: *Risk and Culture: An Essay on the Selection of Technological and Environmental Dangers*, University of California Press, Berkeley, Calif., 1982.
9. Perrow, C.: *Normal Accidents: Living with High-Risk Technologies*, Basic Books, New York, 1984.
10. Rivas, J. R., and D. R. Rudd: Man–Machine Synthesis of a Disaster-Resistant System, *Operational Res.*, vol. 23, no. 1, pp. 2–21, 1975.
11. Toft, B., and B. A. Turner: The Schematic Report Analysis Diagram: A Simple Aid to Learning from Large-Scale Failures, *Int. CIS J.*, vol. 1, no. 2, pp. 12–23, May 1987.
12. Pidgeon, N. F., J. Stone, D. I. Blockley, and B. A. Turner: Management of Safety through Lessons from Case Histories, in *Safety and Reliability in the '90s: Will Past Experience or Prediction Meet Our Needs?*, M. H. Walter and R. F. Cox (eds), Elsevier Applied Science, London, pp. 201–216, 1990.
13. La Porte, T. R.: On the Design and Management of Nearly Error-Free Organisational Control Systems, in *Accident at Three Mile Island: The Human Dimensions*, C. P. Wolf and V. B. Shelanski (eds), Westview Press, Boulder, Colorado, 1982.
14. Turner, B. A.: How Can We Design a Safe Organization?, paper presented to the Second International Conference on Industrial and Organizational Crisis Management, Leonard M. Stern School of Business, New York University, 3–4 November 1989.

THREE

THE APPLICATIONS

THE SAFETY OF LARGE DAMS

M. A. FANELLI

10.1 INTRODUCTION

'Large dams', as defined by the International Commission on Large Dams (ICOLD) are structures more than 10 m high, or retaining more than 10^5 m^3 of water. There are currently in excess of 16 000 of them distributed over the whole world.

Dams are used to store water for a number of uses: civil supply, irrigation, energy production, flood protection, etc.; they are essential to mankind's welfare and progress, and no advanced civilization can do without them. They range in size from relatively small structures (10 m high, a few thousand cubic metres in volume) to cyclopic dimensions (more than 300 m high, many millions of cubic metres of volume). They can be built from a variety of materials (earth and rockfill, mine tailings, masonry, plain or reinforced concrete) that can deteriorate more or less rapidly in a number of different ways. They can be erected on sound rock or on thick alluvial deposits. They can operate in arctic or in tropical climates, in dry countries or in lands where the average rainfall is nearly 10 metres/year. They can be located in seismically inactive regions or in a very active seismic environment. Dams can dominate valleys practically devoid of human settlements or densely populated areas with large cities. They can be centuries old, hand-built without any rational analysis or design, or erected in very recent times using the latest technologies and up-to-date knowledge.

They can be subjected to very careful and frequent surveillance or left practically unattended for lack of funds to install and maintain instruments and to pay skilled personnel. Their capacity to handle (i.e. store and evacuate) large floods may have been ensured with elaborate provisions or may be critically inadequate; their vulnerability to overtopping may be negligible or extremely critical. Finally, dams are built as perennial structures. Their useful life spans lasting—at the very least—over many decades.

It is clear from the foregoing that dams might represent a potential hazard, were it not that their safety receives—at least in industrialized countries—a very large amount of attention and constant care, with the investment of huge technical, human and financial resources tailored to each particular case. It should also be clear, indeed, that each dam is a unique case, that is an individual instance of very complex interplays of factors, extending in time over several decades, subjected to a sequence of events and influences that present only a moderate regularity, yet cannot be considered as purely random. It follows that neither purely deterministic nor 'probabilistic' approaches are able to fully cope with the complexity of each situation.

In particular, probabilistic analysis in the classical sense is ill suited to deal with dam safety issues, insofar as its natural field of application assumes—more or less explicitly—the existence of a large number of very similar individuals, subjected to a rather homogeneous field of influences. It is clear from the above description that if this basic requirement is not satisfied in the case of a particular dam, probabilistic considerations cannot be applied to it without a very careful reappraisal, probably not without major modifications, of their commonly assumed background and meaning.[†] It is also not possible, in the present state of the art, to assign to a given dam such a thing as an objectively defined 'safety factor' (or a 'probability of failure'). It follows that we do not know how to 'measure' in a quantitative sense the actual safety of a dam, and we are obliged to infer its qualitative level from a running evaluation of all the existing knowledge about that dam (factual knowledge as well as monitoring of its behaviour, intended as a response to changes in its environment or to the ageing processes).

The question is, then, what variables or parameters of the dam should best be taken as indicators from which a safety assessment can be inferred? We also need to define, as far as possible, the inference process that ensures a state-of-the-art running safety assessment.

The accomplished mathematical formulation of stress analysis in the nineteenth and twentieth centuries, together with recent explosive developments in computer power, have placed a somewhat excessive emphasis on

---

[†] It is true that the same argument could be applied to many types of one-of-a-kind engineering artefacts (e.g. bridges), but on the other hand there are numerous instances of mass-produced engineering artefacts, such as vehicles, domestic or industrial appliances, etc., for which the assumption of a large population of uniform individuals and of a definite statistical distribution of action is much more acceptable.

the importance of stress–strain distributions as meaningful parameters from which a safety assessment can be effected. In the case of dams, one should be very conscious that local damage (from excessive strain/stress) can be incurred without necessarily impairing global safety, and conversely global failure can occur almost without significant local damage. Displacements appear to be better suited as indicators of the state of safety: indeed, failure of a dam always entails the occurrence of big displacements over all, or a portion, of the dam. However, it should be kept in mind that displacements are often not sufficiently sensitive to the initial stages of development of potentially dangerous damage (see Fig. 10.1).

A conclusion to be drawn from the foregoing considerations (and similar

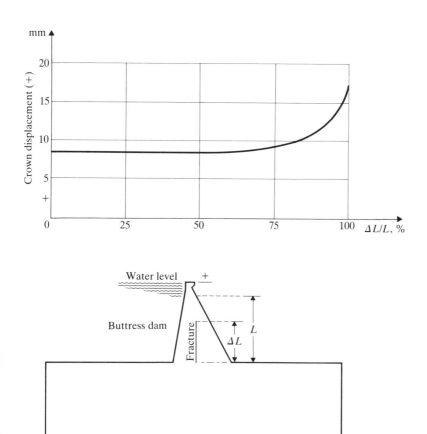

Figure 10.1 Sensitivity of crown displacement of a buttress dam to the length of a vertical crack. *(Source: Water Power and Dam Construction, December 1979.)*

ones that are omitted for brevity) is the necessity of a multivariable control that takes into account all relevant experience from past incidents to dams (of the same type as the one under scrutiny) as well as all the factual knowledge about that particular dam.

Dam design codes, regulations and practices vary widely from country to country. Some underlying trends can, however, be recognized. Whenever possible (e.g. for gravity or buttress dams) global 'safety criteria' are defined against overturning and sliding of monoliths, taking into account both normal live loads and exceptional events (earthquakes, ice thrust, uplift). For fill dams safety criteria against partial failure (slip circles, etc.) are defined; other non-local criteria (such as the liquefaction potential during earthquakes) are also used. It is to be emphasized that these safety criteria are defined in official Codes of Practice in a conservative way, neglecting some of the strength reserves of the physical system under consideration. This is attested by the continued existence, without any mishap, of many ancient dams that do not fulfil those safety criteria. In short, these criteria represent highly conventional 'lower limits' of actual safety factors which remain scarcely amenable, most of the time, to objective evaluation.

The enforcement of these design criteria, in other words, should guarantee public authorities against 'worst case' assumptions concerning both knowledge of the local situation and the professional level of the designer. They usually do not exclude the possibility that a particular design, apparently violating these criteria, could in fact be accepted if the underlying assumptions (more realistic appraisal of secondary strength reserves, of external actions, etc.) are adequately documented by a designer of superior professional standing. On the other hand, in these cases the organization responsible for maintenance should carry the additional burden of checking that the more exacting assumptions made by the designer remain in force all through the service life of the dam; otherwise remedial action would have to be taken.

For structural types where the global equilibrium approach is not feasible (e.g. arch dams) stress analysis should be performed and the local safety factor against ultimate stress must in principle be ensured everywhere. Generally tensile stress is either formally not allowed or very severely limited (e.g. 0.3 to 0.7 MPa). This poses serious problems for localized stress concentrations as well as for diffused thermal stresses.[†]

As already pointed out, official regulations state the above as the minimum requirements for acceptable design; the designer is often implicitly or explicitly allowed to produce a more elaborate analysis. In any case, an official administrative body bears the ultimate decisional responsibility of accepting or rejecting the designer's arguments for safety of the proposed dam.

† Some regulations allow the designer to assume a reduced elastic modulus for the evaluation of thermal stresses.

Risk assessment in a systematic way and according to a well-defined methodology is usually not required as such by existing regulations. The only step in that direction is the requirement by the legislation of an increasing number of countries to carry out computations of the submerged areas downstream of the dam in the event of its collapse. However, this type of exercise is not related to any assessment of the probability of occurrence of this catastrophic event (such an assessment would be extremely difficult in any case, and would entail a host of very delicate problems in the field of responsibility definition, of public opinion management, etc.). The prevailing view is that this probability is very low in developed countries with well-organized technical surveillance procedures; even including the countries that do not fulfil these requirements, the overall historical frequence of occurrence of partial or complete collapse is under 10^{-4} per dam-year, and the trend is a decidedly decreasing one in recent years.

Loads and material strengths are defined in a deterministic way; partial safety factors are not usually defined. It is, however, more and more widely recognized that risk analysis should find a place in some stage of a dam's lifetime: preliminary investigations, design, construction, commissioning, use, maintenance and decommissioning. In each of these stages there are objective risks (such as, for example, the risk of occurrence of catastrophic events like high-intensity earthquakes or disastrous floods) as well as risks of human error. The latter can be further subdivided into insufficient knowledge; incomplete or erroneous information; bad, inefficient or uncontrolled practice; error in judgement and/or decision taking, etc.

A very useful step in ensuring better safety standards, and one that is gradually gaining widespread acceptance, is the adoption of a 'quality assurance' procedure at every step in the operative activities that are concerned with each one of the above-mentioned stages. However, in many countries dam engineering is an established, tradition-bound practice and it may therefore be somewhat slow to switch to more up-to-date techniques.

It is almost universally recognized that the necessity exists for a quasi-continuous appraisal of the safety conditions (or, conversely, of risk status) of every 'important' dam, 'important' meaning in this case that the consequences of a failure could have important adverse effects on lives and properties. In this context, even apparently 'minor' water-retaining structures (sometimes not even officially classified as dams) could have, and have had in a few cases, a remarkable importance.

As already pointed out, the present state of the art does not allow the derivation, from current information, of an objective figure either for the so-called 'safety factor' or for the 'probability of failure' of any particular dam. As a consequence, it is necessary for a running evaluation of safety to be based on an indirect, inferential process of analysis.

10.2 DAM FAILURE

A desired characteristic of any safety-oriented process of analysis of dam in-service behaviour should obviously be an enhanced sensitivity to alterations (either in the dam, in its foundations or in its surroundings) that can have a significant influence towards bringing the dam closer to any one of many possible critical states. However, a difficulty in fulfilling this requirement lies in the fact that not all the critical states are clearly identifiable or foreseeable and that, even for those that can be defined, sometimes sufficient sensitivity is not provided by existing techniques.

The above general considerations can best be illustrated by some cases of actual failures of dams that have occurred in the recent past.

The failure (December 1959) of the Malpasset thin arch dam in Southern France was occasioned essentially by the sliding of a rock dihedron underlying a large portion of the left bank (see Fig. 10.2). At nearly full reservoir, thrust T acting in a vertical plane compressed the rock along surface BC, making it more watertight; on the other hand, along surface AB

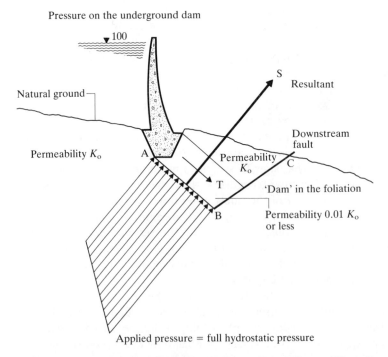

Figure 10.2 Mechanism of collapse for Malpasset Dam. *(Source: Water Power and Dam Construction, November 1985.)*

tensile stresses occurred, giving rise to an opening of the rock joint AB with water infiltration and production of a large pressure resultant S. Downstream sliding of dihedron ABC occurred as a result, causing disconnection of the left abutment and collapse of almost all of the blocks.

The causes that made possible this unexpected failure can be traced back to:

1. Insufficient preliminary investigations/rock characterization. The existence of the dihedron and the stress-dependent rock permeability were discovered only by after-failure investigations.
2. Lack of consideration of the actual failure mechanism.
3. Insufficient monitoring of uplift pressures at the rock/concrete interface.
4. Insufficient, infrequent monitoring of dam displacements and deformations. However, in this last connection it is doubtful that displacement/deformation analysis could *per se* provide sufficient sensitivity to impending danger of sliding. The sliding movement might have taken place in an essentially abrupt fashion, with little or no preliminary warning episodes.

Another 'classical' instance of dam failure relates to the earthfill embankment of Teton Dam (USA) in June 1976 (Fig. 10.3). The dam was about 92 m high, with a wide impervious core of aeolian silt. Small water infiltrations, originating small springs downstream of the dam, were observed two days prior to failure. These developed on the following day and progressed nearer and nearer to the dam, until water sources appeared on the downstream facing and at the toe of the embankment. In a few hours the source grew to a large flow, with erosion of the material, until a large hole developed in the dam body. In about 5 hours the breach reached the crest and complete failure occurred with severe downstream flooding.

A panel set up after the disaster to investigate the probable causes put forward two hypotheses:

1. Seepage under the grout cap in unsealed rock joints led to erosion along the base of the key trench and hence to a piping failure through the key trench fill.
2. Seepage through cracks in the key trench fill, caused by hydraulic fracturing or differential settlements, again led to a piping failure.

Subsequent investigations detected the occurrence of 'wet seams' in some of the construction layers. These could be attributed to unsuccessful attempts to mix dry fill with wet soil on the fill surface during construction, thus creating the potential for low-density zones and generally to deficiencies in earthwork control practices. These heterogeneous layers could have either been fractured hydraulically or undergone differential settlements on wetting. Thus the key trench fill and the grout curtain at its base could have been the seat of intense seepage flows, leading to erosion and piping.

Figure 10.3 Successive stages of development of Teton Dam breaching.

The two cases sketchily illustrated above stress the differences in the mode of failure of concrete and fill dams. In particular, while a concrete structure, especially a slender one like an arch dam, tends to yield suddenly, an earth embankment dam usually yields more gradually (the process may take some hours), thus limiting the magnitude of the peak discharge released downstream (which remains nonetheless very large, quite often in the tens of thousands of cubic metres per second).

The two cases highlight the importance of thorough on-site investigation, of good construction practices and control, and of accurate in-service monitoring towards ensuring safety. Both cases, moreover, emphasize the importance of foundation characteristics and behaviour in determining the overall safety of a dam, and in particular the critical role played by foundation seepage phenomena. Indeed, it is estimated that foundation problems account for at least one fourth to one third of the recorded cases of dam failure.

10.3 BASIC CONCEPTS OF 'MONITORING FOR SAFETY' AS APPLIED TO DAMS

As already pointed out, the present state of the art does not allow a synthetic objective safety index to be evaluated from factual knowledge about a given dam. Consequently, an indirect appraisal is adopted in most organizations. This consists essentially of the following steps:

1. Frequent (in the limit quasi-continuous) monitoring, with suitable permanent sensors installed in the dam, of certain key quantities (displacements, strains, uplift or pore pressures, seepage discharges, etc.) characterizing the 'structural response' of the dams to the continuously changing environmental actions.
2. Simultaneous monitoring of a certain set of quantities (water level in the reservoir, water and air temperatures, facing or internal temperatures if deemed useful, meteorological conditions, etc.) characterizing the environmental actions to which the dam is subjected.
3. Evaluation (more or less in 'real time') of the 'acceptability' of the response of the dam, as determined in step 1) in connection with information gained in step 2. This evaluation can be effected in a number of different ways, of which more will be said later.
4. Qualitative assessment, on the basis of step 3 and of factual knowledge about the dam as well as its past behaviour, of the state of safety of the dam.
5. Decisions, if any, about changes in the management of day-to-day operation of the dam.

Of course, many of the above steps (in particular 1 to 3) can profit heavily, in speed, accuracy and reliability, from the great possibilities of today's automatic information processing. Moreover, steps 4 and 5 could conceivably avail themselves of progress currently being made in the technology of 'knowledge-based systems'.

It is interesting to illustrate in some detail how steps 1 to 3 are carried out in the context of a modern organization of dam operation management. In this connection, the author of this chapter will draw heavily on his own experience in the framework of ENEL (the Italian National Power Agency), without neglecting, of course, important investigations being carried out in other countries:

1. Every major dam is equipped with a considerable number of transducers which are activated by a central processor to measure, at regular intervals of time, the following quantities representing 'structural effects':
   (a) Displacements (absolute or relative) of a certain number of key points. Usually horizontal crest displacements in the upstream–downstream direction are the most significant ones for concrete dams; vertical displacements are of great importance for fill dams. The instruments used are either plumblines or optical collimation, etc.
   (b) Strains (for concrete dams) around a certain number of points, along predetermined directions. The instruments used are strain gauges, compensated for temperature changes.
   (c) Uplift pressures (for concrete dams) by means of piezometers usually placed at the contact with the foundation and provided with pressure transducers. In the case of fill dams, pore pressure is measured at selected points in the embankments (e.g. downstream from drains).
   (d) Seepage discharges, both as a total and separately for different zones of the dam. This quantity is also measured downstream of drains. Calibrated weirs with level gauges are used as measuring instruments.
   (e) Total pressures, by means of special cells, in embankment dams. Sometimes other quantitites are also measured, e.g. tilting of given alignments by means of inclinometers; dynamic response to seismic events; etc. Of course the central processor also activates the recording of measurements on a suitable support for later retrieval and processing.
2. Suitable transducers, also activated at regular time intervals by a central processor, measure the variations of quantities that can be regarded as 'external influences' to which the dam responds with the 'structural effects' illustrated under step 1:
   (a) Water level in the reservoir (so-called 'hydrostatic scales' or, more simply, pressure transducers located under the minimum water level are used as measuring instruments).
   (b) Temperatures. The minimum requirements call for measurement of air and water temperatures. Water temperature should be measured at different depths (a thermocline may exist in the impoundment

depending on the season). For concrete dams, quite often surface temperatures at several points on the facings and sometimes also in the interior of the dam are measured as well. (Notice that the internal temperatures can be regarded as 'thermal responses' to the variations of external temperatures; also, they can be regarded as 'externally originated influences' which produce structural responses.)

(c) Meteorological quantitites: rainfall, air humidity, etc. Of course, this second group of measurements are also recorded for later use under the control of the central processor.

3. Evaluation of structural response in the light of environmental variations. In this step the goal is to estimate whether the structural responses (measured in step 1) are 'acceptable' for the variations that have occurred as a result of external influences (measured in step 2). In former times this judgement was left to the experience of senior engineers with a deep knowledge of the dam and of its past behaviour. Nowadays the preferred course is to set up a definite formalism to carry out the evaluation. This formalism can be established according to a certain spectrum of possible choices, which all concern the type of 'reference model' for the behaviour of the dam, against which actual performance is to be assessed:

(a) Statistical models, based on the knowledge and analysis of past behaviour of the dam over a certain number of years (Fig. 10.4).

(b) Deterministic models, based on *a priori* knowledge of the dam geometry, the mechanical characteristics of its materials (including the foundation!), the equilibrium and compatibility equations of the mechanics of continua, etc. It is to be remarked that these models, however, need the knowledge of past behaviour of the dam, over a period of at least one year, to validate and 'calibrate' them [Fig. 10.5(a) and (b)].

(c) Hybrid models, partaking of models (a) and (b) for different parts of the overall structural response (e.g. using deterministic modelling for the displacements caused by hydrostatic load variations and statistical modelling—for want, for example, of thermometric information—for the displacements caused by thermal variations, etc.)

In all cases, the end-products of the setting up of the reference model, are analytical expressions that relate 'expected values' of quantitites measured under step 1 to quantitites measured under step 2: e.g. for a displacement δ_e one could arrive at a formula for the expected value like this:

$$\delta_e = \delta_0 + \delta_1 z + \delta_2 z^2 + \cdots + \sum_{j=1}^{N} T_j C_j + \sum_{j=1}^{N} \frac{dT_j}{dt} D_j$$

where z is the water level in the reservoir and T_j is the temperature measured at thermometer j, the total number of thermometers being N;

Hypothesis H_o: the dam continues to behave as in the past

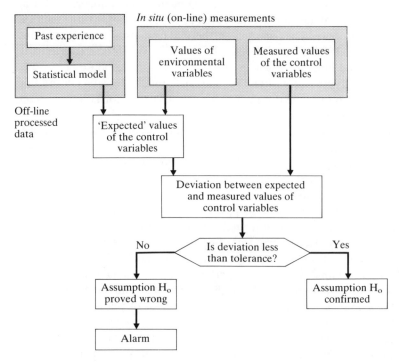

Figure 10.4 Block diagram showing the logical scheme of control operations and inferences to test assumed behaviour in the case of a 'statistical' reference model.

$\delta_0, \delta_1, \delta_2, \ldots, C_j D_j$ are precomputed constants. This expression is typical of a deterministic model for a concrete dam provided with thermometers. The formula for a statistical or hybrid model would still be of the polynomial type for the part reflecting the variations of z, and could contain simply a periodic function of time for the second part representing the seasonal temperature change effects.

This expected value, δ_e, is then compared with the measured value, δ_m. Thus a deviation is evidenced:

$$\Delta = |\delta_m - \delta_e|$$

which has to be assessed. Intuitively speaking, it is evident that if—after calibration—the deviation assumes consistently very small values, a first conclusion to be drawn is that the dam behaves 'as expected'. If, moreover, there are evidences that this expected behaviour corresponds to an acceptable degree of safety (as is the case if a deterministic model is being used, by which the safety of the dam can also be evaluated in traditional engineering

Hypothesis H_0^*: the dam behaves in accordance
with assumed rheological laws

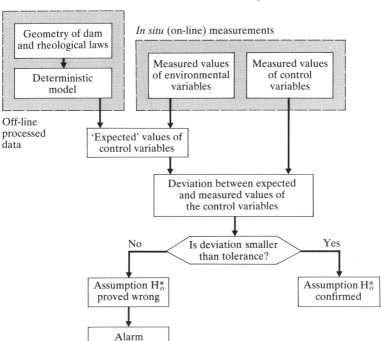

(a)

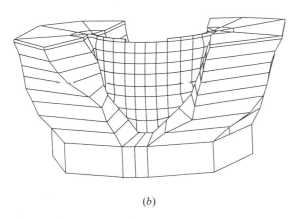

(b)

Figure 10.5 (a) Block diagram showing the logical scheme of control operations and inferences to test assumed behaviour in the case of a 'deterministic' reference mathematical model. (b) Finite element mesh for the setting up of a reference mathematical model of the 'deterministic' type.

ways), then the inference can be made that the structure is indeed safe under the set of conditions for which the comparison was made.

On the contrary, if the discrepancy Δ is a 'large' one, and all the more so if it tends in time to assume larger and larger values, one would be led quite naturally to conclude that the dam is not performing 'as expected' and that some new influence is acting that was not previously considered. As this new factor could quite conceivably lead to harmful consequences, in this case steps should be taken to find out the cause of the unexpected behaviour and to take action to correct it if needed.

The foregoing intutitive reasoning leaves one very important point open to doubt: how do we determine the limit (or 'tolerance' τ) beyond which the discrepancy is to be judged 'too large'? In other words, how can we fix the value such that:

> If $\Delta < \tau \rightarrow$ behaviour 'as expected';
> If $\Delta > \tau \rightarrow$ deviation 'too large'?

It is evident that by fixing τ 'too small' with respect to the inherent accuracy of the whole comparison process, one would run the risk of 'worrying too often' without necessity; conversely, by fixing τ 'too large', one would run the risk of letting a potentially dangerous situation go undetected. In this connections, let us suppose that the data pertaining to the period used for calibration of the model show a frequency distribution of the discrepancies

$$\delta_m - \delta_e$$

that passes the test for normality and has a standard deviation σ. It is then reasonable to use

$$\pm 2\sigma$$

as the half-width of the tolerance band (in other words, $\tau = 2\sigma$). The properties of the normal distribution then assure us that, on the average, 4 times out of 100 there will be an outlier: $|\delta_m - \delta_e| > \tau$, due only to random inherent inaccuracies of the whole measuring–modelling–comparison process. (By choosing $\tau = 3\sigma$, the figure would be 2 out of 1000.) Of course, the above reasoning could be put in more rigorous terms, but the simplified version suffices to show the essence of the question.

If the foregoing logical framework is accepted, then it is quite evident that the way is open to automatic, on-line, real-time monitoring of dam performance. Indeed, by using electrical sensors the measurements can be automatically activated, read and stored in the central processor; the reference model, embodied in very simple formulae such as the one given earlier for the expected value of a displacement, can be programmed in the procedures to be carried out by the processor and periodically inputted with the proper measurements; then the outputs of the reference model, that is the expected values of the structural effects, can be automatically compared with the corresponding measurements; the discrepancies Δ, lastly, can be compared with the pre-set value of tolerance band, τ, and a warning may be issued whenever $\Delta > \tau$. (More sophisticated 'trend analysis', also taking into account, for example, the velocity of an increase of Δ, can be implemented.)

Weighted combinations of discrepancies pertaining to several structural effects should be used in preference to a single indicator. The definition of such 'decisional matrices' is presently a largely empirical art. This is, indeed, the course taken by ENEL (the Italian National Power Agency) for most of its dams (the total number of which is over 260). The corresponding informatics system is commercially available under the trade-name MIDAS through ISMES (a research society controlled by ENEL). The scheme of MIDAS is illustrated in Fig. 10.6 and some of the results obtained are illustrated in Fig. 10.7. Presently the experience accumulated jointly by ENEL and ISMES on MIDAS application is well in excess of a thousand dam-years, with very satisfactory results.

10.4 A LOOK TO THE FUTURE

Although progress is steadily being made towards a better understanding and control of dam safety, yet the present situation is far from being entirely satisfactory. First of all, the quantitites being measured and controlled are not always sufficiently sensitive—as already mentioned—to events that constitute potential impairments of safety (see Fig. 10.1). Secondly, an objective index of the degree of safety (or, conversely, of risk) is not in sight, in the present state of the art, for dams. Thirdly, present-day systems of safety management are an awkward mixture of well-proven, fully formalized engineering procedures (such as the MIDAS system illustrated above) and of non-formalized knowledge about past history and local conditions of the dam. Proper tools are needed whereby these two elements, both necessary to 'good' safety engineering, can be efficiently integrated. Fourthly, a considerable hiatus exists between the technical and the decisional circles. The public authorities, provided with their own technical bodies, do not necessarily interact efficiently with the technical and managerial staff of dam owners.

A better definition and meshing of the respective spheres of influence and responsibility is needed to ensure that safety is pursued at the state-of-the-art level. A step forward, which is being investigated at the feasibility stage, aims at exploiting the potentialities of AI (artificial intelligence) in general and of the techniques broadly designated by the term 'knowledge-based systems' in particular. In this way it is hoped that the different levels

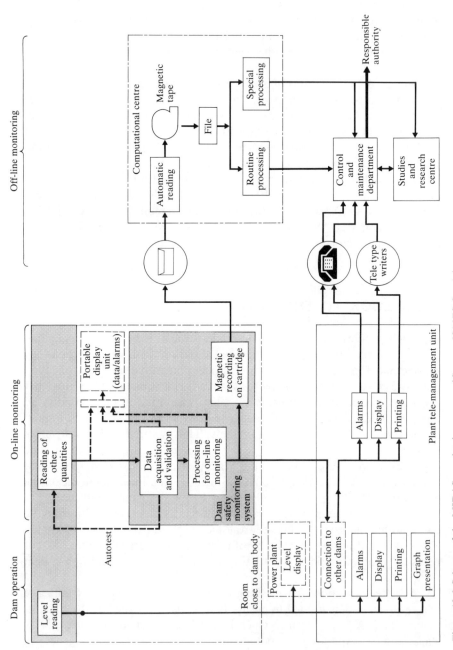

Figure 10.6 Scheme of the MIDAS monitoring system. (*Source*: *ISMES S.p.A.*)

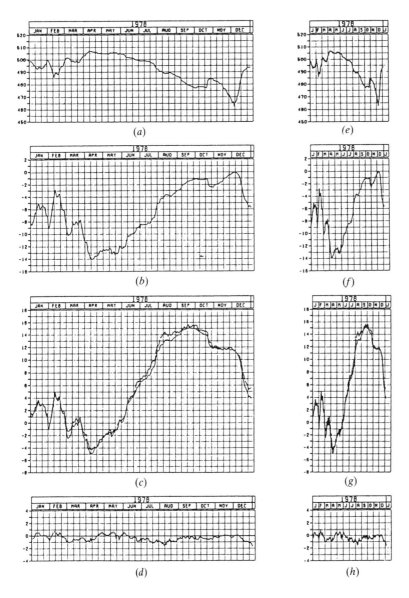

Figure 10.7 Example of deterministic model application with daily frequency recorded situations (year 1978). *(Source: ENEL.)* (*a*) Diagram of storage levels (metres above sea level). (*b*) Diagram of theoretical hydrostatic component (mm). (*c*) Superposition of displacements recorded by tele-recording plumb-line displacement transducer (– – –) and of theoretical relevant values (——). (*d*) Diagram of deviations (mm). (*e*), (*f*), (*g*) and (*h*) same as (*a*), (*b*), (*c*) and (*d*), respectively, but with a different time-scale.

of knowledge about the dam and its environment can be articulated in an efficient, interactive inferential process.

Present-day state of the art allows us in principle to set up a 'model' not only of real-world entitites like the dam, its appurtenant works, its foundations, the environment, the meteorological and seismic events, etc., but also of the different relationships that can be invoked between these entities and the world of cognitive instances: past knowledge and experience (both in general about dams and in particular about 'that' dam), physical laws, specific deterministic models, etc., including human mistakes. In this way the tools of reliability analysis (trees of events, Bayesian probability evaluation, etc.) can also be used in a proper framework and in a context that is 'as well defined as possible'. Thus in the end the question 'How far is that dam from a dangerous situation?' can be appraised in objective, rather than subjective, terms, and those 'algorithmic' tools that can be used (like deterministic models, if this is the case) find their proper place as partial faces of a very complex web of a multiple-level interpretative process.

Such a knowledge-based system can also be conceived from the start as an 'open' one, which can be progressively updated and enlarged; eventually, one would like to think of such a system as a 'learning' one, and this is not excluded by some of the leading figures in the field. Other improvements can doubtless be expected in the development of better, more complete, more efficient deterministic models, as well as in the field of measurements. The development of non-linear, damage-accumulation models, together with the availability of superfast computation, could in principle allow the exploration of many 'scenarios' of the future life of a dam.

However, caution should be used when estimating the possibilities and usefulness of such an approach. Indeed, one realizes more and more that non-linear behaviour models are often extremely sensitive to initial conditions and in general to past history of the system being simulated; consequently the principle of 'continuity' (by which a group of time histories starting from a set of nearly identical initial conditions would stay 'close together' forever, so that a limited sampling of those time histories would suffice to encompass them all) may be completely undermined. This eventuality would not only make almost pointless a limited exploration of future scenarios, such as any exploration is necessarily bound to be, but it would produce, in inexperienced hands, a false feeling of confidence. This does not mean that the development of non-linear, ever more sophisticated models should be discouraged; it only underlines the fact that such tools will in all probability be only short-range, and by no means long-range, forecasting tools. Therefore, the progress both of numerical simulation models and of measuring instruments will allow a more accurate appraisal of the day-to-day evolution of the conditions of any given dam as concerns its safety.

BIBLIOGRAPHY

ICOLD: *World Register of Dams*, vols 1–4, Boulevard Haussman 151, Paris, 1964.

Four Major Dam Failures Re-examined, *Water Power*, November 1985. A report on the International Workshop on Dam Failures, Purdue View, USA, August 1985.

Goubet, A.: Risques Associes aux Barrages (Risks Associated with Storage Dams), *La Houille Blanche*, no. 8, 1979.

Johnson, F. A., and P. Illes: A Classification of Dam Failures, *Water Power and Dam Construction*, December 1976.

MacDonald, T. C., and J. Langridge-Monopolis: Breaching Characteristics of Dam Failures, *J. Hydraul. Engng*, vol. 110, no. 5, May 1984.

Fanelli, M. A.: Investigation and Monitoring of Concrete Dams, *Voltrage Wasserbau—Seminar Wintersemester 1988/89 on Informationsverarbeitung in der Praxis von Wasserbau und Wassewirtschaft*, Aachen, 1989.

ISMES: On Line Monitoring Systems for Dams (Systèmes de Contrôle en Ligne pour les Barrages), ISMES, Bergamo, 1989.

Bonaldi, P., M. Fanelli, G. Giuseppetti, and R. Riccioni: Safety Control of Concrete Dams: The Role of Automated Procedures and Management of Surveillance, Commission Internationale Des Grands Barrages Quatorzième Congrès des Grands Barrages, Rio de Janeiro, 1982.

CHAPTER

ELEVEN

MARINE STRUCTURES

J. B. CALDWELL

O hear us when we cry to Thee,
For those in peril on the sea

But what can He do—and what should we do—in response to those cries?
For as long as mankind has needed to use the sea, it has been seen as both
friend and enemy. We need its bounteous provisions of food, minerals and
energy—and must increasingly turn to the sea as 'mankind's last resource'.
We need to use it as still a most cost-effective medium for transport of goods
and people, for defence and for leisure. But it remains 'the cruel sea',
the 'watery waste', a hostile and largely untameable environment, indifferent
to mankind's needs and aspirations.

So there has always been, especially to the citizens of maritime nations,
a special kind of horrified fascination with disaster at sea. Legend and history
abound with stories and speculations, from *The Marie Celeste* to the
Derbyshire. When such disasters commit large groups of innocent people to
death by fire or drowning, public emotion and pressure for action run
understandably very high. Marine architects and engineers, and all who have
some responsibility for safety at sea, cannot ignore such sentiment. It is not
acceptable merely to argue that the public perception of risk might be very
different from some statistically-defined risk of death at sea averaged over
a long period, true though this may be. Nor is it helpful to remind those
affected that all human activity involves risk and that engineers cannot design
vehicles and structures for zero risk of failure—which again, as noted in
Chapter 1, has to be accepted as a fact of life. What then is to be done?

In the spirit of rational enquiry which underlies this book, it is first necessary to try to clarify the nature and the essential ingredients of the problems of maritime safety; these are discussed in Sec. 11.1. Against this background, Sec. 11.2 reviews the present regulatory framework for the control of safety at sea and illustrates how present regulations affecting ship design treat safety in a largely empirical and implicit way. Clearly there is much to be done before maritime safety can be said to be handled explicitly and rationally; in the final section some pointers to the way ahead are noted from recent developments and safety studies.

11.1 THE PROBLEMS OF MARITIME SAFETY

Although many of these general features of safety engineering discussed in Chapter 1 are relevant to marine work, there are some peculiarities and difficulties in this latter field. Some particular features of the problem of trying to assure safety at sea can perhaps best be identified by reference to a recent and tragic marine disaster, seen in Fig. 11.1.

Figure 11.1 Capsize of *The Herald of Free Enterprise. (Source: Fairplay International Shipping Weekly.)*

The Loss of *The Herald of Free Enterprise*

The bleak facts are not in dispute. On the evening of 6 March 1987, the roll-on, roll-off passenger ferry *The Herald of Free Enterprise*, soon after leaving Zeebrugge harbour, capsized in shallow water with the loss of 193 lives. The ship, built in Germany in 1980, was designed to modern standards of safety and manning, fully in accordance with the prevailing regulations. Sea conditions near Zeebrugge were unexceptional; there was a light easterly breeze and little sea or swell. The passengers had every right to expect the journey to Dover to be just another of the 150 000 Channel crossings by which around 24 million passengers travel safely to and from the Continent each year. Why then were their expectations so tragically dashed?

The subsequent Court of Inquiry had no doubt as to the immediate cause of the disaster. Crew negligence had resulted in the bow doors being left open, and as the ship gathered speed away from port, water was shipped through the open doors onto the open, uninterrupted vehicle deck. This accretion of free water relatively high in the ship reduced its stability to such an extent that it capsized. This happened so quickly that there was no time to launch boats or rafts, and with the ship on its beam, decks became unclimbable cliffs, and transverse gangways deep wells, from which there was little hope of escape. Had the ship been in deeper water and overturned completely, the casualty list would have been even greater.

From the ensuing ferment of public discussion and professional debate, many strands of concern emerged which both called in question current procedures and attitudes to marine safety, as well as indicating some possibilities and priorities for the future.

Frequency and Number of Fatalities

Did this disaster demonstrate that cross-channel transport of passengers, especially in ro-ro ferries, was unacceptably risky? More generally, if acceptable levels of risk are eventually to be used as an explicit criterion of marine safety assessment, how should such levels be decided? These questions raise a number of problems. Thus, if the safety record of UK ro-ro passenger ferries is viewed in terms of the number of accidents per year in which lives have been lost, it must be judged as very good. Of 82 serious incidents to such ships in UK waters in the 34-year period from October 1953 to October 1987, only seven resulted in loss of life. Even the total number of 338 resulting deaths—10 per year—when compared with the many million passenger miles completed, indicates a level of safety not greatly different from other modes of public transport.

However, it is the distribution of those 338 deaths that gives major cause for concern; 327 resulted from just two accidents: 134 lost when the *Princess Victoria* sank in the Irish Sea in 1953 and 193 in *The Herald of Free Enterprise*.

The economies of scale in passenger transport are leading inexorably to ships designed for increasing numbers. Future cruise liners could well accommodate 7000 to 8000 people, simultaneously dependent on the survivability of their temporary home in the event of any one of a formidable range of possible hazards. The potential scale of deaths in such ships must thus influence the level of risk of loss for which they may eventually come to be designed. At present, as noted in Sec. 11.2 below, the size of ship and number of its passengers exercise, via some traditional and empirical regulations, a rather indirect effect on design. A more rational basis for setting safety standards is offered, at least in principle, by the use of curves relating the frequency of accidents involving loss of life to the number of lives lost per accident. Thus if N is the number of fatalities resulting from an accident and F is the annual frequency at which accidents involving N or more fatalities occur, $F-N$ curves can be constructed from historical data on accidents.

Figure 11.2, based on Refs 1 and 2, is an example showing how such $F-N$ curves might be used to define safety limits. Based on recorded fatalities in various activities and modes of sea transport, both the slopes and relative positions of the $F-N$ lines are significant. Aldwinckle and Pomeroy[1] proposed an 'iso-risk' line $FN = 10$ as a criterion for 'events to which the general public is knowingly submitted and which do not cause apparent adverse reaction'. Ships' crews may evidently be exposed to marginally greater risk than implied by this line, as may passengers on non-ro-ro and ro-ro ferries.

International Variations

Even if $F-N$ relationships of this kind, when backed by appropriate statistical data, appear to provide a logical basis for deciding acceptable levels of marine risk, Ref. 3 reminds us of another dimension to this problem. The risks that society appears willing to tolerate vary greatly among the maritime nations. In the aftermath of the *Herald* disaster, Spouge[3] has studied ferry safety in the Philippines, whence emerges a very different picture.

In the 10-year period 1980–1989, 21 major accidents to passenger ferries (three of them ro-ro ships) resulted in the loss of about 6200 lives. This included the worst-ever maritime disaster when the *Dona Paz* sank, following a collision and fire, with the loss of all but 24 of its estimated 4400 passengers. Comparing the UK and Philippine passenger casualty records, Spouge has estimated the risk of death for an individual passenger to be

In UK waters: 0.25 per million ferry crossings
In Philippine waters: 38 per million ferry crossings

Of course many factors, including the age, condition and operational standards of the fleets, sea conditions, rescue services, etc., contribute to the

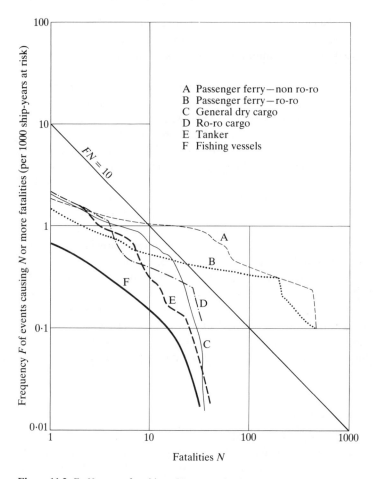

Figure 11.2 $F-N$ curves for ships. *(Source: Lloyd's Register of Shipping.)*

disparity of more than two orders of magnitude between these averaged levels of risk. However, they must also reflect, in some measure, societal and cultural differences in the perception and tolerance of risk, and in the value placed on human life.

Such disparities raise real problems in working towards agreed standards of maritime safety. Many ships are designed to operate internationally, and to standards that are acceptable to all marine nations. As discussed in Sec. 11.2, the principal agency for securing such international agreement is the International Maritime Organization (IMO). Safety assurance can be expensive, and there is understandable reluctance among some maritime nations to conform to standards that they may perceive as unnecessarily high and penally costly. Inevitably IMO deliberations can be protracted.

Not the least remarkable of the outcomes of post-*Herald* deliberations in the United Kingdom was the declaration in a Government-sponsored report[4] that:

> If agreement (on UK proposals for higher standards for ro-ro ferries) cannot be obtained at IMO within a reasonable period, the UK should consider making an approach to other European maritime administrations. Should that approach fail, then the UK should consider applying such a requirement unilaterally, that is, to all ro-ro ferries trading in and out of UK ports, regardless of flag.

This statement not only tacitly recognizes the variability among nations of societally acceptable risks but also points to the need eventually to quantify risk levels, actual and desirable, so that they may be used explicitly in design and safety assessment. One essential ingredient of such an approach is the availability of comprehensive statistical records of marine casualties, from which sound deductions can be made. Herein lie some further problems.

Marine Casualty Statistics

A marine 'casualty' can be classified according to its effect (loss of vehicle or structure, death or injury of personnel, damage to the environment); its severity (total loss, severe damage, minor damage); or in terms of its final cause (fire, collision, stranding, foundering, etc.). Overlaying such categories are many further classifications relating to casualties at sea: the type, size, age and flag of the ship or structure; the nature of its operations; the location, time and environment of the casualty; and others. The resulting multi-dimensional matrix of statistical data presents many difficulties of interpretation, the more so as one approaches specific engineering decisions about design or operation, hoping to base such decisions on a logical appraisal of risk or survivability.

Some substantial sets of marine accident statistics are available, and it is not difficult to use such data sets to make deductions about *general* levels of trends in maritime safety. Figure 11.3 is a typical example. This shows that, considering the world merchant ship fleet as the number of vessels of over 100 tons gross tonnage, which has grown from around 40 000 units in the mid 1960s to about 75 000 units in the late 1980s, the annual rate at which ships have been totally lost through accidents has varied from around 7 per thousand to—in recent years—around 3 or 4 per thousand. Thus the risk of total vessel loss appears to have roughly halved in the past quarter of a century, continuing a trend from the earliest days of casualty recording, when, around 150 years ago, the rates of ship loss and death at sea ran at levels that today would be totally unacceptable.

Of course such global averages conceal wide variations among the fleets of the various maritime nations. There has been a rather consistent disparity between the loss rates in the fleets of the developed countries (generally less

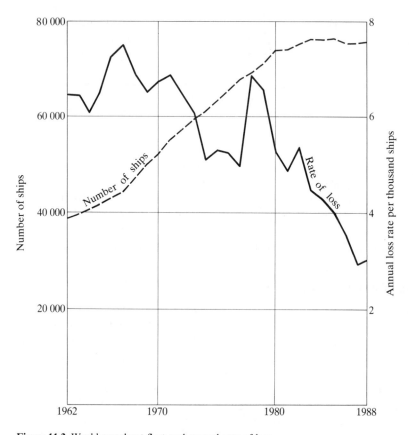

Figure 11.3 World merchant fleet and annual rate of loss.

than half the global average) and those of some developing nations, often associated with 'flags of convenience', where annual loss rates of five to ten times the global average are not uncommon. It has been generally held that such disparities result from variability in standards of competence, main- tenance, etc., on board ship. However, such disparities are diminishing, and with increasing trends towards internationalization of crews, 'flagging out' of ships and more positive surveillance by national administrations, the current trends should not encourage complacency among the allegedly more 'developed' maritime nations.

Other useful general deductions are made and regularly reviewed. Not surprisingly, for example, it turns out that ship's age is a significant factor. Thus for ship losses in the period 1980–1985, the median age of ships lost was 18.6 years, compared with a median age of the global population of ships at risk of 11.9 years. For the UK fleet, the corresponding median ages were 20.9 years (ships lost) and 10.6 years (fleet at risk). Evidently any rational approach to maritime safety should recognize the time-dependent nature of ship survivability, and hence that the expected life of the ship should explicitly influence design decisions.

The Variety of Hazards to Ships

What are the hazards that threaten ships and their occupants, and what are the respective probabilities of their occurrence? It is one of the particular difficulties of marine safety engineering that hazards to ships or offshore structures are many and various, and thus impose potential demands on widely differing capabilities or attributes of the ship, its equipment and personnel.

Here the relative coarseness of current casualty statistics begins to pose serious problems in relating the possible effect of a hazard (the loss of the vessel) to its cause. Figure 11.4 is a typical presentation of statistics of global ship losses classifed by 'cause of loss' over the past 20 years, based on Ref. 2. 'Losses' here include 'serious casualties'. Although the categories of casualties shown in Fig. 11.4 are widely used in marine safety studies, they can be misleading as to the nature of the hazard or the sequence of events that led to the final recorded casualty.

This difficulty of attributing ship losses to precise and specific hazards is well illustrated in the enquiries and debates that follow the occasional

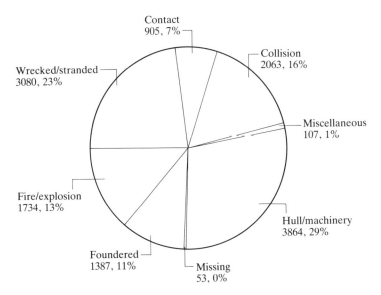

Figure 11.4 Serious casualties including ship losses 1980–1989. (*Source: Lloyd's Register of Shipping.*)

disappearances of ships with all hands and without prior warning. The tragedy that overtook the 169 000 tonne OBO (oil/bulk/ore) ship *Derbyshire* in 1980, somewhere in the North West Pacific, with the loss of 44 lives, engendered not only great concern that an apparently well-found, competently manned ship could vanish with negligible trace but also much professional speculation and investigation into possible causes. Among many proffered explanations, three very different hypotheses illustate the variety of hazards contemplated:

1. The ship experienced a major structural failure leading to a rapid break-up and sinkage.
2. Moisture in the iron ore cargo, coupled with severe ship motions, transformed the cargo into a slurry whose fluidity induced a rapid capsize.
3. Heavy seas breaking over the forward hatches penetrated the hatch covers to such an extent that the added mass of water in the holds exceeded the reserve buoyancy and the ship sank.

The Court of Inquiry could only conclude that the cause of the disaster was 'unknown'. On any of the above hypotheses, the ship 'foundered', but the corresponding implications for future design and safety assurance are very different.Thus there is a pressing need for marine casualty statistics to be refined, and definitions improved, so that more can be learned from them.

The Variety of Hazards to Life at Sea

Losses of lives, as of vessels, can likewise result from a variety of quite different causes, which may bear little relation to the causes of vessel losses. Consider, for example, the hazards confronting those who work at sea. Figure 11.5, compiled from annual statistics prepared by the UK Department of Transport, shows the annual death rates per 1000 crew (officers and ratings) on ships in the UK registered merchant fleet. The data refer to ships of over 100 gross tons, and exclude fishing vessels.

The results in Fig. 11.5 are annual values averaged over three five-year periods from 1972 to 1986. The steady decline from 18.8×10^{-4} to 10.0×10^{-4} in the overall death rate is indicative of a clear trend, although the *Herald* disaster in 1987, in which 39 seamen were lost, will doubtless be reflected in a higher overall rate for the five-year period 1987–1992. But a noticeable feature of the results in Fig. 11.5 is that deaths resulting from casualties to vessels (by foundering, collision, fire, explosion, etc.) account for only a small proportion (15 per cent in 1972–1976, 9 per cent in 1982–86) of total deaths. By far the largest single cause of death at sea is disease, responsible for more than half the deaths throughout the period. There has been a reduction, from around 10 per cent to just over 2 per cent, in deaths

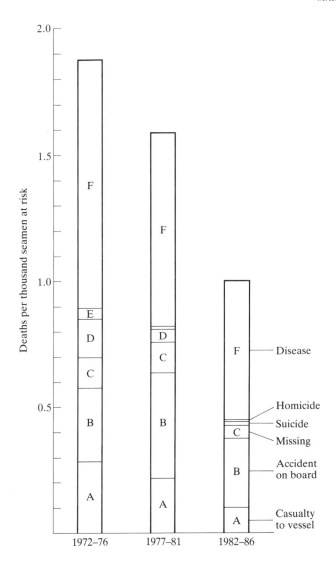

Figure 11.5 Rates and causes of death in the UK-registered merchant fleet.

from homicide or suicide. However, the proportion of deaths due to accidents on board has increased from 15 to 28 per cent in the 15-year period.

Such statistical information can help in ordering the priorities of those engineers who are seeking to reduce levels of personal risk to seafarers. Improved medical facilities, together with more deliberate attention to designing equipment, arranging deck layouts and access, and improving working practices to reduce accidents, could evidently be more beneficial than higher levels of stability or subdivision in making life at sea safer.

Statistics of loss of life can also help to counter emotive views about maritime safety. Thus, if it is noted that the annual risk of death voluntarily incurred by motorcyclists at about the middle of the period covered by Fig. 11.5 was around 200×10^{-4} and the risk of death from all causes for a 30-year old male was estimated to be 13×10^{-4}, then it appears that working on ships should not now be regarded as a particularly hazardous activity.

The Sequential Nature of Marine Casualties

There is, however, a more serious impediment to the scientific use of current marine casualty statistics as a basis for a more rational approach to safety at sea. The loss of a ship can rarely be attributed to a single cause or event, such as 'capsize'. Generally there is a sequence of events, each representing some mischance, malfunction or malfeasance, which eventually leads to the 'top event', the casualty itself. The *Herald* tragedy exemplified this.

In Lloyd's Register Casualty Return for 1987, the *Herald* is recorded as having 'foundered'. Even though such categorization would be of more value to the naval architect if a distinction could be made (in Fig. 11.4, for example) between 'capsizing' (due to loss of stability) and 'foundering' (due to loss of buoyancy), it cannot be denied that the final cause, the top event, that precipitated the loss of the vessel and lives was 'foundering'. Is the correct response to such a tragedy then to seek ways to ensure that ships of this kind, or of all kinds, are more resistant to foundering? Would this suffice, or should other remedial measures be taken?

The answers to such questions lie in unravelling the complex train of events, and non-events, which together led to the final capsize. Thanks to the Formal Investigation presented in the subsequent report of the Court of Inquiry, the anatomy of this disaster is now rather clear; Fig. 11.6 is a schematic reconstruction of the course of events, based on the Court's report. The general sequence is well known from the publicity following the tragedy and need not be repeated here, but it may be noted from Fig. 11.6 that there were four principal ingredients contributing to the casualty.

1. Error or neglect by individual crew members
2. Absence or inadequacy of on-board systems or equipment
3. Architectural features of the ship affecting its vulnerability to rapid capsize
4. Absence or inadequacy of the Owners' safety policy and orders, and their enforcement.

Clearly, defects both of engineering (items 2 and 3) and in human and managerial aspects (items 1 and 4) interacted in a complex way in this

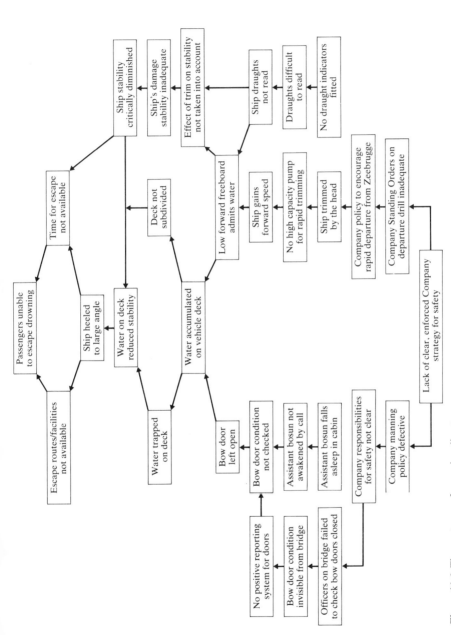

Figure 11.6 The anatomy of a marine disaster.

disaster, and the Court rightly concluded that remedial action was needed in all four areas. Some further comments on the human, managerial and engineering dimensions of marine safety are given below.

Here it is the sequential, interactive nature of so many marine accidents, of which the *Herald* was not untypical, that needs to be emphasized. Not only can this result in misleading or incomplete conclusions being drawn from hazard assessments based on coarse statistics of casualties; it also makes difficult both the identification of remedial measures and the assessment of the safety of new designs or of changes in design. In the writer's view, future progress must lie in more detailed, retrospective studies of those, albeit fewer, casualties where the sequence of events can be reliably reconstructed, than in the collection, and sometimes misleading interpretation, of statistics of final causes of marine casualties. Thus, as noted in Chapter 1, more emphasis is needed on 'learning from failure' than on the mere recording of undersirable events.

Human Factors in Marine Safety

In a paper on ship collisions presented to the Royal Society of Arts in 1882, Colomb wrote:

> ... for the year 1879–80, there were 522 collisions reported off the coasts of the United Kingdom, of which the causes were assumed to be known. We may roughly separate these into two classes: those, namely, which are blameless, and those which are blameworthy. The latter embrace 60 per cent of the whole, and include 'anchoring in foul weather', 'bad look out', 'neglecting to show light', 'neglect of rule of road', 'error of pilot', 'general negligence' and 'error in judgement'.

Colomb, himself a mariner, went on to question whether 60 per cent of ship collisions, although evidently involving a human element, could indeed fairly be attributed to what he termed the 'moral obliquities' of seamen. He believed that many collisions resulted more from the laws and rules under which seafarers were required to operate, and suggested that more attention should be paid to the circumstances leading up to the collision.

More than a century later, the debate continues. Figures, now more commonly nearer 80 per cent, are quoted to support the view that the human element is the prime factor in marine safety. Rich in anecdotal evidence—'the bridge was manned only by a large dog'—the case for attributing a high proportion of accidents to the 'moral obliquities' of seamen appears strong. Certainly their standards of training and competence, and the extent to which these are enforced, are major determinants of accident rates. The responsibilities here lie as much with national administrations and with company managements as with individuals.

This predominance of the human dimension in marine safety might suggest that design and engineering now have a diminishing role in raising safety levels. The *Herald* inquiry stressed the need to address human factors, both individual and organizational, as a major contribution to improved safety; and the growing use of smaller and more multinational crews with more diverse qualifications, experience and abilities increases the importance of the human component of safety. But of course design and engineering cannot be divorced from such concerns. Much valuable work has been done on ergonomic aspects of design, for example in the equipping and layout of ships' bridges to maximize user-kindliness and to enable efficient and safe operation with crews now much reduced in size because of the inexorable pressure of rising crew costs. Elimination of poor details of design, siting and construction of equipment can be a continuing contribution to reducing accidents through maloperation or carelessness.

But 'to err is human'; and it will always be so, however good the training, however rigorous the Standing Orders or however strict their enforcement. Sooner or later, other ro-ro passenger ferries will have their vehicle decks flooded, if not via the open bow doors, perhaps following a collision occasioned by human error. So the concomitant of human imperfectibility must surely be 'damage tolerance'—the inherent ability to survive the consequences of plausible, conceivable human failure. It was the *Herald's* tragedy that it could not tolerate the consequences of a rare, but culpable, failure. How the designer could, or should, provide the necessary damage tolerance in such ships has been the subject of much subsequent research. Questions and problems remain, to which we return later.

The Problems of Management

Event trees such as Fig. 11.6 point to the question: 'Whose responsibility is the safety of a ship, its cargo or passengers?' It is a long-established maritime tradition that it is the ship's master who is responsible for its safety. By a logical extension, he may be held responsible if an accident occurs, such as befell the *Exxon Valdez*, which pollutes the environment. While ships' captains have in the past welcomed, and indeed insisted on, taking responsibility as the man in charge, events are forcing changes in custom and practice. There are a number of reasons.

Firstly, the tendency towards costly litigation, with implications or accusations of criminal liability, threaten to put shipmasters in an increasingly exposed and intolerable position. Secondly, the pressure on owning or operating companies to have an explicit policy for safety and an identified structure of safety management underlines the position of shipmasters as being, in a strategic sense, responsible for the implementation of policies, Standing Orders or other procedures created by the company. These procedures will in turn comply with, and be influenced by, national or international regulations on maritime safety.

Thus the responsibility for maritime safety is multilevel, and the essential needs, clearly identified in the *Herald* inquiry, are for safety to be ensured and implemented through:

- a clear and firm management and command structure;
- proper channels of communication between ship and shore;
- attention at all times to all matters affecting the safety of the ship and those on board;
- strict discipline;
- clear and concise orders.

However, it is yet another of the peculiarities of the maritime scene that even these admirable and clear precepts can be difficult to observe. Consider the kind of management scenario quoted in a recent report:

> A Panamanian ship is lost which is beneficially owned in Luxembourg by an international syndicate, who employ a foreign crew through a Pacific island managing agent....

Evidently both the chain of command and of accountability can be tortuous. Such situations strengthen the need for a clear statement and acceptance of roles and responsibilities at every level, from Chairman to bosun's assistant. Replacement of traditional, ill-defined and variable practices and attitudes to safety by such policies is a prime contribution that management can make to the future of life at sea.

Thus the emphasis in marine safety, as in other disciplines, is shifting towards organizational and managerial influences. Reviewing recent major disasters including Zeebrugge and *Piper Alpha*, Reason[5] points out that the 'technical age' of safety concern, in which the focus was on engineering aspects, was followed by the 'human error age' with concentration on human fallibility. Now we see the emergence of a 'sociotechnical age', which recognizes that interactions between technical and social aspects of a system may be a key determinant in its safety record. Reason goes on to suggest that 'resident pathogens' in a sociotechnical system may combine with local triggering factors to overcome its immunity and so to produce a disease of unsafety which could be mild, chronic or fatal. On this model, identification and neutralization of pathogens (latent failures) may be more beneficial to safety than measures to reduce active failures. The correlation of marine accidents with the managerial culture and style of shipowning companies suggests that this should be a rewarding area for further enquiry (Chapter 9).

The Cost of Safety

It might be expected that a strong link between the qualities of a ship (in design, construction and operation) and its profitability would be effected through the insurance market. Although underwriters do of course take some account of factors such as age and condition of a vessel, the possibility of reduced insurance premiums has not hitherto appeared to be a significant incentive for setting safety standards higher than required by prevailing regulations. Thus it has been the cost of safety, rather than its cost–benefit balance, which has attracted most discussion. Additional measures to maintain or increase safety involve costs that are immediate and quantifiable for their effects on profitability. The resulting benefits, whether in the increased confidence of users or in the potential reduction of death, injury, loss of property or environmental damage in the improbable event of an accident, are vague and dependent on faith in statistics. When to this is added the lack of precision or agreement in quantifying the value of a life that may be lost or of a damaged coastline, it is perhaps not surprising that decisions regarding desirable levels of safety, insofar as they are articulated at all, are founded more on qualitative than quantitative considerations.

But there are reasons to expect this situation to change. There is a growing, if in some circles still reluctant, acceptance that future assessment and assurance of maritime safety must be increasingly founded on a more scientific, numerate approach to the costs and benefits of safety. One incentive is the rapidly escalating costs, awarded after litigation following major marine disasters. It has been estimated, for example, that, following the *Exxon Valdez*, more money has been paid per dead seabird than is currently given in compensation for the loss of a seaman's life. Thus the growing social concern to preserve the environment in all its forms is influencing the potential financial consequences of unsafety. These combined forces of social and economic disbenefit must accelerate acceptance of a more quantified basis for marine safety. We return to this in Sec. 11.3.

There are positive developments also in the search for commercially desirable levels of safety. The notion that there exists a level, for example of structural reliability, at which the 'life-cycle' costs of a structure are minimized, originated in aeronautical engineering. Higher reliability increases initial cost, but should diminish the expected costs of repair or replacement. In principle, if the relevant costs are known, a level of reliability can be found at which the total life cost will be minimized. If this reliability is not less than that required by relevant regulations, then it can represent a target for reliability-based design. Such procedures have not yet influenced the design of ships but are finding application in offshore structures.

Design for Safety

To conclude this brief survey of problems confronting those seeking to improve levels of safety at sea, let us consider the matter from the standpoint of the designer—the naval architect. The task of designing vehicles and structures that will perform their specified functions efficiently, economically, profitably and safely has become more challenging during the past quarter of a century. This has been a period of profound change: in sea use, leading to a greater variety of marine artefacts; in types of vessel, such as OBOs and ro-ros, hydrofoils and hovercraft, multihull and SWATH (small water-plane area twin hull) ships, all of which have established themselves in this period; in sizes of vessel, with a tenfold increase in the size of some types of ship; in materials of construction, with, for example, glass-reinforced plastic now in common use; with crew reductions from around 35 on a typical cargo ship to 12 or less—all taking place against a background of growing concern for the safety of life at sea and the preservation of the maritime environment.

This unprecedented period of diversification and technological develop-ment has imposed new demands on the naval architect. Until about 30 years ago, the procedures of ship design and methods for the assurance of safety had resulted mainly from a process of evolution, in which performance at sea and identification and rectification of defects observed in service enabled design procedures to be progressively refined and improved. Of course, because, from around 150 years ago, a theoretical framework of knowledge of mechanics and hydrodynamics gradually emerged, this enabled some science to be injected into a process long founded on art, intuition and experience. But this diffusion was very slow, so that ship design, right up to the middle of this century and beyond, was dominated by empiricism and copious rules of thumb.

The codes of practice that resulted from this evolutionary process are among the most detailed and prescriptive aids to design to be found in any branch of engineering. The Rules of the Classification Societies (such as Lloyd's Register of Shipping, The American Bureau of Shipping, Bureau Veritas, Det Norske Veritas) provide, in respect of the structural design of merchant ships, remarkably detailed guidance on the dimensions and materials required in all parts of a ship. Adherence to such Rules, or otherwise satisfying the Classification Society, enables the ship to be 'classed'—a process that, to owners and insurers alike, certifies the structure of the ship as fit for service.

This time-honoured and well-tried process of design-by-rule has served ship designers well. It permits economical and expeditious structural design, and the record of structural failure, from which it is estimated that only 5–8 per cent of major ship casualties are of structural origin, testifies to the general reliability of rule-based design.

However, recent developments, noted above, have exposed some serious limitations in overreliance on rules that are largely grounded in experience and empiricism. The dramatic structural failure of *Esso Malaysia*, one of the early designs of VLCC (very large crude carrier), was attributed to its unprecedented size which had necessitated extrapolation of the existing structural design rules far beyond the range of ship size on which they had been predicated. This was but one, albeit influential, example of the inadvisability of applying experience-based rules to a design that involves any innovation, whether in concept, materials, size or function, for which past experience is largely irrelevant.

Even though, since the *Esso Malaysia* experience in 1968, ship structural design rules have progressed to a more scientific basis, less dependent on experience and giving more scope for the designer to innovate, two particular disadvantages are relevant to this discussion. The first is that the assurance of adequate safety and reliability is widely seen to be the responsibility of those who formulate the rules. Thus the satisfaction of rule requirements is commonly regarded by designers as sufficient guarantee. However, compliance with prevailing rules is not a legally inviolable defence against a charge of professional negligence, for which the 'Bolam test', as noted in Ref. 6, provides the accepted definition. Moreover Classification Societies, who formulate structural design rules for ships (see Sec. 11.2), prudently indemnify themselves against such liabilities.

Secondly, there is the consequent problem that actual levels of safety are deeply implicit in the rules. It is thus often extremely difficult to identify or quantify the margins or factors of safety embedded in the various formulae, tables or procedures specified in these codes of practice. Although they meet well the busy designers' need and preference for rules which are simple and uncomplicated to use, they do not yet provide means, for example, to quantify the effect of a proposed design change on the subsequent safety of that design. Because many of the rules and regulations governing ship design are of this empirical, evolutionary kind (as is illustrated further in Sec. 11.2), the naval architect has special problems in developing 'design for safety' into an explicit, rational procedure.

We may, however, contrast the situation in merchant ship design—a mature, long-established activity, with a legacy of tradition and empiricism— with that in offshore engineering. The history of offshore structures is little more than 40 years old, so that tradition and experience have had much less impact on the development of design procedures while the scientific approach has had correspondingly more. Safety considerations are more explicit and prominent in offshore engineering, and it is probable that this influence will be increasingly felt as ship designers seek more rational approaches to safety. We shall return to this point in discussing, in the final part of this chapter, possible future developments in marine design for safety.

Here it may be useful, however, briefly to review the difficulties in moving towards a more explicit rational basis for ship design for safety. Some have already been mentioned, such as the absence of agreed criteria or defined acceptable levels of safety or risk, the variety of hazards, the sequential nature of most marine accidents and the potential incompatibility between profitability and increased safety. Another problem, common to the design of mobile artefacts, is that the probability of loss of a ship (or a life) is influenced both by the probability P_1 of encountering a hazard and the probability P_2 of not surviving that hazard. The estimation of P_1 for a ship whose future service over perhaps 25 years is ill-defined or unknown and which may be exposed to a great variety of hazards from the environment (winds, waves, icebergs, rocks, ships) or from within (fire, explosion, cargo shift, negligence) is clearly formidable. Having identified and quantified a particular hazard, the evaluation of P_2 requires that certain limit states be defined, beyond which the ship should be considered lost. It might be expected that the concepts of 'demand' on, and 'capability' of, engineering systems, which have provided a good basis for reliability analysis of, for example, engineering structures, could be usefully applied in ship design. Thus if one could develop probability density functions for, say, the 'demand' D made on the stability of a ship by its environment and could likewise estimate the probability density function of its 'capability' C to resist capsize (as affected by the ship condition, loading, etc.), then the probability that $D > C$ would define the probability of loss of the ship by capsize.

Such a process turns out[7] to be impracticably difficult in the present state of knowledge, for at least three reasons. Firstly, ship capsize in a seaway is a highly complex dynamic process which has hitherto defied attempts to model it mathematically; indeed, there are those who regard ship rolling motions as being essentially 'chaotic'. Perhaps 'chaos theory' can lead to new insights into ship capsize, from which new criteria for safety can be derived.

Secondly, there is the related difficulty that in many ship hazards, demand and capability are intimately interrelated. Thus, as shown, for example in Ref. 8, the capability of a ship to absorb, without fatal damage, the energy of a collision also depends in part on the properties (shape, energy absorption) of the striking ship. Hence the concepts of limit states and of capabilities, as inherent to the ship being designed, cannot easily be applied.

Thirdly, there is the well-known problem of shortage of data, especially on the range and variability of those factors influencing both P_1 and P_2. Although there is an impressive and growing bank of data on sea conditions (winds, wave heights, directions, periods) in most of the major areas of sea use, much more is needed on, for example, component reliabilities and on other factors influencing a ship's capabilities to survive specific hazards.

Clearly much remains to be done to narrow the gap between what, in principle, could be done and what, in practice, it is possible or, at present, mandatory to do to assure or assess the safety of a proposed design of ship. To chart a possible course of progress it is useful to know the starting point—the state of present practice in marine safety. In the next section, therefore, a short review is given of the current situation, with particular reference to the principal organizations and instruments involved in the provision of safety at sea and to the kinds of regulations they prescribe.

11.2 METHODS OF CONTROL OF SAFETY AT SEA

The first part of this chapter has reviewed the manifold problems and peculiarities of maritime safety, and emphasized the variety and complexity of the risks facing seafarers. That the *general* levels of risks to individuals, to owners of ships or their cargoes and to the environment have over the years been brought down to levels that are broadly acceptable to society might suggest that the methods that have evolved for controlling those risks have proved effective. However, tragic events such as the loss of *The Herald of Free Enterprise, Derbyshire, Alexander Kielland* and *Piper Alpha* or environmental disasters such as *Exxon Valdez* or *Amoco Cadiz*, inevitably call in question the efficacy of current procedures intended to assure safety at sea. It is relevant therefore now to present a brief survey of the present regulatory framework for marine safety, together with a few illustrations of typical procedures affecting specific aspects of risk control, before moving, in the final part of this chapter, to consider some trends and possibilities for improvement.

This review is largely from the standpoint of the United Kingdom's concern for maritime safety. The situation is not very different in the other developed maritime nations, but, as noted earlier, the public perception of safety can vary widely among other less-developed nations, and this, together with their prevailing economic conditions, inevitably affect attitudes and resources directed to reducing risks at sea.

In view of space limitations, attention is focused here on non-military aspects of sea safety. The procedures and processes for risk control in naval vessels are different; for a recent survey of safety assurance in UK warships the reader is referred to a recent paper by Brown.[9]

The Regulatory Framework

The global and very diverse nature of maritime operations has led to the evolution of a network of agencies and regulatory bodies whose work contributes to maritime safety. They range from international organizations to local industry and company authorities, whose roles and responsibilities interact to affect all aspects—design, construction, operation and maintenance—that influence safety.

The International Maritime Organization (IMO)

This is the principal intergovernmental body, established as the Intergovernmental Consultative Organization (IMCO) in 1948 as an agency of the United Nations with responsibility for promoting legislation affecting maritime safety and pollution control. Its authority and influence effectively date from 1958, when 21 nations became parties to the IMCO Convention. Since then its membership has expanded to include, by 1989, 132 member states including all the major maritime nations. The IMCO became IMO in 1982.

The essential role of IMO, whose Head Office is in London, is advisory and consultative. Because it is an intergovernmental body, it cannot exercise legislative or executive powers over its member states. However, it does provide an invaluable forum for discussion, exchange of information and proposals, upon which can be based intergovernmental agreement to introduce new or improved regulations affecting safety and the environment. To reach such agreement between so many diverse nations, and then to implement any resulting regulations in the member states in a way that will not disadvantage their fleets, can be extremely time-consuming, as noted earlier.

Nevertheless, the products of IMO's work—conventions, protocols, codes, regulations, amendments, resolutions, guidelines and standards—represent a global consensus of fundamental importance to maritime safety. Thus, within IMO, the hierarchy of functions and responsibilities is headed by its *Assembly* on which all member states are represented and which meets every 2 years to discuss and, where appropriate, to ratify IMO instruments. The Assembly has links with, or inputs from, other UN agencies (for example FAO, WHO) who have interests in marine affairs and various non-governmental agencies or consultative bodies, such as IACS (International Association of Classification Societies) and ICS (International Chamber of Shipping).

A smaller *Council* of IMO, comprising representatives of 24 states, meets twice a year to consider matters of policy and the work of its two principal technical committees. The Council is supported by three subsidiary bodies to assist in general policy matters: the Facilitation, Legal and Technical Cooperation Committees.

Much of the detailed work of IMO falls to the Marine Environment Protection Committee (MEPC) and the Maritime Safety Committee (MSC), both normally meeting twice a year. The central role of MSC and the large scope of its work are evident from the list of its subcommittees:

- Bulk Chemicals (reporting also to MEPC)
- Containers and Cargoes
- Carriage of Dangerous Goods
- Fire Protection
- Life-saving, Search and Rescue
- Radiocommunications
- Safety of Navigation
- Ship Design and Equipment
- Stability, Load Lines and Fishing Vessel Safety
- Training and Watchkeeping

From the work of these subcommittees, via discussions in Committees,

Council and Assembly, emanates a flow of material reaching into most aspects of ship design and operation. Such material periodically coalesces into major Conventions which have become milestones in the history of marine safety. Well-known examples include International Conventions on:

- Safety of Life at Sea (SOLAS), 1913 (following the *Titanic* loss), 1929, 1948, 1960, 1974
- Load lines, 1966
- Tonnage Measurement, 1969
- International Regulations for Preventing Collision at Sea, 1972
- Safety of Fishing Vessels, 1977
- Marine Pollution (MARPOL), 1973
- Standards of Certification, Training and Watchkeeping (SCTW), 1978.

To most of such Conventions, for which IMO is the Depositary, various Amendments are agreed from time to time. Although Conventions and Amendments are formally adopted in the year indicated, their 'entry into force'—that is, enactment by national administrations—may be delayed for some years. Originally this required a specified number of states to become signatories, but because of the ensuing delays, the procedure now is for such agreements to become effective after a specified time unless a minimum prescribed number of objections has been received by parties to the convention.

The Department of Transport

Unacceptably high losses of ships and lives at sea in the nineteenth century led to the first UK Merchant Shipping Act in 1894. This, and the subsequent Acts, to date exceeding 20, embody the major legislative measures affecting shipping. Responsibility for implementing this legislation, which incorporates both national policies and international (IMO) agreements, rests with the Department of Transport (DTp) and specifically with the Marine Directorate of DTp. The two principal organs within the Directorate are the Shipping Policy Division, with policy responsibilities for non-technical aspects of general shipping, defence and security, and foreign shipping relations and the Marine Division. It is this latter division on which the major onus lies for implementation of legislation affecting safety of seafarers and the marine environment.

These responsibilities range from standard setting and certification of the crew, manning levels, pilotage, search and rescue, and prevention or restriction of pollution, to the design, construction, equipping and operation of ships. A key role in the execution of these functions and in the exercise of 'port state control' is played by the Division's district offices and suboffices. Their manifold duties include, for example,

- Survey and/Certification of
  - Passenger ships
  - Radio and other safety equipment
  - Crew accommodation
  - Fire protection
  - Life-saving appliances
- Inspections of stowage of
  - Dangerous goods
  - Bulk cargoes such as timber, grain
- Random inspection of ships trading in UK waters
- Investigation of casualties
- Examination of ships officers

Certification, as required by merchant shipping legislation, also provides formal evidence of compliance with IMO conventions to which the United Kingdom is party. It is thus a key element in the national effort to control marine risks. Certificates have to be renewed at specified intervals after satisfactory survey and must always be available for inspection. To assist in this heavy load of inspection, survey and certification, the DTp authorizes suitably competent agencies to undertake some of these functions on its behalf. One such agency is Lloyd's Register of Shipping, described further below.

Communication of legislative and other changes to designers, builders, owners and operators is critical to their rapid enactment. The principal medium is the 'Merchant Shipping Notice' issued by the DTp which may also include guidance to assist compliance and other relevant information.

Clearly, then, the DTp has a central position on the marine safety scene. Not only does it provide the main link with, and influence in, international developments, but the Department also acts in both the development and enforcement of national safety standards and procedures, as well as monitoring their efficacy. Some have questioned whether these various roles should indeed be vested in a single organization. Certainly they place severe demands on a relatively small, hard-pressed staff, leaving rather little effort to spare for long-range strategic work on the methodology of marine safety assessment or assurance.

The Classification Societies

Lloyd's Register of Shipping (LRS) is one—the oldest and largest—of nine major Classification Societies whose principal *raison d'etre* is to assure the owners of ships that their design, construction and maintenance conform to rules that should ensure the highest standards of fitness for service. LRS originated in 1760 from the wish of marine insurance underwriters to have some standard of reference and reliable guarantee of seaworthiness. More recently a proliferation of societies in many emerging nations reflects a desire for maritime status and independence, and their capabilities are of a very different order from those of the major long-established bodies. Lloyd's Register can be taken as an exemplar of the marine Classification Society, a type of organization with which there are few, if any, parallels in other sectors of activity.

LRS is international, with offices in more than 100 countries staffed by more than 1500 surveyors. Their responsibilities include not only the ships of many flags or ownerships, and other mobile and offshore structures, but also a wide range of land-based industrial plant, materials, equipment and services. In its primary concern to assure the fitness of ships for service, two interesting features may be noted. Its Rules, which embody unrivalled experience and expertise and reflect international statutes and legislation, cover only the ship's hull, equipment and machinery—the 'hardware', but not the 'human-ware'. Secondly, in its principal governing body, the General Committee of Lloyd's Register of Shipping, a large majority of the members are from, or are closely associated with, shipowning companies. This close association between owner and Society reflects their mutual concern to advance safety standards, and brings the great benefit, frequently absent in other sectors of engineering, of facilitating a rapid feedback of service experience. This ability to learn from failure was noted in Chapter 1 to be an essential ingredient of progress towards higher standards of safety. Certainly the scarcity of major casualties attributable to the failure or inadequacy of the classification process testifies to its efficiency and value.

The principal instruments for the classification of a ship by a Society are its Rules, to which a ship must conform in its construction, machinery, equipment and materials. To maintain its class certificate, a ship must satisfy periodic surveys, as well as surveys of modifications or repairs. The Rules, as noted earlier, are remarkably comprehensive and prescriptive. They cover a wide variety of marine artefacts, and include:

- Rules of classification of:
  - Ships
  - Yachts and small craft
  - Mobile offshore units
  - Submersibles and diving systems
  - Fixed offshore installations
- Rules for:
  - Inland waterway ships
  - Floating docks
  - Ships for liquid chemicals
  - Application of glass-reinforced plastics to fishing craft (provisional)

The Classification Rules cover major technical aspects of hardware, such as materials, structures, machinery, systems and equipment for control, electrical, fire and refrigeration, corrosion protection and certain features affecting construction and manufacture.

In addition to these Rules, the Society issues periodic Guidance Notes (especially for novel developments) and Codes; maintains a comprehensive record of service performance; provides consultancy, computing and laboratory testing services; undertakes extensive research and development; and participates in the work of many international organizations. Among the latter, the International Association of Classification Societies (IACS), which was established by charter in 1968, has developed into a significant influence on the global scene. The original seven member societies of IACS have increased to twelve, including three Associates. The IACS Council meets annually and is supported by a general policy group to whom about 12–15 specialist working groups report on specific topics.

Some may see in the growing scope and influence of IACS a basis for moving towards a single world-wide Classification Society, but there are powerful arguments against this.[10] Nevertheless, the positive, unifying influence of IACS is evident in two ways. Firstly, it is indeed acting to reduce previous disparities or inconsistencies between the various Societies, so that in many important areas, for example fire protection, propellers, machinery, pipes and pressure vessels, materials and welding, unified requirements are now in place.

Secondly, IACS is helping to establish common views on certain technical aspects of IMO's work and to communicate these via the Councils of the two organizations. If this can help to expedite international agreement on maritime safety, then IACS will increasingly be seen as a beneficial influence on the global scene.

The Marine Industry

At the level of the corporate UK (or other) shipping industry and within individual companies, the system of responsibility for, and enforcement of, safety procedures and standards is less clearly defined. Of course the industry and its constituent companies are bound to conform with prevailing legislation and regulation; but, as noted earlier (see Fig. 11.6, for example), safety at sea is crucially influenced by the existence and observance of appropriate operational standards and practices.

Figure 11.7, from Ref. 2, summarizes the main constituents of safety control in merchant shipping. Safety has both 'inanimate' (the ship and its contents) as well as 'animate' (people and practices) components. The international and national regulatory framework, outlined above, exercises control over the former, but only over certain aspects of the latter, such as training and manning and some operational procedures. But at the vital

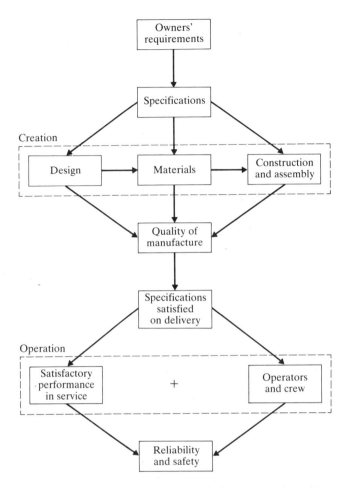

Figure 11.7 Reliability and safety depend also on operations. *(Source: Lloyd's Register of Shipping.)*

day-to-day operating level, including emergency situations as well as routine duties and responsibilities, control of the human element of risk is mainly through 'in-house' practice, custom and guidance. In this, although industry-wide guidelines and recommendations are promulgated, through, for example, the General Council of British Shipping, there is much variety in the policies and procedures adopted by individual companies.

Recent events, especially post-*Herald*, have highlighted this imbalance between the regulatory and operational dimensions of marine safety control. One consequence has been the decision by IMO to pay greater attention to human factors in the work of its technical committees. Another has been increasing pressure on companies to develop clearly defined strategies, policies, responsibilities, communications, codes of practice and standing orders which will create a more safety-conscious climate at all levels. A persuasive case by Gilmour[11] for the urgent development of a 'management system' for safety reflects a widespread view that it is at this level that the greatest contribution to reducing marine risks can now be made.

It must not be inferred from this, however, that regulations affecting 'hardware' have yet reached a satisfactory state. For the designer of that hardware, a difficult question arises. It is sufficient for the designer, as a professional engineer, to claim that, in respect of safety, his/her responsibilities have been discharged satisfactorily provided that his/her design satisfies all the relevant legislation, regulations and codes? The argument for a negative answer, by drawing a distinction between ethical and legal aspects of the designer's work, has been clearly made by Rawson.[6] On this argument the designer has a responsibility to try to anticipate the hazards that may attend the ship and those on board, and to ensure to the best of his/her ability that the risk of accident or death is acceptably small. If, in the designer's professional judgement, the regulations as currently framed are inadequate, or the assurance of adequate safety will involve additional costs to the client, then it is his/her professional duty to say so.

Here we come, full circle, to a key problem, touched on earlier, in 'designing for safety'. How is the designer able to judge, on present knowledge, the levels of safety afforded by conforming to the prevailing regulations? To illustrate this central difficulty, let us consider examples of specific regulations affecting vital aspects of the safety of a ship.

The Practical Application of Regulations Affecting Safety

Two, among many, ways in which a ship may become a major casualty are through:

1. Capsize resulting from loss of stability following a collision or other incident following which seawater enters the hull
2. Major structural failure of the hull by the application of an excessive longitudinal bending moment to the ship.

Both types of hazard have been of continuing importance and concern to naval architects, and regulations or design codes intended to minimize such risks have been progressively refined over many years.

Stability standards The basic intention is that when a ship suffers a prescribed amount of flooding which causes some of its watertight compartments to be 'laid open to the sea', it should be capable of remaining afloat. In its original purely deterministic form, this requirement led to 'one-compartment' or 'two-compartment' ships, defined as ships that could survive one, two (or more) adjacent compartments being flooded without exhausting the residual buoyancy (or floatability) or stability of the damaged ship. The required compartmentation (or subdivision) standard—1, 2 or more—was dependent on the function of the ship, its length and (for passenger ships) the maximum number of passengers permitted to be carried.

Recent formulations by IMO of these standards have increasingly recognized the essentially probabilistic nature of the hazards that may impose demands on a ship's capability to remain afloat. This had led to regulations that specify that a ship will be deemed safe if its 'Attained Subdivision Index A' is greater than the 'Required Subdivision Index R'. For passenger ships the latter is defined by

$$R = 1 - \frac{1000}{4L_s + N + 1500}$$

in which

L_s = 'subdivision length' of the ship (which is approximately the length of the ship at its waterline), in metres
$N = N_1 + 2N_2$
N_1 = number of persons for whom lifeboats are provided
N_2 = number of persons (including officers and crew) that the ship is permitted to carry in excess of N_1

This indicates the implicit intention, noted earlier in this chapter, that the risk of ship loss should decrease as the number of passengers and size of ship increase.

For dry cargo ships the Required Subdivision Index is

$$R = (0.002 + 0.009L_s)^{1/3}$$

so that the crew complement, which does not appear explicitly, is evidently assumed to be roughly proportional to ship size L_s.

The designer's task then is to arrange the compartmentation and other relevant features of the ship so as to ensure that $A \geqslant R$, where

$$A = \sum^i p_i s_i v_i$$

in which

i represents any compartment or group of compartments that may be laid open to the sea
p_i accounts for the probability that only the ith compartment or group of compartments will be flooded
s_i accounts for the probability that the ship will survive the flooding of the ith compartment or group
v_i accounts for the probability that only the ith compartment(s) will be flooded within the assumed vertical extent of damage

Thus in calculating the Attained Subdivision Index A, which is a measure of a ship's ability to survive (i.e. not to founder or capsize) after its watertightness has been impaired, the designer postulates a range of damage scenarios, each associated with certain calculated probabilities of occurrence. For each scenario, defined by the range and extent of resultant flooding of compartments, the designer must then investigate the effect of the water entering the ship on its stability, draught, angle of heel, etc. Here factors such as the 'permeability' of compartments, the ship's freeboard, metacentric height and other static stability characteristics strongly influence the term s_i.

The calculations are complex and need not be detailed here. Regulations of this kind not only exert a critical influence on ship design and its survivability but also illustrate some important trends in ship safety assessment:

1. A move from a deterministic to a probability-based approach, in which historical statistics of collision damage are used to evaluate the probabilities (p_i, v_i) associated with various locations and extents of damage to the hull.
2. A corresponding increase in the complexity of the calculations required to satisfy the regulatory authorities.
3. An increase in the calculations required to determine the effect of design changes on the Subdivision Index A. Computer-based procedures and expert systems are being developed to assist designers.

However, even if these new approaches represent a notable advance on the previous empiricisms of one- and two-compartment standards, they are unlikely to be the last word on the matter. Two particular aspects call for further attention:

1. The evaluation of s_i from a basis of the statical stability of the ship (i.e. in calm water) can only be an uncertain guide to its survivability in a dynamic environment of waves, wind and possibly shifting cargo. Nor does it recognize, or indicate, the *rate* at which a ship might founder or capsize as a crucial element in the risk of death for those on board. The tragedy of the *Herald* was not that it capsized, but that it capsized so quickly as to give no chance to many on board to escape.
2. Although the setting of a target Required Subdivision Index R enables the new standards to be calibrated against previous ships, it is not at all clear how R (or A) is related to the actual risk of loss of a ship.

Thus the new approach to ship stability standards, outlined above, can be seen as only a step along a difficult road towards the rational assesssment of maritime safety. We look further along this road in the final section of this chapter.

Longitudinal strength As a second example of current procedures in safety assessment, consider what can happen (illustrated in Fig. 11.8) if a ship is subjected to a bending moment that exceeds its ultimate longitudinal strength. How can the naval architect seek to ensure that such a back-breaking and potentially disastrous event will not occur during the life of a ship?

The structural behaviour of a large ship can be likened to that of a non-uniform free-ended beam supported by the buoyancy of the sea and loaded by its own distribution of weight. Calculation of the resulting bending moments and shear forces, including dynamic effects where they may be significant, is a key stage in ship structural design, and is intended to ensure that the capability C of the beam (the hull)—that is its longitudinal strength—will exceed the demand D (for example the maximum applied bending moment) which may result from the actions of weight and buoyancy.

It has been well established by experience and experiment that the *general* structural behaviour of conventional, mono-hull forms of ship structure approximates to the expectations of the simple 'engineers' theory' of bending. Significant departures from the resulting linear distribution of stress across the hull cross-section can, however, result from:

1. Discontinuities such as hatch openings, superstructures or other sudden changes of cross-section

Figure 11.8 Structural failure of the tanker *Energy Concentration.*

2. Shear lag effects in having higher ratios of breadth to depth
3. Any occurrence of buckling of compressed elements (plates, stiffeners, panels) in the cross-section
4. Material failure due to yielding, fatigue or fast fracture

Thus the present method of assuring adequate capability C in ship longitudinal strength requires that the elastic section modulus Z of the hull cross-section should not be less than a prescribed value which depends on the predicted bending moment in association with a maximum permissible bending stress in the hull. Buckling control is effected through stability checks and/or dimensional restrictions, and material properties are specified to minimize the likelihood of fast fracture. Fatigue has (rightly or wrongly) been judged to be adequately controlled by working within the imposed stress limits, by guidance in detail design and by standard procedures of quality control in construction.

How is the demand D on a ship's hull strength to be determined and specified? The designer will in general not be able to define precisely:

1. The expected life of the ship
2. The routes, and hence the environments, in which it will operate during its life
3. The range or distribution of cargo loads
4. The rate at which corrosion might diminish its structural capability

Much research has been done, and many elaborate procedures devised, to try to arrive at a rational basis for prescribing values of the maximum applied bending moment M to be used in design. Two principal components of M are recognized:

1. The still water bending moment that results from the distributions of weight and buoyancy, the latter depending only on the underwater form of the hull.
2. The wave bending moment that also depends somewhat on the hull form, but primarily on the properties (height, length, period) of the most severe waves that a ship is deemed likely to encounter during its life.

In determining a realistic design value for the wave bending moment a probability-based approach is clearly essential. It turns out that the number of waves that a sea-going merchant ship encounters during a 20-year life is of the order of 10^8. Hence, by combining long-term global ocean wave statistics with analytical models of ship dynamic behaviour in various sea states and studying the effects of ship size and geometry upon the resulting bending moments, it has been found possible to devise methods for predicting extreme values of bending moments and shear forces for use in design. These extreme values typically relate to a 1 in 10^8 probability of exceedance.

Based on such methods, the Classification Societies have put forward formulae for longitudinal bending moments to be used in association with the section modulus Z, as described above. Until recently, these formulae varied somewhat between the Societies, but in view of their critical importance in determining safety against structural failure and the undesirability of having a variety of standards, the International Association of Classification Societies agreed in 1990 to publishing a unified set of longitudinal strength requirements.

These are exemplified in the following extracts from Lloyd's Rules. The permissible still water sagging and hogging bending moments are to be taken as the lesser of the following:

$$|\bar{M}_s| = F_D \sigma Z_D \times 10^3 - |M_w| \qquad \text{kN m} \qquad (11.1)$$

$$|\bar{M}_s| = F_B \sigma Z_B \times 10^3 - |M_w| \qquad \text{kN m} \qquad (11.2)$$

where M_w is the appropriate hogging or sagging hull wave bending moment at amidships, given by

$$M_w = \pm f_1 f_2 M_{w0}$$

in which

$M_{w0} = 0.1 C_1 C_2 L^2 B (C_b + 0.7) \text{ kN m}$
$\quad f_1 = 1.0$ for unrestricted sea-going service, and is to be specially considered for other service
$\quad f_2 = -1.1$ for sagging moment (negative); $1.9 C_b (C_b + 0.7)^{-1}$ for hogging moment (positive)
$\quad C_b = $ block coefficient (a measure of fullness) of the ship's underwater hull form; C_b is not to be taken as less than 0.6
$\quad C_1 = $ a coefficient whose tabulated values depend on ship length
$\quad C_2 = 1.0$ with lower values towards the ends of the ship
$\quad L = $ ship length
$\quad B = $ ship breadth

Clearly the required section moduli Z_D (referred to the upper deck) and Z_B (referred to the ship's bottom) are related to the total bending moment $M_s + M_w$ through a permissible bending stress σ and the factors F_D and F_B. M_s can be readily calculated from the ship's loading conditions which give maximum values of hogging and sagging moments, and

$$\sigma = \frac{175}{k_L} \text{ N/mm}^2$$

in which

$$k_L = \frac{245}{\sigma_0}$$

σ_0 = specified minimum yield stress, N/mm^2

F_D and F_B are reduction factors which are applicable if the maximum hull bending stress σ_D at deck or σ_B at bottom is less than the permissible stress σ. Thus

$$F_D = \frac{\sigma_D}{\sigma}$$

$$F_B = \frac{\sigma_B}{\sigma}$$

but neither can be less than 0.67 for plating or 0.75 for longitudinal stiffeners.

Even if such semi-empirical formulae still have a somewhat arcane appearance, with a large element of experience and Classification Society expertise implicit in the various coefficients, nevertheless they illustrate current efforts to place ship structural design and safety assurance on a somewhat more rational, consistent and internationally acceptable basis.

Inevitably such procedures lag behind ideas being studied and discussed in the research community. Further refinements can be expected in the prediction of environmental loads, in the modelling of structural behaviour and in definition of limit states affecting safety. A strong theme in recent research has been (as in the stability work previously discussed) to find ways of expressing structural safety in terms of risk. This would recognize that both the demand D on a structure and its capability C to survive that demand are essentially probabilistic. The capability C is influenced by variabilities in material properties, dimensional accuracies and quality of construction, and should therefore not be regarded as single valued. On this approach, the measure of structural safety would be

$$P(C - D) > 0$$

which is the probability that the strength will exceed the loads on the structure throughout its life.

This approach has clearly had its origins in other fields of engineering and was introduced to the marine community as long ago as 1967.[12] A good example of a recent application of this reliability-based approach to ship structural safety is in Ref. 13.

But in returning to our original example of structural failure (Fig. 11.8) there is a final irony. This ship was *Energy Concentration*, a very large crude carrier, 326 m long, 48.2 m broad and 25.2 m in depth and of 216,269 tons deadweight. This huge structure broke its back in July 1980, not because its strength capability was less than prescribed by the authorities when she was built in 1970, nor because corrosion had significantly reduced that strength, nor because the ship had experienced some extreme sea condition causing an unpredictably high wave hogging moment. In fact, the collapse occurred in calm water as the oil cargo was being discharged. By mistakenly emptying the centre tanks first, a very large 'static' hogging bending moment developed which eventually exceeded the ultimate longitudinal bending strength of the ship's structure.

This remarkable episode constituted a very valuable, if unintentional, experiment, and a full account of the event and some retrospective analyses have recently been given,[14] in which the authors have sought to learn from this failure as much as possible about those limit states that should eventually form the basis of ship structural safety assessment.

However, it was a human failure—a blunder—that broke the ship. Could, or should, such an occurrence be included in the probability density function of loads on the structure? What, indeed, are the circumstances that the designer should contemplate in assessing the safety of a design? Here is a question to which a more explicit answer is required in the future.

11.3 THE WAY AHEAD

We have seen, from Sec. 11.1 of this chapter, that the assurance and improvement of safety at sea pose a great variety of problems, some of which are common to other branches of engineering while some derive from the peculiar nature of marine affairs and technology. We have also seen, in Section 11.2, that present methods of control of safety involve a complex network of national and international agencies, together with company policies ashore and at sea, which make the creation of a consistent, guiding strategy for marine safety very difficult. At the technical level also, the evolution of rules and regulations from a necessarily empirical basis now presents designers with procedures that appear to be an uneasy mix of tradition, empiricism and rationality. There are, in the author's view, compelling reasons for believing that maritime safety assessment and control are now in a transitional stage. Various forces are at work which will encourage, perhaps enforce, change towards a more consistent, defensible and beneficial approach.

The Driving Forces

There is plentiful recent evidence of the force of public concern as a stimulus to progress. Increasing respect for life has long been a measure of advancing civilization; to this must now be added respect for our 'global commons' and our environment. Witness the speed at which the normal processes of regulatory change have been accelerated by public outcry following the *Herald* and *Exxon Valdez* disasters—to name but two from many. The former resulted in a great variety of measures and recommendations, listed in Ref. 4, which have affected the design, equipment, operation and management of UK passenger ferries. The traumatic effects of *Exxon Valdez* culminated in the passing by the US Congress of OPA 90—the Oil Pollution Act, 1990—whose effects on the design and economics of tanker operations have not yet been fully evaluated. (Indeed doubt has been expressed as to whether the requirement of OPA 90 that tankers should have double bottoms whose depth shall not be less than one-fifteenth of the ship's breadth, will in fact reduce pollution risk levels to the extent intended.) Thus the growing awareness of the potential toxicity and lethality of certain marine operations on communities likely to be at risk in greater numbers and concentrations must surely be a potent force for change, in both developed and developing countries.

Closely related to this, and pervading the engineering community generally, are the twin threats of liability and litigation. Current efforts within the Royal Institution of Naval Architects to define the naval architect's roles and responsibilities in relation to risk[6] mirror the work, on behalf of the whole engineering profession, by the Engineering Council to define a Code of Conduct that addresses risk issues much more explicitly than heretofore. Professional codes of this kind should affect the engineer's work at two levels, firstly, by raising the corporate consciousness of company and institutional responsibilities towards safety and, secondly, by emphasizing and clarifying the duty of the individual engineer to recognize and minimize the risks to which the work may expose the public.

This trend will inevitably bring all technical codes and regulations under increasing scrutiny. In the marine field, the semi-empirical nature of many regulations (exemplified in Sec. 11.2 above) will cause difficulty. Will it suffice for a designer, perhaps of a ship involving some new concept or technology, to say that by satisfying such regulations, he/she is professionally satisfied as to the safety of the design? Caught between the pressures of professional responsibility for safety and compliance with regulations in which safety levels are obscure, or at best implicit, this position seems likely to become increasingly untenable.

Thus the development of more rational and explicit codes, and of procedures for safety assessment that are accessible to designers of average competence, must now be major priorities in marine safety work. Some recent work[7,15] has suggested ways in which this might be done. Fortunately, advances in safety engineering in other fields, together with improvements in methods and data for predicting marine vehicle behaviour under extreme conditions, are making these objectives more realistic and feasible. That formal, rational safety assessments for marine vehicles and structures are now becoming available, and will become mandatory (see below), must surely be the most potent forces for change in marine safety. Let us review some recent evidence.

Towards a Rational Approach to Marine Safety

The increasing range and variety of techniques for safety assessment are evident from many chapters of this book. It is not appropriate, therefore, to present in any detail here the basis of methods of risk and reliability analysis, hazard and operability studies, failure mode and effect analysis, fault tree analysis, simulation, consequence analysis, etc. That such techniques exist is well known to marine safety authorities. The main need now is for such procedures to be assessed for their relevance to marine safety, and then adapted or adopted for routine use.

Unfortunately, two of the principal organizations whose work, as noted in Sec. 11.2, exerts a strong influence on marine safety, are not well equipped to carry out this kind of development work. IMO has severely constrained resources and must rely on participating nations for such effort; nor are most national administrations able to spare significant effort for methodological research. Therefore, in recent years, work to promote the use of more modern approaches to marine safety has largely been in the hands of

- Classification Societies (in UK, Lloyd's Register)
- Other statutory bodies concerned with health and safety (Health and Safety Executive)
- Private companies specializing in safety assessment (e.g. Technica Ltd)
- University research groups (e.g. Glasgow, Newcastle, UWIST)

The following brief summaries of two recent studies illustrate the progress of such work, and demonstrate that despite the special problems, noted in Sec. 11.1, of the marine environment, formal procedures of safety assessment can be applied and should increasingly (in the author's view) form the basis of a more rational approach to marine safety.

Safety assessment for an offshore floating production unit (FPU) Thompson and Prentice[16] showed how, at the conceptual design stage, a safety assessment could be used to quantify the risks associated with a variety of major hazards to which units of the kind shown in Fig. 11.9 may be exposed. The FPU enables oil, delivered from a subsea well via flexible risers, to be transferred to buffer oil storage in a converted tanker, and thence to a shuttle tanker for export from the unit. Since the FPU is intended to remain on station for the life of the oilfield, it will be exposed to a wide variety of hazards, with the potential for injury or fatality, environmental damage or damage to material.

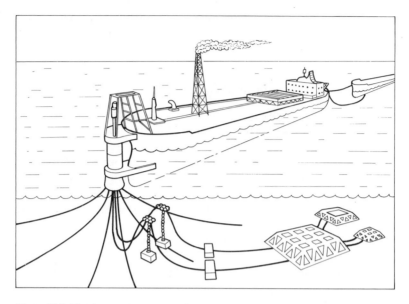

Figure 11.9 Floating production unit (safety assessment in Ref. 16). *(Source: Lloyd's Register of Shipping.)*

The study commenced by identifying and selecting major hazardous events. Application of Failure Mode and Effect Criticality Analysis (FMECA) required standard failure modes to be identified for each component of hardware and control systems, and the effects of such failures were categorized into eight groups ranging from injury/fatality, production shut-down and material damage to pollution, fire or explosion. Possible causes of such failures were then grouped (e.g. due to inadequate design, maintenance or instructions, human error, etc.) and 'criticality factors' introduced which reflected the technological status (proven, extrapolated or novel) and the failure consequences (high, medium, low). Formal, albeit only qualitative, appraisal of all systems and components, using standard FMECA work-sheets, led to the identification of elements requiring special attention and to the selection of 15 hazardous events for detailed quantitative analysis. These ranged from well blow-out, flowline or riser failure, fire, explosion or hydrocarbon release at various locations, to ship collisions or helicopter crashes.

To quantify the risks associated with each of these hazardous events, a wide range of techniques, assumptions and estimates had to be used. In some cases, such as for assessing the risk of riser failure due to overload, a fault tree was used to evaluate probabilities. Similarly, the variety of events that could lead to an engine room fire on the storage ranger was modelled using event trees. Throughout this quantitative phase of the study, which was done by Lloyd's Register Safety Technology Department, access to LR's extensive casualty database was of crucial importance in providing credible estimates of component failure probabilities, collision risks or frequencies of fire and explosion.

The final phase of the study was to use the foregoing results to compile a 'risk database'. This presented, for each of the major functional areas of the FPU, the estimated annual frequency of each relevant hazardous event, the ensuing probability of the loss of the unit, the quantity of the resulting pollution and the probabilities of various numbers of serious injuries or fatalities. Finally by multiplying the consequences for each hazardous event by its frequency of occurrence, the total risks were evaluated by summation. Figure 11.10 illustrates the $F-N$ type of end result, from which oil spills of up to 10 tonnes can be expected about once a year, and spills of at least 1000 tonnes could be expected once every ten years. The major risk to life

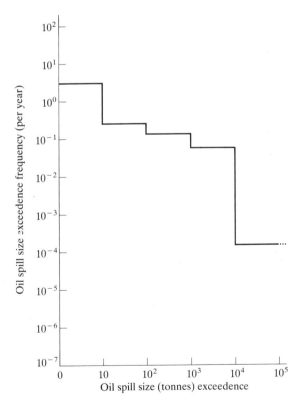

Figure 11.10 Frequency–size curve for oil spill from floating production unit. *(Source: Lloyd's Register of Shipping.)*

was shown by this study to result from fire or explosion in the production or process modules and from fire in the engine room. The study did not address the question as to whether the estimated risks were acceptable. It does, however, demonstrate the feasibility and value of risk assessment techniques in evaluating and comparing preliminary designs of a marine system, even where such designs contain novel features.

Risk assessment for ships carrying hazardous cargo in port areas Although there has not yet been any release of liquefied petroleum gas from an LPG ship due to collision or impact, the possible consequences of such an incident occurring in populated port areas are so grave that the UK Health and Safety Executive, together with the Safety and Reliability Directorate and Technica Ltd, have recently developed risk assessments for this particular marine hazard. Some results are reported by Spouge.[17]

The general approach to estimating the probability that a release of LP gas will occur in a particular port area due to ship collision can be seen from Fig. 11.11. If an LPG ship is struck by a passing ship while at the jetty, gas will only be released if the impact occurs in way of a cargo tank, if this tank is loaded and if the collision is at an angle of sufficient severity to penetrate the tank. Clearly the estimates of the probabilities of such component events occurring are best derived from accident data to ships in port and from analysis of the resistance of LPG ships structures to penetration by collision. Both present difficulties at present, and the resulting estimates must be regarded as provisional.

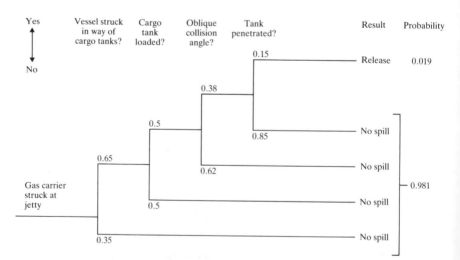

Figure 11.11 Event tree for gas carrier striking.[16]

The probability of such ship collision incidents for the port in question was estimated to be 9×10^{-6} per ship passing movement. If, while a gas carrier is at the jetty, typically 10 ships pass it and 20 gas carriers per year use the jetty, then the expected annual frequency of LPG release is

$$0.019 \times 9 \times 10^{-6} \times 10 \times 20 = 3.4 \times 10^{-5}$$

which is a chance of 1 in 30 000 per year.

To convert this result, using consequence calculations, into estimates of fatalities among the nearby population requires various possible toxic, flammable or explosive effects of the resulting gas drift and dispersion to be modelled, together with the location and explosure risks of the population. For this, techniques developed in the petrochemical industry were used, together with local meteorological data, to derive risk contours, annual fatality rates or $F-N$ curves, to represent the societal risks in the port area.

Thus, as Table 11.1 shows, for the particular port being considered, an overall annual fatality rate of 4.1×10^{-3} is expected from the operations of gas carriers and product tankers. Of the various hazardous events listed, transfer spill from product tankers is clearly shown to be a major target for risk reduction measures. Would the extra cost of an improved emergency shut-down system (ESD) be justified? Spouge argues that if the value of a human life is assessed as, say £2 million, and the ESD would reduce the risk of transfer spill by 50 per cent, then the benefit would be

$$3.0 \times 10^{-3} \times 0.5 \times \text{£2 M} = \text{£3000 per year}$$

Table 11.1 Estimates of fatalities from operations of gas carriers and product tankers

Event	Annual fatality rate	%
Gas carriers		
Collision on approach	1.1×10^{-6}	0.0
Grounding on approach	5.0×10^{-8}	0.0
Fire on approach	2.2×10^{-7}	0.0
Striking at berth	2.4×10^{-4}	5.8
Impact at berth	6.7×10^{-6}	0.2
Fire at berth	7.3×10^{-6}	0.2
Transfer spill	4.7×10^{-4}	11.4
Product tankers		
Explosion at berth	3.8×10^{-4}	9.3
Transfer spill	3.0×10^{-3}	73.1
Total	4.1×10^{-3}	100.00

Thus it could be argued that if the amortized net annual cost of the ESD were to be less than £3000 per year, it should be considered necessary.

Such extension of risk assessment work into cost–benefit analysis raises controversial questions which, despite pleas such as those in Ref. 15, have not yet been properly addressed by the marine community. This must eventually be done, but perhaps the more immediate need is that the credibility and applicability of risk assessment methods must first be established among those concerned with maritime safety. Studies of the kind outlined here can do much to help this necessary cultural change.

Implications of the *Piper Alpha* Disaster for the Future in Marine Safety

On the evening of 6 July 1988, an explosion occurred on the production deck of the *Piper Alpha* oil platform, which was located 110 miles north-east of Aberdeen and had been producing oil and gas for a consortium of owners since 1976. A fire developed from which a fireball erupted and the ensuing dense smoke and further explosions caused failure of most of the emergency systems. Further major explosions followed when gas risers ruptured, destroying one of the rescue craft and causing major structural collapse of the platform. Out of the 226 persons on board 165 were killed as well as 2 crew from the rescue craft. This was the highest death toll in the history of offshore operations.

The report[18] of the Public Inquiry into this disaster, published as this chapter was being completed, is likely to be a milestone in the history of the safety of marine structures, with implications that will reach beyond offshore hydrocarbon recovery into other areas of marine work.

The Inquiry concluded that the triggering event for this disaster was the leakage of condensate from a blind flange assembly, causing a cloud of flammable gas which was then ignited, possibly by an electrostatic spark. The subsequent train of events, the behaviour of the systems for control, shut-down, evacuation and rescue, and the causes of death, have been reconstructed in great detail.[18] The working practices on board the platform, its owners' managerial procedures and attitudes to safety, as well as the inspecting and monitoring roles of the Department of Energy were also critically examined. Based on this very comprehensive appraisal of the technical, operational, managerial and regulatory aspects of the disaster, the report derives some far-reaching recommendations for the future. And just as the technology of some long-established traditional industries can derive fresh impetus from new, more sophisticated developments in related fields, so it is probable that the management of safety in traditional marine activities such as shipping and fishing will come to be influenced and improved by developments in offshore safety consequent upon this disaster. The Inquiry's proposals could thus provide, if not a blueprint, at least a powerful stimulus for a reappraisal of the management of marine safety generally.

Four main features of these proposals relate particularly to matters discussed in this chapter, and are adapted below to point the way ahead. Firstly, it is proposed that operators of major marine installations, vehicles and structures should be required to carry out a *formal safety assessment* (FSA) of major hazards, to demonstrate that such hazards and their risks to personnel have been identified and appropriate controls provided. The FSA, updated at regular intervals, would thus assure the operators, the public and the regulatory authorities that the operation of the structure is acceptably safe. In the case of ships, especially those carrying passengers, the FSA should also address the evacuation and rescue of personnel and demonstrate that adequate time and resources are available. The FSA is expected to make extensive use of modern techniques, including hazard and operability studies, quantitative risk assessment and others used in the studies noted above.

Secondly, operating companies should be required to demonstrate that an effective *system of safety management* is enforced. We have already seen, in the context of the *Herald* disaster, discussed in Sec. 11.1, that this need had been identified by the *Herald* Inquiry. The *Piper* recommendations stress the importance of regular safety audits by operating companies, monitored and, if necessary, supplemented by inspections by the regulatory body. In the shipping industry, with its often complex structure of ownership and operations, noted in Sec. 11.1, means must therefore be found for allocating these responsibilities for safety management.

Thirdly, the *regulations* governing safety of marine structures must increasingly be *based on stated performance objectives* rather than on prescriptive solutions or on guidance notes or rules, which are often seen to be inflexible and restrictive. Section 11.2 has illustrated the nature of current maritime regulations affecting design, and comment has been made on the difficulty of moving to performance-based regulations. Nevertheless, it has been an underlying theme of this chapter that if maritime safety assurance is to be placed on a more durable and defensible basis, this must be high on the agenda for marine technological development.

Fourthly, the *Piper Alpha* Inquiry report points to the need for *a single, strong regulatory body* within the offshore safety regime. We have already noted in Sec. 11.2 the complex structure of national and international authorities involved in marine safety, a structure that contrasts sharply and unfavourably with that in the aviation industry. Resolution of this problem is as much a political as a technical problem, but it must be tackled. That the Inquiry recommended the Health and Safety Executive, in preference to the Department of Energy, as the regulatory body for the offshore industry reflects their belief in the need for such a body to have the philosophy, management culture and expertise appropriate to the task of safety regulation into the next century. Similar arguments must surely apply to marine safety generally, although the international nature of maritime operations and regulation, together with the legacy of tradition and practice, are formidable obstacles to change.

11.4 FINALE: AN AGENDA FOR CHANGE

Starting and ending with two major recent maritime disasters, this chapter has reviewed (in Sec. 11.1) the particular problems of the marine industries in relation to safety, and the traditional and current means of controlling the risks to life, property and the environment (Sec. 11.2). A brief survey of recent developments in Sec. 11.3 has shown that, despite the technical, organization and regulatory complexities of marine safety, and despite the inertial mass of its traditions and practices, some important lessons have been learnt and enacted from recent disasters. New views are emerging regarding the control of, and responsibilities for, marine safety.

However, there is still much to be done, especially in the four areas noted above from the recommendations of the *Piper Alpha* Inquiry, which encapsulate much of the comment of this chapter. The work needed ranges from basic research to create more valid models for predicting vehicle behaviour in extreme conditions, development of performance-based codes and regulations and study of design implications, to the reappraisal of management and regulatory responsibilities and organizations to ensure the more rational and consistent approach to safety that is needed.

Two other things will help to promote marine safety: education and technology transfer. Safety engineering and design for safety need to become more explicit, but integral, features of education in marine technology at all levels. Too much reliance has been placed on codes of practice as the guarantors of safety; too little exposure to modern ideas and methods of safety engineering has resulted. Advances in other disciplines of engineering are, as we have seen, often highly relevant to marine work. If, by bringing together in this book safety expertise across many disciplines, these objectives of technology transfer and education have been advanced, then the cause of maritime safety will have been well served.

REFERENCES

1. Aldwinckle, D. S., and R. V. Pomeroy: Reliability and Safety Assessment Methods for Ships and Other Installations, Lloyd's Register of Shipping, technical report no. 82, 1983.
2. Aldwinckle, D. S.: Review of Shipping Record, *Conf. on Safety at Sea and in the Air*, Royal Aeronautical Society and Royal Institution of Naval Architects, London, 1990.
3. Spouge, J. R.: Passenger Ferry Safety in the Philippines, *Trans. R. Inst. Nav. Architects*, vol. 132, 1990.

4. Department of Transport: Ro/Ro Safety, Report of Steering Committee, Department of Transport, 1990.
5. Reason, J.: How to Promote Error Tolerance in Complex Systems in the Context of Ships and Aircraft, *Conf. on Safety at Sea and in the Air*, Royal Aeronautical Society and Royal Institution of Naval Architects, London, 1990.
6. Rawson, K. J.: Ethics and Fashion in Design, *Trans. R. Inst. Nav. Architects*, vol. 132, 1990.
7. Caldwell, J. B.: Prospects for a Rational Approach to Marine Safety, *Int. Conf. on Marine Safety*, Glasgow, 1983.
8. Sen, P., and J. A. Cocks: Collision Resistance, *Conf. on Safety and Survivability of Ro-Ro Ships*, Royal Institution of Naval Architects, London, 1990.
9. Brown, D. K.: The Management of Safety of Warships in the UK, *Trans. R. Inst. Nav. Architects*, vol. 132, 1990.
10. MacLeod, Sir Roderick: Shipowners and Classification, 100 A1, Lloyd's Register, 1989.
11. Gilmour, B. E. K.: A Management System towards Improving the Safety of Passenger Ro-Ro Ferries, *Kummerman Int. Conf. on Ro-Ro Safety and Vulnerability*, Royal Institution of Naval Architects, 1987.
12. International Ship Structures Congress: Report of Committee 10 on Design Procedure, Oslo, 1967.
13. Thayamballi, A. K., Y. K. Chen, and H. H. Chin: Deterministic and Reliability Based Retrospective Strength Assessments of Oceangoing Vessels, *Trans. Soc. Nav. Architects and Mar. Engng.*, New York, 1987.
14. Rutherford, S. E., and J. B. Caldwell: Ultimate Longitudinal Strength: A Case Study, *Trans. Soc. of Nav. Arch. and Mar. Engng*, San Francisco, 1990.
15. Goss, R. O.: Rational Approaches to Marine Safety, *Trans. North East Coast Inst.*, vol 105, 1989.
16. Thompson, I., and D. Prentice: Safety Assessment Considerations for Offshore Floating Production and Storage Units, *Trans. R. Inst. Nav. Architects*, vol. 132, 1990.
17. Spouge, J. R.: The Use of Risk Assessment for Ships Carrying Hazardous Cargo in Port Areas, *Conf. on Safety at Sea and in the Air*, Royal Aeronautical Society and Royal Institution of Naval Architects, London, 1990.
18. Department of Energy: *Report of the Public Inquiry into the Piper Alpha Disaster*, Cm 1310, HMSO, London, 1990.

TWELVE

WATER SUPPLY AND POLLUTION CONTROL

P. W. JOWITT

12.1 INTRODUCTION

At a special meeting of the General Assembly on 10 November 1980, the United Nations formally launched the International Drinking Water Supply and Sanitation Decade 1981–1990. At that time, the mortality rate in the developing world from water-related disease was of the order of 1 in 1200 of the exposed population, 80 per cent of all diseases in the world were water related, 100 million people had gastroenteritis, 200 million suffered from schistosomiasis (bilharzia or snail fever), 30 million had onchoceriasis (river blindness).[1] Diarrhoeal diseases alone accounted annually for the death of 4 million children under the age of five. Ten years later and despite the efforts of various world agencies, national governments and charities, the outlook for millions is still bleak. The United Nations has now launched a successor initiative: Safe Water 2000.

In the developed world, the basic threats to public health from inadequate water supply and unsafe wastewater disposal are negligible in comparison, and any residual danger is generally latent rather than potent. The primary sources of risk, so prevalent in the developing world, have been reduced to a series of secondary risks. For example, the accidental poisoning of water supplies at the Lowermoor drinking water treatment plant in south-west England in 1988 involved the chemical aluminium sulphate (alum), routinely used as a flocculating agent to separate out impurities present in untreated water as colloidal solids. In this instance, the resulting alum concentrations in the water supplied to 20 000 people in the Camelford area of North

Cornwall were 6000 times the permitted European Community limit. However, even at its normally low rate of application aluminium is suspected as being a factor in the occurrence of Alzheimer's disease and has brought the use of alum into question. Indeed, concern over aluminium may have been a contributory factor in another example of secondary risk which occurred at a treatment plant near Oxford in 1988. Supplies from the treatment plant were temporarily withdrawn after the discovery of the bacterium *Cryptosporidium* at the plant. There has been some speculation that growth of this bacterium may not have occurred had the aluminium flocculating salt not been substituted by an equivalent iron salt.

The complexion of the public health risks relating to water supply and waste disposal varies greatly between the developed and developing world. The beginning point of water pollution control requires improvements in basic health brought about by the provision of potable water supply and safe means of waste disposal. Refinement of these measures leads to a requirement to monitor and maintain quality at specified levels. Improved design criteria, novel processes and better operational control allow standards to be tightened and extended to other parameters of concern. The simplicity of this pattern of development is beguiling, and a variety of uncertainties affect the outcome of any pollution control programme.

In the developing world attempts to reduce pathogen concentrations and interrupt disease pathways are complicated by the paucity of design data and incomplete knowledge of pathogen transmission mechanisms and means of attenuation. Notwithstanding the massive underfunding of water supply and pollution control programmes in the developing world, great uncertainty and risk are associated with the institutional, financial and technical conditions under which pollution control schemes are operated and developed. In such circumstances the major difficulty is in achieving water quality standards that even remotely conform to the sometimes rather arbitrary pollutant control standards as given by such as the World Health Organisation, the European Community, etc.

In contrast, the developed world is beginning to contend with a rather different problem, involving the assessment and attenuation of transient phenomena such as accidental toxic waste spillage and the control of an ever-increasing range of micropollutants and known and alleged carcinogens. Under such circumstances, the uncertainties to be resolved are associated not only with the effective monitoring of substances at very low concentrations, but also the nature of the dose–response relationship, and thereby the very nature of the imposed standards themselves.

12.2 HISTORICAL CONTEXT

While the primary sources of water-related health risks in the developed world are under control, it has not always been so, and the major developments have really only occurred within the last 150 years. Previously the situation was similar to that currently prevailing in much of the developing world, where lack of progress results not so much from a lack of understanding of the magnitude and nature of the risks but from a combination of cultural inertia, lack of financial resources, sociopolitical difficulty and institutional and technical failure.

The occurrence of water-borne diseases such as cholera and typhoid is characterized by a classical faecal–oral transmission cycle and typically involves the use of a water supply contaminated by sewage-laden wastewater, followed by outbreaks of disease. Even if the precise health effects and mechanisms of such pollution were largely unknown until the mid nineteenth century, the undesirability of pollution water courses has long been appreciated: at an Inquisition in the reign of Edward I of England (16 Edw 1) in 1288 it was

> ... determined that the water course of Walebrook (i.e. the Walbrook, a stream running into the Thames from a swamp called Moorfields), north of the City wall in London should be free from dung and other nuisances....[2]

In London in the following centuries a number of efforts were made to separate the source of supply from the means of disposal, with each new attempt generally prompted by the failure of its predecessor: thus the occurrence of such London place names as Lamb's Conduit Street, New River Head, etc., which are a clue to those early attempts to bring fresh water from further afield. By the mid nineteenth century the situation in London had once again reached crisis proportions. One of the leading lights of the movement for sanitary reform was Edwin Chadwick, a lawyer, who wrote in a letter to Councillor John Shuttleworth, Manchester, on 9 October 1844:

> For all purposes it would be of the greatest importance that you should get the advice of trustworthy engineers, of whom I am sorry to say there are marvellous few—a more ignorant and jobbing set of men ... I have rarely met with.[3]

It was not until 1854 that the cause of cholera was firmly established, when Dr John Snow demonstrated that an outbreak in Soho, London, was due to contamination by sewage of the water supply taken from the Broad Street pump. His advice was simple: 'Take away the pump handle.' A long-term solution, however, depended on a more strategic initiative, and in particular to Joseph Bazalgette. His scheme was to construct a system of major intercepting sewers to take wastewater to the east for treatment and safe disposal in the downstream reaches of the Thames, away from the centres of population. With new sources of supply taken from upstream areas to the north and west of London, together with some borehole supplies in the south, the cycle of water-borne disease was broken. Bazalgette's sewerage system still forms the basis of London's wastewater collection system, and he was later responsible for many similar schemes elsewhere. The old London rivers running into the Thames are no more the major elements of the supply/disposal system, although they do retain the role of storm relief sewers. In consequence, the Thames is no longer a major cause of disease and nuisance. The pattern of problems faced by a city such as London and the steps taken to resolve them are reflected in experiences elsewhere. Accounts of the pattern of development in Scotland and France can be found in O'Hanlon[4] and Goubert.[5]

The methods of water and wastewater treatment which have proved so effective in providing supplies of safe water and proper means of waste disposal are now well established, and most treatment plants are generally based on three basic types of process:

1. Physical processes
   (a) Screening
   (b) Sedimentation
   (c) Filtration
   (d) Flotation
   (e) Comminution
2. Chemical processes
   (a) Coagulation
   (b) Precipitation
   (c) Disinfection
   (d) Ion exchange
3. Biological processes
   (a) Anaerobic digestion
   (b) Biological oxidation

Typically, two or more of these processes are used in combination. Conventional water treatment for a river abstraction source might involve initial screening followed by coagulation/sedimentation (assisted by the addition of a chemical coagulant such as aluminium sulphate). These processes might typically be followed by filtration and then disinfection. The treatment plant would also include a sludge thickening process to deal with the waste material arising from the sedimentation and filter backwashing components. In contrast, a good quality groundwater source may simply require disinfection. With regard to wastewater treatment, a typical process chain for a conventional activated sludge (biological oxidation) plant would be screening/comminution, primary sedimentation, aeration tank, secondary settling/final clarification.

The inflows to water and wastewater treatment plants are generally of variable quantity and quality. The various plant processes are intended to buffer transient peaks and remove/reduce the overall levels of undesirable water quality parameters. For the most part, treatment plants are able to cope with a wide variation in loading. However, their normally robust character can sometimes become unstable or vulnerable to toxic substances, to the extent that the overall performance of the plant may render the quality unacceptable. It is therefore important that operational criteria for the management and process control of such plants are established and adherence to such good practice is encouraged by an appropriate framework of regulations, legislation and professional practice.

12.3 WATER QUALITY STANDARDS

The temporal and spatial availability of water is usually asynchronous with human demands. The component tasks of water resources development are thus concerned with the location, collection, long-term storage, treatment, short-term storage and distribution of a suitable supply. The water supplied to consumers should be of sufficient quantity and acceptable quality. In the United Kingdom the definition of quality has centred on the notion of 'wholesomeness', and now, in common with other member states of the EC, water quality is governed by extensive and complex EC directives. For example, the governing Directive for drinking water quality is 80/778/EC. These directives in turn are generally related to other international standards.

The more general term 'wholesome' can be regarded as combining the two properties of potability and palatability. Thus the water treatment processes employed prior to consumption must ensure that the water is free from bacterial and other biological matter associated with faecal pollution and water-related diseases and harmful organic (e.g. trihalomethanes) and inorganic (e.g. heavy metals such as cadmium, lead) compounds. The supply should not be aggressive, for example by virtue of an extreme pH value. In addition, the supply should not have excessive colour, taste or odour, and should not be excessively turbid or contain harmful or undesirable dissolved matter. Other factors that have to be guarded against are issues such as plumbo-solvency, caused by soft, acidic waters and resulting in a tendency for lead to be drawn into solution from lead supply pipes. The Directive 80/778/EC lists 64 parameters, comprising 16 general physicochemical parameters, 12 inorganic anions, 16 metals, 15 organic substance parameters and 5 microbial parameters. The Directive also has various footnotes, covering such matters as the presence of pathogenic bacteria (e.g. 'in addition, water intended for human consumption should not contain salmonella, pathogenic staphylococci ...'). Interestingly, member states are allowed to relax the standards for total bacteria in bottled water within their own borders, provided that all other microbiological standards are observed.

The quality standards for water to be used for direct abstraction to potable supply is governed by another EC Directive (75/440/EC), covering 39 determinands, 4 biological indicators and a number of other particularly dangerous determinands (i.e. the so-called List I substances given in the

Dangerous Substances Directive 76/464/EC, and including such parameters as mercury, dieldrin, chloroform, etc.) Directive 75/440/EC provides for different degrees of treatment:

A1: simple physical treatment and disinfection;
A2: normal physical and chemical treatment including disinfection;
A3: intensive physical and chemical treatment and disinfection.

The Directive specifies quality standards in terms of guide and/or imperative values; these in turn are defined as 90 percentiles (guide values) or as 95 percentiles or maximum allowable concentrations (imperative values). Furthermore, the methods of measurement and frequencies of sampling are contained in yet another Directive, 79/869/EC. The frequencies depend on both the intended type of treatment (A1, A2 or A3) and the size of the population to be served. For small populations, the 'competent national authority' is given some discretion. At the other extreme, a minimum frequency of 12 times per year is specified for populations in excess of 100 000 and where the abstraction requires intensive (A3) treatment. This minimum sampling frequency is still not very high and the statistical difficulties posed by such low rates of monitoring will be addressed later.

Various other directives are intended to protect aquatic life (including shell fish and freshwater fish), provide safe bathing waters, groundwaters, protect land from the harmful effects of sewage sludge, etc. Thus discharges of effluent are also controlled. Regular discharges of treated effluent operate under a regime of a discharge consent standard, covering the volume and quality limits of the waste, with respect to specific and composite determinands. There has been a similar tendency to use percentile standards to specify discharge constant standards, although annual average and maximum allowable concentrations are also used.

The natural quality of waters used for abstraction or to receive (treated) effluents is highly variable. In addition, treated effluents vary in quantity and quality, due in part to the variability in type and volume of the raw effluent and the performance variability of the treatment processes themselves. Consequently, specification on a sound statistical basis of water quality standards and the accompanying frequency of sampling is not a straightforward task. The issues are complicated further by the imprecise relationship between the various contaminants and their deleterious effects.

12.4 THE DEVELOPMENT OF DISCHARGE CONSENT CONDITIONS

It is useful to examine the UK origins of standards for effluents discharging into rivers, in particular the well-known 30:20 standard deriving from the Eighth Report (1912) of the Royal Commission on Sewage Disposal.[6]

The Commission undertook various monitoring experiments of receiving waters and examined the practices of the then extant River Boards. The Report takes ammoniacal nitrogen as an indicator of *recent* sewage pollution but fixes upon biochemical oxygen demand (BOD) as the major indicator of the *character* of the pollution, and in particular its nuisance value (paras 7–9). The Report then concludes (paras 10–11) that an in-stream BOD figure of 4 mg/l can generally be taken to be a useful dividing line between a river free from pollution (BOD < 4 mg/l) and a river that will show signs of pollution and nuisance (BOD > 4 mg/l). The effects of BOD on the health of the river are temperature related and the Royal Commission adopted 65°F (18°C) as the benchmark temperature for such tests.

The preliminary section of the Report quotes from the earlier Fifth Report, noting that the terms of reference require it to have regard to the '*economical* and efficient discharge' and 'not requiring local authorities to incur further expenditure on sewage disposal than the circumstances of its area require', and that the 'law should be altered so as to allow local circumstances such as the quality of the receiving water to be taken into account'. The required effluent quality in terms of BOD, say, c mg/l, would thus be determined via a simple mass balance calculation involving the river and effluent flow rates Q, q (m^3/s) and the in-stream river BOD concentration C mg/l (though, of course, the values of Q, q and C are all variable and would require careful specification). Thus the effluent quality standard is determined from

$$\frac{qc + QC}{q + Q} < 4$$

or

$$c < \frac{4(q + Q) - QC}{q}$$

The Report then states three objections to such a variable and local policy:

1. Administrative difficulty
2. Inequity between authorities in the burden of purification
3. Excessive differentiation in the required effluent quality than is necessary to ensure economy

The last of these objectives seeks to avoid the inefficient management of a treatment plant merely because a lower quality effluent could be tolerated.

Instead, the Commission proposed a single, normal standard which would be suitable for the majority of locations, with provision for higher or lower standards where justifiable. The first element of this normal standard related to BOD and was taken to be 20 mg/l BOD. This value was partly based on the observation that well-managed treatment plants regularly achieved such a figure, and it was justified by the hopeful anticipation that the effluent discharge would be to a receiving water assumed to be 'clean' (BOD = 2 mg/l) and that the effluent would be diluted eightfold. Such a discharge would result in an in-stream BOD of 4 mg/l, the figure identified by the Commission as representing the upper limit for a river to be pollution free. In addition, an effluent suspended solids standard of 30 mg/l was advocated, once again based on the observation that such a standard could generally be achieved at well-managed plants. The suspended solids test was also regarded as the primary test. This resulted in the 30:20 standard, which has been a corner-stone of effluent discharge standards in the United Kingdom and which has proved such a sound and durable instrument for water pollution control.

The Report also outlined the conditions under which the normal 30:20 standard should be relaxed or tightened up, though the Report cautions against the 'tendency to undue laxity' that might result from relaxed standards. Despite such caution, it would seem that the Report's acknowledgement of the possibility or occasional reasonableness of such local variation in discharge standards has resulted in extensive adoption of local emission standards rather than the 30:20 uniform emission standard they advocated as the norm. The outcome is that the United Kingdom has taken a different course to the rest of the EC in the implementation of EC Directives.

Thus, while the impression may have been given that the 1912 Royal Commission had advocated a uniform emission standards (UES), the practical reality has been otherwise.[7] Nevertheless, custom and practice in the water industry has continued to categorize a plant on its ability to deliver a 30:20 effluent. The UK practice of setting emission standards in relation to local conditions has resulted in a range of more and less stringent consent conditions, in some cases down to 5:5. The UK practice is referred to as the environmental quality objective (EQO) approach, though it is anticipated that there will be greater concordance between the EQO and UES approaches.

In 1987 the Third Report of the House of Commons Environment Committee[8] notes that the UES approach allows emissions to be set as low as technologically possible and that they are less cumbersome to implement. The Report also notes that the use of UESs is a reflection of 'Continental countries where the Napoleonic Code of establishing norms has prevailed'. This latter aspect has the effect in principle, if not in practice, of imposing the same burden of cost for producers of similar effluents from similar activities, irrespective of the good fortune one might enjoy over another by virtue of adjacency to a large, clean, receiving water.

The Environment Committee Report also noted (paras 24–27) that the Department of the Environment (DoE) had little information on sewage works effluent compliance prior to 1985. Comprehensive statistics, sought for the first time by the DoE in 1986, show that about 22 per cent of the 4355 consents issued by the DoE to sewage works were breached. It should be noted that the definition of compliance used by the DoE referred to a 95 percentile standard, so that these failing works were deemed to be discharging more than the concentration stated in the consent conditions for more than 5 per cent of the time.

Of course, in the event of a gross pollution incident, such as the incident involving aluminium sulphate in the Camelford area in 1988, or such common incidents as unauthorized discharges of farm slurry into water courses, it should be immaterial whether an EQO or UES approach is adopted. Obviously, legal prosecution of gross incidents could be pursued successfully without the need for specific water quality legislation, insofar as evidence of actual damage, such as fish kills and adverse health effects, should be sufficient to establish a case. On the other hand, in the day-to-day control of water quality parameters, it is difficult to associate a particular pattern of a contaminant in an effluent discharge with a particular effect. In such cases, a *technical* offence is required, which is based on the breach of a statutory (if somewhat arbitrary) limit. This is the realm of water quality legislation and should govern the bulk of water quality monitoring and control for the bulk of the time.

12.5 PERCENTILE STANDARDS

A major factor affecting the specification of discharge standards and the consequence for the receiving waters is the temporal variation of the effluent flow and its contaminant concentrations and the corresponding in-stream quantities in the receiving water itself. All other things being equal, the effect of the discharge on the receiving water will be worst when the river flow is at its minimum and the effluent flow is at its maximum. Thus the eightfold dilution implicit in the establishment of the Royal Commission 30 : 20 standard might be based on some low flow conditions in the receiving water and some condition of maximum treated effluent flow. For the latter, three times 'dry weather flow' (DWF) might typically be used. (Provision is usually made for storm flows to be stored temporarily in stormwater tanks and treated when raw effluent flows have sufficiently subsided). The notions of a 'low river flow' or a 'dry weather effluent flow' may seem intuitive, but, in truth, precise definitions are rather arbitrary.

This variability of quality and quantity in the effluent flows and receiving waters has led to the notion of percentile standards for some water quality parameters referred to earlier. For example, Directive 75/440/EC for water abstracted for supply gives in respect of nitrate a 'guide' value of 5.65 mg/l NO_3-N as a 90 percentile non-exceedance value, with an 'imperative' value of 11.3 mg/l NO_3-N as a 95 percentile value. In contrast, for drinking water the requirements are more stringent and the corresponding parameter is governed by a 100 percentile (i.e. maximum admissible) concentration. It should be noted, though, that the actual figure of 11.3 mg/l NO_3-N used in both Directives conveys an illusory precision, since it derives from the rather more arbitrary value of 50 mg/l NO_3, which is exactly the same standard but expressed in terms of nitrate rather than its equivalent nitrogen content.

The general notion of specifying standards as percentile non-exceedance values has some appeal, especially for naturally varying parameters. Indeed, percentile compliance was acknowledged in the 1912 Royal Commission Report, which recommended that an infringement of the standard should not be deemed to have occurred unless, out of 12 samples, at least 3 exceeded the prescribed standard, amounting to an approximate 80 percentile sample compliance. A practical consequence of a percentile definition of water quality standards is that a particular raw water source is not condemned by an occasional high value.

The variability of effluent quality presents legislators and practitioners in the water industry with the twin problems of framing of discharge consent conditions and developing an appropriate system for monitoring compliance. Prominent among those who have sought to establish within the UK water industry a sound and consistent approach to these problems are Warn, Brew, Matthews and Ellis.[9-12]

A situation in the United Kingdom had developed in which the operational criteria, policy strategy and legal interpretation of compliance were in conflict. Reference has already been made to the 1912 Royal Commission's implicit recognition of percentile sample compliance for sewage effluents. In the late 1970s, the National Water Council (which was a statutory body responsible for water-related affairs in England and Wales) advocated a system of river water quality objectives (RQOs) based on 95 percentiles. However, for discharge content conditions the Council recommended *fixed* figures which could not be legally exceeded, thereby shifting the Regional Water Authorities' (RWAs) policy from the 80 percentile sample compliance deriving from the Royal Commission standard to a 100 percentile (i.e. maximum admissible) limit. In fact, a 95 percentile standard for effluent discharges was adopted as a compromise, placing them on the same statistical basis as the in-stream RQOs. This decision produced an inconsistency between the legal and operational definitions of compliance.

Further difficulties were anticipated as a consequence of the implementation in 1985 of Part II of the 1974 Control of Pollution Act (COPA II), including the potentially conflicting roles played by the Water Authorities in England and Wales. The RWAs, while themselves dischargers of effluent, also had the legal responsibility for initiating proceedings against polluters. The 1989 Water Act, establishing the National Rivers Authority (NRA), has resulted in a separation of roles and responsibility, with the administration of the requirements of COPA II in effect being brought under the control of the NRA.

12.6 STATISTICAL VARIATION OF WATER QUALITY AND METHODS OF COMPLIANCE ASSESSMENT

Water quality parameters (and the corresponding flow variables) are time-varying random variables, and the overall probability density functions (p.d.f.'s) and the serial correlation of the variables need to be considered. Confining attention for the moment to the p.d.f. (i.e. independent of the temporal ordering of the data), then the general shape of the p.d.f. of a naturally occurring substance might be expected to reflect a number of properties, such as:

1. Bounded at some lower bound concentration (e.g. $x = 0$)
2. $f(x)$ tends to zero as x tends to zero.
3. $f(x)$ tends to zero as x becomes large.
4. $f(x)$ has a dominant peak.
5. $f(x)$ has positive skewness.

Commonly used forms of $f(x)$ [such as the normal (Gaussian), lognormal, triangular, gamma] tend to be unimodal and first-order continuous. The lognormal, which is widely used to represent water quality variations, is unimodal, positively skewed and smooth; it is also restricted to positive values of the random variable x. The lognormal is capable of reflecting coefficients of variation Cv (standard deviation/mean) ranging from zero to infinity. For typical values of Cv (0.3 to 0.7) the upper 95 percentile ranges from 1.55 to 2.31 times the mean. For $Cv = 0.5$, the 95 percentile is 1.95, or approximately twice, the mean value. Thus, specification of an upper 95 percentile, together with the broad assumption that the underlying p.d.f. is roughly lognormal with a 'typical' value of Cv, is implicitly making a series of assumptions, such as tying down the parameter in terms of its mean value and the way in which $f(x)$ tends to zero beyond the specified 95 percentile figure.

In many cases, these assumptions are unjustified, and the consequences of such an assumption may be significant. For example, it might happen that a particular parameter arises from two sources and is governed by two distinct p.d.f.'s. Suppose one of the sources predominates and has a low mean, the other source having a much higher mean. The overall p.d.f. will be bimodal and, although it will be possible to use sample data to parameterize a lognormal function with the requisite 95 percentile, the fit will be poor and the fitted p.d.f. will not reflect the data. Decisions based on an inappropriate p.d.f. may thus be seriously in error. In practice, such a bimodal pattern of parameter variability can arise in situations where the dominant causes of pollution are under control (such that the background pollutant levels vary about some low level) but where the occasional occurrence of a high pollutant load from a different source (such as a spasmodic agricultural discharge) becomes more obvious statistically and more significant in its effect. Unfortunately, though, such isolated pollution episodes may not be detected within routine monitoring programmes, yet they become obvious by their consequences.

Of course, discharge consent conditions are not described in terms of particular p.d.f.'s, but in terms of various statistical parameters which reflect the intended purpose and in-stream objective. For example, a specified upper limit on the mean or median value offers control over general levels without particular regard for extremes. On the other hand, an upper percentile would be appropriate if the intention was to focus attention on high values without particular reference to general levels, allowing the same 95 percentile to be achieved by low mean/high variance or high mean/low variance processes. For particularly toxic materials, even 95 percentiles might be deemed to offer insufficient protection, and a maximum allowable concentration (100 percentile or MAC) could be specified.

The suitability and use of these various parameters in the context of consent conditions has been studed in depth by Ellis.[11,12] Of the matters that Ellis considers there are two that have been the source of some confusion, namely the inappropriate use of 'sample compliance' rather than 'determinand compliance' and the issue of multideterminand compliance. For example, Directive 75/440/EC (Surface Waters Intended for Water Supply) requires that:

1. 95% (90% for some determinands) of samples [must] comply and for failed samples
   (i)   deviation from the parametric values in questions must be less than 50% (except for pH, temperature, dissolved oxygen and microbiological determinands,
   (ii) there is no danger to public health,
   (iii) consecutive water samples at significantly suitable intervals do not deviate from the relevant parametric values.
   ⋮
3. Higher values than the required parametric values can be ignored if resulting from floods, natural disasters or abnormal weather conditions.

The Directive's requirement that a fixed percentage (in this case 95 or 90 per cent) of samples must comply is a statistical nonsense; the absurd effects that can result from such a requirement have been detailed by Ellis[12] and by Warn and Matthews.[10] The nonsense arises from the simple fact that for a given water quality, the likelihood of acceptance *according to this given rule* varies with the frequency of sampling. Suppose that the 'true' compliance of some determinand is such that there is a probability p that the determinand concentration is less than the prescribed amount. If n independent samples are taken, then the probability that exactly r of them will be less than the prescribed value is the binomial probability $B(r; n, p)$. The overall probability that *at least* 95 per cent of the sample values have concentrations less than the prescribed value is then the sum of $B(r; n, p)$ from $r = 0.95n$ (rounding up as necessary) to n. In the trivial case when $n = 1$ (so that rounding up $0.95n$ is also unity) then the chance of overall success in meeting the criterion that at least 95 per cent of samples comply is simply p. However, as n increases, the chance of meeting the stated condition reduces irrespective of the prescribed concentration value of the determinand, the true water quality and the probability p. When $p = 0.95$ then the chances of meeting the stated condition reduce asymptotically with n to 0.5, that is to say, compliance could just as equally be decided by the flip of a coin. Thus

$$\text{Pr (at least } 0.95n \text{ of } n \text{ samples comply)} = \sum_{r=0.95n}^{n} \frac{p^r(1-p)^{n-r}n!}{r!(n-r)!}$$

so that for $n = 1$, $\text{Pr}(>0.95n \text{ samples comply}) = p$ and for $n = $ large and $p = 0.95$, $\text{Pr}(>0.95n \text{ samples comply})$ tends to 0.5.

There is an obvious absurdity in such a criterion for assessing the overall compliance of a river or an effluent. Despite this, performance criteria based on such a definition of compliance has been implied in various National Water Council policy statements and EC directives themselves.

Instead, a more rational approach, and one advocated by, among others, Warn and Matthews and Ellis, is to frame the criterion to make the chances of compliance broadly the same regardless of the sampling frequency. This could be achieved by using the n sampled data to estimate the true (or 'population') value of the 95 percentile and then comparing this value to the value specified in the criterion. A variety of parametric and non-parametric estimators of percentile values are available. In statistical parlance, the risk of a type I error is maintained at a fixed value for all sizes of sample [type I error = Pr(null hypothesis rejected when it is actually true)]. The sample size serves only to control the type II error [type II error = Pr(null hypothesis not rejected when it is actually false)].

For the purpose of assessing the compliance of discharges with emission standards, Warn and Matthews proposed (and implemented within what was then the Anglian Water Authority) a more conservative approach involving the estimation of a suitable (e.g. 90 per cent) two-sided confidence region for the population 95 percentile. This results in a pair of lower and upper performance values. If the required 95 percentile exceeds the upper performance value, then compliance is deemed to have been achieved and the emission is classed as satisfactory, whereas if the low performance value exceeds the required 95 percentile, the emission is deemed unsatisfactory. If the confidence region bounded by the two performance values includes the required percentile, the status of the emission is deemed unresolved. The advantage of higher sampling frequencies is that this region of doubt is decreased.

Ellis[12] advocates an equivalent system of determining compliance. He has also addressed the problem of multideterminand compliance.[11] At least one Water Authority had been operating a compliance assessment scheme in which overall compliance within a water sample required individual compliance of all determinands simultaneously. The consequence of this was that the greater the number of determinands involved, then the greater would be the required true individual compliance to give an overall 95 per cent compliance. Specifically, for a set of n statistically independent determinands all enjoying an individual probability p of compliance, then the probability q that all n determinands simultaneously comply is given by $q = p^n$. If the individual percentile compliance is 95 per cent (that is $p = 0.95$) then for the case of $n = 3$ (or 12), the overall compliance corresponds to $q = 0.8575$ (or 0.5404). Conversely, the corresponding required values of p to secure an overall compliance of 95 per cent ($q = 0.95$) for $n = 3(12)$ determinands are $p = 0.9872$ (0.9957).

Notwithstanding the consideration of correlation between the occurrence of particular determinands, or the possible health or other consequences caused by the interaction of particular determinands, it should be clear that a general system of overall/simultaneous compliance makes little sense. On the one hand, retaining required individual compliance levels at 95 per cent means that when a large number of determinands are involved the overall compliance levels fall to derisorily low levels; on the other hand, attempting to maintain overall compliance at 95 per cent say, means that individual compliance levels are required to be at technically impossible levels and/or at levels that cannot be sensibly monitored at typical sampling frequencies.

The notion of discharge consent conditions and water quality standards requires, as Ellis has demonstrated, a clear purpose, a consistent and logical framework, and acceptable criteria for testing compliance. A 95 percentile provides an effective control on the upper range of a particular determinand, and for most determinands emanating from a single and/or temporally consistent source (i.e. such that the underlying p.d.f. is not markedly dissimilar from a typical unimodal form) then the 95 percentile also offers some further control. However, as mentioned earlier, extreme determinand values often arise from a different mechanism or from an unusual/abnormal operating condition, and it is perhaps prudent to set a maximum acceptable concentration (MAC) in addition to the 95 percentile values. Such a two-tier approach has been recently suggested in the United Kingdom by the newly established National Rivers Authority (NRA). Indeed, the NRA also suggested returning in effect to the 80 percentile implicit in the 1912 Royal Commission recommendations, though it now appears that the 95 percentile will be retained.

As indicated in Directive 75/440/EC, the occurrence of high concentrations arising from national disasters, flood flows, etc., cannot realistically be taken to be within the regime or control of the various Directives. A system of maximum acceptable concentrations serves the purpose of limiting the extremes of bad operational practice and containing what is reasonably controllable.

12.7 TOXICITY, DOSE–RESPONSE RELATIONSHIPS AND THE SETTING OF EXPOSURE LIMITS

The statistical aspects of how consents are framed and monitored have now broadly been established, though clearly important matters still remain, such as how to deal with seasonally varying determinands, etc. Although brief reference has been made to the rather arbitrary nature of some of the specified exposure limit values, the actual determinand concentrations to be specified within the standards have not so far been discussed in any detail. The relationships between a particular determinand and its effect on aquatic life or human health are imprecisely known (and in some cases as yet unsuspected). They may depend on a variety of other related factors and may vary in their particular effect from one individual to another. The specification of what the public might expect to be a 'safe' exposure limit is far from straightforward, and has become increasingly so as attention has shifted from those generally biological parameters that have an epidemiological impact, through substances that have short-term toxic effects, to the substances that have long-term toxic effects (including carcinogenesis), even at very low concentrations. The general approach used to establish exposure limits is the construction of a dose–response relationship. The characteristic features of such relationships include the LC50 (concentrations at which 50 per cent of the exposed population displays the response within some specified time interval) and the possibility of a threshold concentration below which there is no response.

The accuracy and precision with which such relationships can be established depends on a variety of factors. In some cases clinical trials with human volunteers have been used; in others, clinical data on the actual incidence of disease in the population at risk and an assessment of dosage may be available. Clearly, though, for some parameters and their effects, experiments involving human volunteers are not acceptable and reliance is placed on other techniques, such as the interpretation of experiments on animals. In any event, the low-dose/low-response region of such relationships will be very ill-defined, and this difficulty will worsen as an ever-increasing number of substances of concern are incriminated or at least come under suspicion.

For example, much attention has been paid in recent years to the effects of nitrates in drinking water, in particular its implication in the occurrence of methaemoglobinemia (blue-baby syndrome) and in stomach cancer in adults. This concern is such that some UK water suppliers have had to seek so-called derogations (relaxations) from EC directives in respect of nitrates and expensive denitrification plants have been installed at some sources. However, as noted in para. 80 of the Third Report of the Environment Committee,[8] such connections now look increasingly tenuous. There is also a general concern that a number of the limits for health-related parameters are based on a lifetime exposure at this concentration, and, as such, are unduly harsh. Nevertheless, there is no imminent prospect that the EC and related limits will be uniformly relaxed.

Rather, the standards expected of governments and water suppliers by the population at large often exceed those that individuals in that population are prepared to expect of themselves. This trait is not confined to aspects of public health but applies to a variety of activities.[13] Furthermore, there is an apparent discrepancy of perceived and actual risk and greater acceptability for risks that are well defined and confidently understood.[14] These latter considerations reinforce the tendency to set low exposure limits that are cautiously, if not arbitrarily, low.

In some cases, concern over one parameter results in one risk type being substituted by another. For example, recent concern of the use of chlorine in water treatment as a disinfectant [in particular, its reaction with man-made and even natural substances such as formic acid to produce carcinogenic trihalomethanes (THMs)] has resulted in a trend to alternative methods of disinfection, such as the use of ozone.[15] Although ozone has been used for disinfection since 1906, its use is not currently widespread and it may itself turn out to have equally undesirable but as yet unforeseen consequences. In this connection Kenneth Cantor of the US National Institute for Health has cautioned against 'moving from a known quantity (i.e. chlorination) to one where we know the benefits but not the risks (i.e. ozonation)', and urges instead moves to reduce the presence of organics and improvements in the chlorination process.[15]

There is a clear need to maintain a sense of balance and perspective in assessing the risks posed by the various water pollutants, and in turn in specifying the 'safe' exposure limits that are contained in standards such as the EC Directives. It could be argued that the protection that the Directives require against obscure but carcinogenic micropollutants is out of proportion to the risks posed by more familiar substances. For example, supplies of Perrier mineral water were recently withdrawn temporarily because of the presence of traces of benzene (a known carcinogen). The concentrations were small and almost certainly represented a potential exposure far less than that associated with the inhalation of petrol fumes by a motorist, which in turn is 50 times less than the exposure faced by a cigarette smoker.[16]

Henschler has argued that the multiplicity of substances to be controlled and the economic and technical limitations to understanding and controlling the precise nature of their effects requires a concentration of effort on those risks deemed to be of real significance.[16] He also argues that the participants (scientists, politicians and administrators) charged with the responsibility for setting priorities and establishing standards should themselves observe what he terms the 'principle of reasonableness'. Henschler contends that the tendency for high-ranking EC representatives to negotiate at length on whether the limiting exposure to a radioactive parameter should be set at 300 or 350 becquerel is not only a violation of this principle but is 'grotesque, and ... as being on the verge of foolishness'.[16] Given the absence of unambiguous and known safe exposure limits for health-related water quality parameters, then the requirements of water quality legislation have no doubt also been the outcome of a degree of negotiation.

If water quality and health were simply commodities of exchange in an economic market, then investment would be set at a level where a further £1 spent on water quality control provided less than £1 worth of expected health/environmental benefits and £1 less on water quality control would lead to a reduction of more than £1 worth of expected benefits. It is notoriously difficult to establish perceived monetary cost for morbidity, acute ill-health or, in extreme cases, death. Any such perceptions vary between individuals and may reflect their economic status, the extent to which they are themselves polluters, the extent to which they contribute to pollution control through taxation, the extent to which they can afford to provide extra provision and the extent to which they will individually benefit. The simple equation between marginal increase in cost and marginal increase in benefit is thus rather difficult to justify and apply across a whole population. Furthermore, the full implementation of the principle that the 'polluter should pay' is still some way off.

Planned investment in the United Kingdom in wastewater treatment over the next ten years to bring water quality into line with EC directives is in excess of £30 billion. It has to be accepted that, even at this level of investment, not all sources of risk will be addressed and brought under control. The possibility will always remain of such unconsidered incidents as accidental spillages and elements of human error contributing to the overall probability of failure.

12.8 HUMAN ERROR: CAMELFORD

Elements of the statutory framework for the protection of water quality, together with the engineering measures and sampling strategies to comply with its requirements, have been described above. In defining the associated MAC or 95 percentile limits and implementing a sampling regime, it has been implicitly assumed that the process under consideration possesses reasonable stability and can be reasonably controlled and that moderate excursions from typical operating points will not be of major importance. This sophisticated view of things can be rendered irrelevant by gross incidents unimagined in the normal operation of the treatment process. Incidents that can have deleterious effects on the water supply or a receiving water include unforeseen and accidental major pollution incidents, recklessness, negligence and even acts of wilful pollution. It is not clear how these fit into that part of the risk control strategy which is the concern of water quality standards, though, of course, the various water and pollution acts may make the offenders liable under the law. However, it is clear that such factors need to be assessed.

The incident already referred to at Camelford is just such an example of how a sophisticated operational control strategy and equally sophisticated pollution legislation are seen to offer no protection to an unforeseen sequence of blunders. The raw facts relating to the Camelford case are that on 6 July 1988 an unsupervised delivery to the Lowermoor water treatment works of aluminium sulphate (used routinely as a flocculating agent) was poured into the contact tank of treated and disinfected water (and about to go into supply), rather than into an adjacent aluminium sulphate storage tank. The delivery was made by a relief driver who had been given a key to the works and the storage tank; the key also fitted the contact tank. There were delays in responding to numerous consumer complaints (which ranged from unpleasant acidic and metallic taste, curdling of milk, to complaints of diarrhoea), with the true cause remaining unsuspected for some considerable time. Instead, South West Water Authority (SWWA) staff underestimated the significance and severity of the complaints, and wrongly attributed it to the failure of a lime dosing pump. Under more usual circumstances, such a pump failure would indeed fail to neutralize properly the acidity left by the residual but low levels of aluminium sulphate that arise from normal operation of the plant. Such pump failures are relatively commonplace and, based on evidence of complaints of acidity, the inference that a lime dosing fault had developed might not be unreasonable. An element of the usual response to such an incident would be to flush the mains. The adoption of such an action at the Lowermoor works had the effect of drawing further contaminated water into supply and of causing the death of 50 000 fish in the rivers Camel and Allen.[17,18]

At a subsequent court case in January 1991, SWWA was convicted of causing a public nuisance by supplying water that endangered public health. They were fined £10 000 with £25 000 prosecution costs. The conviction opened the door to up to 1000 civil cases being prepared by consumers affected by the incident. The district manager with responsibility for the plant was dismissed by SWWA after an internal inquiry and later had an appeal to an internal SWWA tribunal rejected. He continued to claim that he had been made a scapegoat and that his earlier recommendations to make changes to the locks/keys had not been implemented by SWWA. He sought to put his case before an industrial tribunal in January 1989. In the event, the parties arrived at an out of court settlement. Independent inquiries into the incident were highly critical of SWWA and its procedures.

It is easy to see in hindsight how any one of the events in the chain that led to this most unfortunate pollution episode might have been avoided. It is less easy to claim with any conviction how such a series of mistakes might have been foreseen. Clearly, the conjunction of events was apparently regarded as so improbable that those in a position to prevent such an outcome did not take the appropriate measures. The extent to which this was a failure, an oversight or just bad luck is a matter of contention. As is often the case, what happened resulted from one or more of what can at best be described as unfortunate blunders, which, taken together with other events, led to an unanticipated and scarcely credible outcome. Much has been made of the apparently slack way in which keys to various SWWA installations were widely available, and that among other things the contact tank and the alum storage tank could be opened by the same key. Certainly, the locks have since been changed and a special connector fitted to the storage tank that mates with a connector on the delivery tanker. It is worth remarking though that the usual purpose of a 'lock' is to offer security against vandalism or criminal activity; it is unlikely that the lock was ever envisaged as an instrument of quality assurance in connection with normal and authorized operations, as opposed to unauthorized interference. At the most basic level the Camelford incident has forced a reappraisal of the precise role of such an everyday object as the simple lock in the maintenance of quality rather than merely security. To operatives and others whose work involves regular access to installations at treatment plants, a cumbersome set of different mechanical keys and locks could be perceived progressively as an inconvenience and therefore prone to misuse. It is clearly preferable that more modern security measures, such as electromagnetic systems, be introduced which can combine convenience, security and quality assurance.

There were a number of pivotal elements in the sequence of events that led to the Camelford incident. Some of them, like the matter of the keys and other working practices, were long-standing, and in hindsight can be regarded as components of an accident waiting to happen. Other components of the event involved decisions made as the episode unfolded. A chronology of some of the major elements of the incident are as follows:[17,18]

1. Key fits variety of similar locks.
2. Availability of keys widespread.
3. Unsupervised alum delivery made on 6 July 1988 by relief driver unfamiliar with site, and briefed only verbally.
4. Driver does not follow delivery note instruction to telephone SWWA staff

on arrival at site, and instead unlocks incorrect tank and deposits 20 t of alum in treated water about to go into supply.
5. Subsequent complaints wrongly attributed to failure of lime dosing pump, and corrective measures adopted which are ineffective, continue to expose other consumers to contaminated water supplies and cause numerous fish kills.
6. SWWA staff notice on 8 July 1988 that the aluminium sulphate storage tank level is low.
7. Actual cause identified on 8 July 1988, driver interviewed on 12 July 1988 and public informed via press advert of nature of event on 22 July 1988.

It is instructive to examine how the almost totally unanticipated nature of the actual alum misplacement (in effect, an example of the closed world assumption) led in turn to the misattribution of the cause of the spate of customer complaints. In seeking to diagnose the cause of consumer complaints, the plant operators could be assumed to resort to an informal form of Bayesian reasoning, in which the chances of some cause a_i is assessed on the basis of some evidence b_j. This process can be written formally using Bayes' theorem:

$$p(a_i|b_j) = p(b_j|a_i) \frac{p(a_i)}{p(b_j)}$$

where

$$p(b_j) = \sum_j p(b_j|a_i)p(a_i)$$

and in which $p(b_j|a_i)$ and $p(a_i|b_j)$ are conditional probabilities and $p(a_i)$ and $p(b_j)$ are marginal probabilities. The probability $p(a_i)$ is a prior assessment of the proposition a_i, and $p(a_i|b_j)$ is a posterior assessment based on the evidence b_j. What follows is rather simplistic but suppose propositions are defined as follows:

a_1 = water contaminated as a result of 20 t alum being placed erroneously in contact tank
a_2 = water contaminated as a result of failure associated with lime dosing
a_3 = water contaminated as a result of something else
a_4 = water not contaminated
b_1 = many consumers complain of metallic/acidic taste

There is a real difficulty in establishing acceptable numerical values for the various probabilities. The following values are offered without justification but for the purpose of illustration:

Probabilities $p(a_1), p(a_2), p(a_3), p(a_4)$ in the ratio $10^{-6}:10^{-3}:10^{-3}:1$

(which does at least reflect the layman's notion that what actually happened was a 'chance in a million') with the conditional probabilities:

$$p(b_1|a_1) = 0.99$$

$$p(b_1|a_2) = 0.1$$

$$p(b_1|a_3) = 0.1$$
$$p(b_1|a_4) = 0.001$$

Application of Bayes' theorem to take into account the evidence of consumer complaints gives

$$p(a_1|b_1) = 0.00099/1.20099 \sim 1/1200$$

$$p(a_2|b_1) = 0.1/1.20099 \sim 1/12$$

$$p(a_3|b_1) = 0.1/1.20099 \sim 1/12$$

$$p(a_4|b_1) = 1/1.20099 \sim 10/12$$

and which are now in the approximate ratios of $10^{-3}:10^{-1}:10^{-1}:1$. Also of interest are the ratios of posterior to prior probabilities $p(a_i|b_1):p(a_i)$, which are roughly 1000, 10, 100, 1 for a_1 to a_4, respectively.

In absolute terms what turned out to be the true situation (a_1) is still highly unlikely, and it is not surprising that the operators focused on the possibility of a lime dosing failure (a_2) or 'something else' (a_1). Indeed, as Bayes' theorem shows, the most likely possibility (although less so than at the outset) is no water quality problem at all, but with b_1 being the result of a spate of spurious complaints.

If, in recognition of the slack procedures known to have been extant, the prior probability of the alum misplacement is set on a par with the other two causes (i.e. the fairly commonplace 'lime dosing failure' or the catch-all 'something else') such that probabilities $p(a_1)$, $p(a_2)$, $p(a_3)$, $p(a_4)$ are in the ratio $10^{-3}:10^{-3}:10^{-3}:1$, then:

$$p(a_1|b_1) = 0.99/2.19 \sim 10/22$$

$$p(a_2|b_1) = 0.1/2.19 \sim 1/22$$

$$p(a_3|b_1) = 0.1/2.19 \sim 1/22$$

$$p(a_4|b_1) = 1/2.19 \sim 10/22$$

and which are now in the ratio $1:10^{-1}:10^{-1}:1$, with the alum misplacement having a likelihood of about 50 per cent.

The ratios of posterior to prior probabilities $p(a_i|b_1):p(a_i)$ are now roughly 500, 50, 50, 0.5 for a_1 to a_4, respectively, once again with the chances of a_4 showing the most marked change.

As expected and as shown from this simple analysis, the improbable event *can* emerge from Bayes' theorem with sufficiently strong support so long as the event is not assigned such a comparatively low prior probability. Two questions emerge:

1. Are there other signals in the output of Bayes' theorem (such as the large ratios of posterior to prior probabilities for some propositions as noted above) which should, *taken together with the importance of the corresponding consequences*, have an alerting effect? If so, how could this be achieved without resulting in a warning system that was unnecessarily alarmist and over time ceased to be credible?
2. Is the improbable event (in this case the alum misplacement) really so improbable that its prior probability is equivalent to a chance in a million?

Considering this latter question, then, to be sure, if the number of well-known cases of alum misplacement in the United Kingdom over the past 50 years at all water treatment plants were to be compared to the total number of alum deliveries, then from a frequentist viewpoint, one in a million estimate might not seem unreasonable.

There is also something rather seductive about the assumption of common sense and the tendency for the context and semantics of the issues involved to distort apparently reasonable judgements. Consider the pair of statements and questions:

Statement 1. The same key fits the aluminium sulphate storage tank and a nearby disinfection contact tank at a water treatment plant. A delivery of 20 t of aluminium sulphate is ordered from the regular supplier. Although the driver making the delivery is unfamiliar with the plant, he is given instructions and directions to the aluminium sulphate storage tank by the regular delivery driver.
Question 1. What is the probability that the delivery driver misplaces the aluminium sulphate in the contact tank?
Statement 2. The same key fits tank X and nearby tank Y at site S. A delivery of chemical C is ordered from the regular supplier. A driver unfamiliar with the plant is given instructions and directions to tank X by the regular delivery driver. The driver is unaware that the same key fits both tanks.
Question 2. What is the probability that the delivery driver places chemical C in tank Y?

The first statement is much richer contextually, and it is important that this richness does not excessively precondition the probability assessment of the possible outcomes. In the Camelford case, part of the directions given to the relief driver were that the aluminium storage tank was 'on the left'. In fact, the layout of the Lowermoor treatment plant site is such that both tanks can be regarded as being 'on the left', depending on the direction from which they are approached. However, if the driver had known which tank was which, the fact that the key fitted both would have been immaterial. As it was, the driver did not know which tank was which and the fact that the key fitted a particular tank could have been taken as confirming the identification of the correct tank.

12.9 CLOSURE

The *primary* and more obvious and regular risks are those that in the developed world have been brought largely under control through the construction and operation of appropriate abstraction, treatment, distribution and disposal systems, and reinforced by legal requirements of quality and the requisite monitoring. Sadly, much of the developing world awaits such basic provisions.

Two broad categores of *secondary* risk can be distinguished, both of which require the establishment of suitable analytical and decision support tools:

1. Risks related to occasional and gross pollution incidents, which may arise from apparently improbable and unanticipated causes. Assessment of such risks requires a greater acceptance of an 'open world' view of uncertainty analysis and a more critical reappraisal of preconceived attitudes of confidence.
2. Risks that are associated with relatively low-level exposure to both known and as yet unspecified substances and micropollutants, whose effects are imprecisely known or suspected. The establishment of standards and the provision of appropriate levels of protection to exposed population groups requires the adoption of a principle of reasonableness.

REFERENCES

1. Bourne, P.: Improving the Quality of Life, *Water*, vol. 35, pp. 2–4, November 1980.
2. Barton, N. J.: *The Lost Rivers of London*, Historical Publications, Barnet, p. 101 (148 pp.), 1982.
3. Binnie, G. M.: *Early Victorian Water Engineers*, Thomas Telford, London, p. 172, 1981.
4. O'Hanlon, H. M.: Water and Drainage: 1840—EEC Directives, 1840-1990: One Hundred and Fifty Years of Civil Engineering at the University of Glasgow, University of Glasgow, 1990.
5. Goubert, J.-P.: *The Conquest of Water: The Advent of Health in the Industrial Age*, Polity Press, Oxford, 1989.
6. *HMSO Royal Commission on Sewage Disposal (Eighth Report)*, Wyman, 1912.
7. Water Research Centre: Emission Standards in Relation to Water Quality Objectives, technical report TR17, Water Research Centre, Medmenham, June 1976.
8. House of Commons: Pollution of Rivers and Estuaries, Environment Committee Third Report, Sessions 86–87, paras. 111–116, 13 May 1987.

9. Warn, A. E., and J. S. Brew: Mass Balance, *Water Res.*, vol 14, pp. 1427–1434, 1980.

10. Warn, A. E., and P. J. Matthews.: Calculation of the Compliance of Discharges with Emission Standards, *Water Sci. Technol., York*, vol. 16, pp. 183–196, 1984.

11. Ellis, J. C.: Multi-determinand Compliance, technical report ER579-M, Water Research Centre, Medmenham, 1983.

12. Ellis, J. C.: Determination of Pollutants in Effluents: Part A: Assessment of Alternative Definitions of Effluent Compliance, technical report TR230, Water Research Centre, Medmenham, 1985; Part B: Alternative Forms of Effluent Consents: Some Statistical Considerations, technical report TR235, Water Research Centre, Medmenham, 1986.

13. Kates, R. W.: *Risk Assessment of Environmental Hazard, Scope Report 8*, International Council of Scientific Unions, Wiley, Chichester, p. 112, 1978.

14. Waldegrave, W.: Sustaining the Environment in a Developing World, First NERC Annual Lecture, reprinted in *Civ. Engng. Systems*, vol. 4, no. 3, pp. 115–123, 1987.

15. Fowler, D.: In Your Water Tomorrow, *New Civil Engineer*, pp. 12–13, 26 July 1990 (Thomas Telford, London).

16. Henschler, D.: Environmental Protection and the Principle of Reasonableness, *Siemens Rev.*, vol. 4/89, pp. 38–41, 1989.

17. Fowler, D.: Civil Engineer Sacked over Acid Poisoning, *New Civil Engineer*, p. 10, 6 October 1988 (Thomas Telford, London).

18. Fowler, D.: Unravelling the Camelford Case, *New Civil Engineer*, pp. 19–20, 26 January 1989 (Thomas Telford, London).

THIRTEEN

BRIDGE SAFETY

N. SHIRAISHI and W. B. CRANSTON

13.1 INTRODUCTION

Bridges have been a challenge to engineers from the earliest days of civilization. Nineteenth century engineers in the United Kingdom often carried the title 'Bridgemaster', confirming the special expertise required as well as the importance of bridges in the infrastructure.

While the majority of modern bridges are short-span ones, giving rise to relatively simple design procedures, there is continuing pressure to use larger and larger spans. This has led to 'stretching' of established designs and the adoption of new concepts and new materials. Innovation has also been evident for short spans, with the introduction of standard prestressed beams and composite steel–concrete decks, requiring development of new design procedures.

With the emphasis on development and innovation, it is not surprising that many bridge failures have been due to factors that were not foreseen at the design stage. There is the additional factor, illustrated later in this chapter, that bridges are particularly vulnerable to natural hazards such as wind, earthquake and flood, as well as hazards arising from human errors.

No records exist of failures of the early attempts by engineers in Roman times, but we can be sure that the impressive multiple arch design used for the famous Pont du Gard aqueduct in France was based in part on experiences of failures with earlier arch structures. In more recent times, failures have been the subject of detailed enquiries as to the causes, which has led in turn to additional and extended design criteria being established.

For example, the Tay Bridge disaster led to detailed studies of wind loading, the Tacoma Narrows collapse led to aerodynamic studies and the failures during construction of both steel and concrete box girder bridges led to requirements for detailed structural analysis of construction stages.

This chapter continues with a short discussion of actual bridge failures, followed by sections on applications of probability analysis to bridges, on bridge assessment and testing, and on the concept of robustness as applied to bridges. An extensive section of case histories follows, and conclusions are drawn. The chapter concludes with thoughts on future developments.

13.2 BRIDGE FAILURES

Csagoly and Jaeger[1] reported in 1979 that around 250 bridges a year were estimated to collapse annually in the United States and Canada, and listed the causes as:

1. Overload due to live load (mainly older short span bridges being subjected to a single heavy truck)
2. Collision of heavy vehicles with the structure
3. Fatigue, with or without brittle fracture
4. Failure or excessive movement of substructures or
5. Deterioration of structural components or connections

Hadiopriono[2] studied a selection of major failures that occurred in the period 1977–81. Failures were of two types, the first being actual collapses and the second being the discovery or occurrence of 'distress' such that the structure was taken out of service. Of the 147 cases he studied, 57 were of bridges, and Table 13.1 gives the types. It was found that 53 per cent of failures were due to external causes and 21 per cent failed during the construction process. An analysis of these causes of failure is given in Table 13.2.

The external causes are dominated by collisions involving vehicles, trains or ships. Pedestrian bridges tend to fail through overloading when used as viewing stands for festivities.

Examples of failure during the construction process include inadequate welding practice for steel bridges and insufficient lateral bracing of falsework for concrete bridges.

Probabilistic Risk Analysis as Applied to Bridges

Probabilistic analysis has been used in preparing the 1983 Ontario Highway Bridge Code and the UK Code (BS 5400) for the Design of Bridges, with the levels of safety factors being calibrated to existing practice. Work is in progress on the US AASHTO Code, with the safety factors now being varied

Table 13.1 Bridge failure cases studied by Hadiopriono[2]

Type of bridge	Number of failure cases (1977–1981)
Steel truss	13
Steel plate girder	14
Steel box girder	2
Concrete girder	2
Concrete box girder	8
Cable suspension	3
Floating bridge	1
Tied arch/steel arch	4
Bascule span	2
Pedestrian	8
Total	57

Table 13.2 Bridge failures: frequent events and occurrences[2]

Frequent principal causes and events	Number of occurrences	Type of failed bridge	Remarks
External causes			
Vehicle/train impact	15	Steel truss, plate girder	Collapses occurred primarily in US and Europe
Ship impact	5	Steel truss	
Overload by people	5	Narrow pedestrian	Overloading during festivities
Others	5	Varies	
Construction deficiencies			
Inadequate welding procedures	6	Steel plate girder, tied arch	Cracks occurred in several Ohio River bridges
Falsework related problems (inadequate bracing and weak foundations)	2	Concrete box girder	Events led to partial collapses during bridge construction in US
Others	4		

depending on the type and span of bridge. All these codes are in limit state terms.

In the case of the Ontario Code, both the patterns of loading and the safety factors were based on extensive surveys of actual truck loadings. More recent work by Jaeger and Bakht[3] assumes that for a given truck size there is a maximum observed load at about 3.5 standard deviations above the mean. Using the Poisson probability distribution method they calculated reduction factors for the design of short-span (up to 20 m) bridges with more than one lane loaded. The multipresence factors that emerged were found to be slightly more advantageous than those then specified in the 1983 Ontario Code. For intermediate-span (20–125 m) bridges strict probability calculations would allow even larger reductions, which were rejected because of the possibility of critical non-random groupings of loaded trucks. Such groupings can occur at certain times of day on bridges close to industrial plants and on bridges close to large construction sites.

The concept of a maximum observed load is, at first sight, perhaps rather difficult to accept. It is likely to be more acceptable in the future since the presence of in-truck load sensors (as used in some delivery vehicles in the United Kingdom) as well as police monitored automatic weigh-in-motion check-points are likely to become universal in developed countries. However, there will still be a possibility of overloading of single rear axle trucks used for short journeys.

For long-span bridges (greater, say, than 125 m) it has been usual to take a considerable reduction of load, assuming that loaded trucks would be very unlikely to cover the whole bridge. However, studies of traffic on the Severn suspension bridge in England showed that in the period 3 a.m. to 6 a.m., traffic in the eastbound lanes could be almost exclusively loaded trucks coming from docks in Wales. In the event of an accident blocking the eastbound lanes, the bridge was found to be unsafe, and strengthening measures have been undertaken. An alternative would have been to install emergency control measures to restrict entry on to the bridge, as in the next example.

A historic suspension bridge over the River Tweed in Scotland forms a vital pedestrian link between the village of Gattonside and the town of Melrose. Following a structural appraisal, users are at the moment (1991) advised by notice to proceed such that not more than six individuals are present on the bridge at one time. On days when rugby football championships are held in Melrose, a police patrol ensures that this limit is observed.

In conclusion it seems that imposed loading by traffic on bridges is now well understood, and can be modelled statistically. There is a growing tendency for an upper cut-off loading value through law enforcement.

Bridge Assessment and Testing

Bridges are normally subject to regular inspection, which may lead on to an appraisal and to the bridge being posted for a lower load than normal. The Ministry of Transportation in Ontario has conducted detailed appraisals by instrumenting bridges to measure strains and deflections and then studying the effects of applying specially loaded trucks. In sensitive cases the trucks are driven on to the bridge using remote control. These appraisals[4] have often led to the raising of the posted load, which had been previously assessed by calculation or judgement alone.

A key factor in assessment is establishing the material strengths, which in the case of older bridges is made more difficult by the lack of any records of any testing during construction. To obtain reliable data a large number of samples needs to be taken. Bartlett and Sexsmith[5] show how the use of prior judgement as to the likely specified material strengths in conjunction with Bayesian statistics can dramatically reduce the number of concrete cores or samples of rebar that need to be taken from a given structure. The level of reliability of prediction of material strength aimed at is the same as that implied in the sampling regimes specified in current design codes. The bridge appraisal then proceeds by ensuring that the margins of strength present are greater than or equal to that demanded by the safety factors of the current code.

Novak, Neaman and Ting[6] show how reliability studies can be extended to include the effects of deterioration. In a theoretical example they show that a conventional analysis of bridge response (essentially as in the previous paragraph) could lead to immediate posting or even closure of a bridge, while a full analysis would show the probability of collapse to be acceptable. The bridge can thus remain open, and remedial action to halt deterioration undertaken at a reasonable pace and cost.

Robustness

The word 'robust' is defined in *The Concise Oxford Dictionary* as meaning 'strong and sturdy'. In construction it has a special meaning perhaps best defined in the statement in the UK Code BS 8110 for Concrete Structures that 'the structure should not be unreasonably susceptible to the effects of accidents'.

Two accepted methods are available to do this. The first is to effectively isolate sections of structure from one another by making them statically determinate—collapse is then limited to the portion suffering immediate damage. The second is to provide an alternative path for loading should any individual structural component be rendered ineffective through damage. Csagoly and Jaeger[1] argue strongly for this concept to be applied to bridges. Their argument is based on a study of actual failures of bridges in North America where collisions and other external hazards caused complete failure of single components in individual bridges. They found that, in many cases, other secondary elements were found to take over and prevent total collapse, avoiding loss of life and allowing swift repair with minimum economic loss to the bridge users.

Their recommendation was that back-up or alternative path systems should be made mandatory, arguing that the increased costs in design and construction would be a small fraction of the savings that would result from the large reduction on actual collapses. This recommendation is included in the 1983 Ontario Bridge Code.

While the economic case for this recommendation is clearly and convincingly argued from a probabilistic viewpoint, it is recognized that design personnel with a deep understanding of structural behaviour are needed to design and analyse the back-up structure.

Planning for Bridge Safety

In order to construct any sort of bridge, it is necessary to evaluate economic viability, social serviceability and technical reliability. In 1975 Bylington investigated various measures to be taken into account for the planning of expressway construction.[7] He summarized these factors as follows:

1. Convenience of transportation—reduction of travelling time, reduction of psychological stress through traffic congestion, release from traffic signals
2. Safety transportation—decrease of traffic accidents
3. Environmental serviceability—decrease of traffic noise and of air pollution
4. Regional benefit—increase of employment, tax and fare, mobilization, regional development
5. Economics—construction and maintenance costs

Ideally all of these factors should be taken into account when assessing the reliability required for a given bridge. It could be low for a bridge serving a small community but must be correspondingly higher for a bridge carrying a busy urban freeway. For a busy route where closure would involve large detours and heavy traffic congestion, an even higher reliability is required.

13.3 FAILURE CASE HISTORIES

During Construction

The differences between safety problems of completed structures and structures under construction can be characterized as follows:

1. At the construction stage, the structural form may vary through time and the structural resistance may not be easy to characterize.
2. In most bridge design codes, some design loads for bridges under construction are specified, but in practice it is possible for the structure to be overloaded.

3. While standard methods of construction are usually available for a given type of bridge, modifications are nearly always necessary to meet site-specific conditions, which may in turn not be fully foreseen at the start of the construction contract.

As an illustration of a construction problem in failure we will consider the Ohkumo Bridge. On 16 January 1976, the weather was fine in the northern part of Kyoto in Japan even though there was 5 cm of snow from the day before. The seventh span of the bridge was a simply supported girder of integrated concrete slab and two steel plate girders stiffened by a lateral truss at the lower part of the plate girders. According to the construction schedule, pouring of the concrete for the deck started at 11 a.m. When approximately 30 m^3 of concrete had been poured, a small strip-like fall of 15 cm was found. An engineer looked over the fall, examined the supporting system as well as the falsework and found no deficiencies. Suddenly the bridge deflected horizontally and fell down into the Yura River with an explosion. There were two fatalities and six injuries. An investigating committee found that the failure was a typical one of lateral buckling of the girder due to the loading of the wet concrete. It was noted that at this construction stage the cross-section of the bridge was a so-called U-letter shape, consisting of two steel plate girders and lateral truss so that the shear centre of the section was located at a far lower position than the lowest part of the section. At the design stage, no attention had been paid to the location of the shear centre so that no examination of the overall structural instability and lateral buckling had been made. Even though failure had occurred during the construction stage, the main cause of failure was due to a lack of knowledge of a particular structural characteristic, namely the location of the shear centre of a channel section. This should have been considered at the design stage.

Four box girder bridges collapsed during construction in a period of two years from 1969 to 1971. They were the Fourth Danube Bridge, Vienna, in November 1969, the Milford Haven Bridge, UK, in June 1970, the West Gate Bridge, Melbourne, Australia, in October 1970 and the Koblenz Bridge, Germany, in November 1971.

The case of the West Gate Bridge is in many ways a typical example. It was a big challenge since it was to be an eight-lane bridge of steel and concrete, the biggest in Australia—two and a half times as long as Sydney Harbour Bridge—and the new gateway to Melbourne. The project began in April 1968. The Lower Yarra Crossing Authority had secured a well-qualified group of designers (including Freeman Fox and Partners, one of the UK's most experienced and respected international consultants) and contractors (World Services Constructions Pty Ltd, a Netherlands-based company of world reputation, for the steelwork, and John Holland, a leading Australian company, for the concrete). At first, morale among engineers and workers on site was high but because of the company's poor on-site supervision, enthusiasm waned and World Services was 7 months behind schedule by the end of 1969. In order to speed up the work, the contractor agreed to turn the major part of the steel contract to John Holland. However, friction developed between Holland and Freeman Fox: vital questions referred to London were answered slowly if at all. The news of the collapse at Milford Haven on 2 June 1970 had a calamitous impact on the already sliding morale of the Melbourne bridge builders.

The most critical work on the West Gate Bridge turned out to be the erection of the span between Piers 10 and 11. In order to make its nearly 400 feet length more manageable during erection it was decided to assemble the two separate half box longitudinal sections on the ground. These two spans would then be lifted to the tops of piers 10 and 11 and be bolted together side by side to form the support for the roadway. This type of assembly was uncommon but with sufficient care it was thought that the two spans would fit together. However, when the two sections of 10–11 span were brought together, high above the riverbank in late August, at mid span the northern half was 4.5 inches higher than the southern span. The two spans could have been lowered to the ground for correct reassembly, but a quicker solution was sought. Unused concrete blocks each weighing about eight tons, were placed at the middle of the northern span to bring it down the necessary few inches. On 6 September it was noticed that a major buckle developed at the seam between the fourth and fifth of the eight boxes on the northern span. The method chosen to correct the buckle was to undo certain bolts between boxes 4 and 5, which would allow the steel to settle into proper alignment, and then rebolt. On 15 October 1970 workmen began loosening the bolts. After 37 bolts had been undone, the operation appeared to be having some success—the bulge had been flattened from 4.5 inches to $1\frac{1}{8}$ inches. Then all at once the buckle spread. At the last moment an attempt to save the bridge was made but with a thunderous rumble the span collapsed onto the bank. Unfortunately there were site huts immediately beneath the span onto which the steelwork fell and 35 of the 68 men on the site died.

Of all those involved in the project, the Royal Commission set up to investigate the accident found only the various suppliers of building materials to be blameless. The Commissioners said: 'In greater or lesser degree, the Authority itself, the designers (to which the greater part of the blame must be attributed), the contractors, even the labour engaged on the work, must all take some part of the blame.'[8]

An earlier example (1958) is the Second Vancouver Narrows Bridge, where the failure occurred because of inadequate bracing to a grillage of steel I beams. It is possible that this failure would have been averted if the contractors had been aware of a similar failure during the construction of the Frankenthal Bridge over the Rhine in 1940, details of which were not published until 1972.[9]

There have been many reports of collapses of bridges and viaducts during the pouring of the concrete for the deck structure. For example, in 1970, a 125-foot simply supported concrete span in Los Angeles collapsed while concrete was poured. In 1972 about 150 feet of highway bridge collapsed in California killing six workers and injuring six others. Two men were killed and six injured in the collapse of the Ohkumo-bashi (Ohkumo Bridge) in 1976 in Kyoto, Japan. Similar accidents occurred in Indiana in 1982 (12 killed, 17 injured), Elwood, Kansas, in 1982 (1 killed, 8 injured) and in 1989 falsework collapsed under a 100-foot overpass crossing the Baltimore–Washington Parkway.

Perhaps the key factor in construction collapses is that design and construction are usually carried out by different offices (even in the same organization). The construction engineer, while being skilled in many wider aspects such as project management, will often not appreciate the finer detail of structural response. This suggestion is borne out by the conclusion by Hadiopriono[2] that lack of bracing to falsework is a significant contributor to failures in construction. Behaviour in buckling can be difficult enough for skilled structural engineers!

Collisions

Hadiopriono[2] identified collisions as being a major contributor to bridge collapses. This is inevitable when one considers that a large proportion of bridges are over roads, railways or navigable waterways.

Many collisions occur because the vehicle passing under the bridge is carrying a load that extends above the legal height limits, although such incidents generally only cause damage. Railway collisions usually occur when trains are derailed, although a case is on record where the walls of wagons overloaded by sodden sugar-beet deformed outwards to such an extent that a steel trestle supporting an overbridge was torn away.

Ship collisions with bridges over waterways have become an important issue in modern times. A paper by Fransen[10] gives an extensive survey of bridges that have collapsed due to such collisions. Over half of these occurred due to human error by the ship's master or pilot. Around a quarter occurred because of steering failure and the remainder due to ships breaking loose from moorings during storms. Such external hazards cannot be prevented and should be considered in design.

An important case was that of the 278-m steel arch Tjorn Bridge near Gothenberg in Sweden built in about 1960. The arch consisted of two 3.8-m circular tubes with 14 to 22-mm plate thickness. The navigation channel under the arch had a height of 41 m on 50 m width. On 18 January 1980 at 1:30 a.m. in bad weather the arch was struck by a 27 000 dwt ship which had lost navigation control on account of ice formation on the ship hull. The bridge collapsed totally. Eight people lost their lives through driving their cars over the edges of the remaining viaducts, before the traffic could be stopped. The arch fell partly on the ship without causing any injuries. The new bridge was built at the same place, but as a cable-stayed steel box beam of 366-mm span in November 1981. In order to make sure that the new bridge could not be hit by a ship the towers were situated on rocks about 25 m inland. There is no doubt that the original steel arch solution was highly efficient and economical against the design criteria adopted. One should not be too hasty to judge the designer who failed to recognize the collision danger. The bridge could easily have gone on to survive for a further 50 years without mishap.

A contrasting example to the Tjorn Bridge is the Chesapeake Bay Bridge, Virginia, USA. This is a three-mile-long concrete trestle, with prefabricated 75-ft spans on pile bents. During the five-year period from 1967 to 1972, there were three occasions when ships out of control were thrown repeatedly against the bridge, severely damaging several spans. In this case there seems no alternative but to accept occasional damage. It would be interesting to know whether the designers of this bridge did consider ship impact. In any event the use of simply supported spans precluded any possibility of progressive collapse.

A further instructive example is the Tasman Bridge built in 1964 over the Derwent River, Tasmania, Australia. It is a 1025-m long viaduct with approach spans of 40 m and a 94-m navigation span. Protective fendering was provided to the piers supporting the navigation span, although it was recognized that this would only deal with a glancing collision. The approach spans were designed to be continuous, with specific weak links installed at supports to avoid a progressive 'domino'-type collapse should a ship accidentally collide with the 40 m-high support piers. The yield stress of the steel over the supports was held by specification to a close tolerance, ensuring that it was significantly weaker than the adjacent reinforcement to which it was lapped. In 1975 a ship out of control brought down two approach span piers. Only three spans fell, leaving the remaining structure undamaged. The foresight and skill of the designers were confirmed.

Csagoly and Jaeger[1] refer to a case of collapse of a through-truss bridge on the eastern part of the United States caused by collision of a commercial vehicle with the end-diagonal member. Such members are particularly likely to be hit, and the provision of an adequate back-up system is difficult.

Effects of Scour

The Toukaido line of the Japan National Railway crosses over the Fuji River on three bridges. The upstream bridge, constructed in 1956, was used as the route to Tokyo and was a three-span continuous half-through bridge supported by a pneumatic caisson. The middle bridge, constructed in 1910, was on the route to Osaka and was a truss bridge with a well foundation.

The third bridge, the downstream bridge, was constructed in 1889 and was no longer used. In August 1982, typhoon number 10 attacked the mainland of Japan with extraordinarily heavy rain. In the resulting floods the foundations of the middle and downstream bridges were scoured locally. One of the foundations and two truss girders collapsed. The causes, other than the very heavy rain, were thought to be the construction of a dam upstream of the Fuji River as well as the lowering of the river bottom by excavation for river gravel.

In April 1987 a bridge located west of Amsterdam, New York, on Interstate 90, crossing the Schoharie River, suddenly collapsed after heavy rain. Approximately 300 feet of the 540-foot bridge was destroyed and at least three cars and one truck disappeared into 25 m deep waters. Eye-witnesses reported that around 10:45 a.m. the central part of the bridge collapsed with an exploding sound. One and a half hours later two other spans with two of the four remaining piers collapsed. The collapse was thought to be due to heavy rain resulting in an unexpected amount of water together with the action of floating debris.

Two railway bridges have recently failed in the United Kingdom following heavy river floods, one on the main line just north of Inverness and the other in Wales. As a result, a programme of inspection has been set up for substructures, now possible at reasonable cost because of improvements in diving techniques. In addition in some cases scour sensors are being installed at some depth below the normal river bed level, to give early warning and allow bridges to be closed to traffic.

Fatigue and Corrosion

A few decades ago it was believed that it was possible to design and to construct so-called maintenance-free bridges. As a result concrete bridges were frequently believed to be much safer and more economical than steel bridges. However, it has been realized that repeated live loading, accompanying impact effects, as well as rusting and corrosion can cause deterioration of bridge structures both locally and totally. In order to maintain the required functioning of a bridge, inspection and feasible maintenance treatments are required.

Usually the level of deterioration necessary to seriously affect the load capacity of the bridge is visually evident to a simple inspection. However, this is not always the case, as the following four examples show.

In December 1974 a truck suddenly fell into a collapsed hole on the West Side Highway crossing the Hudson River. This route had been used by approximately 20000 automobiles per day until this collapse. Later inspection revealed that all reinforced steel deck plates for almost 10 miles of the route had rusted, resulting in deteriorated beams and road deck. No previous inspection had been carried out so that no repairs whatsoever had been done. Blocked drains together with the use of salt in winter are thought to have been the main technical causes of this failure.

The Ynys-y-Gwas Bridge in Wales was one of the first UK prestressed bridges, built in 1953. Spanning a modest 60 feet and carrying two traffic lanes, the design was nonetheless quite sophisticated, consisting of I beams formed of nine segments stressed together both longitudinally and transversely. The bridge was subject to regular inspection and to a particularly close examination in 1981 when an abnormal load was permitted to pass over it. In particular there were no warning signs such as rust staining, cracking or deflexion of the beams. At 7 a.m. on 4 December 1985, a car drove on to the bridge deck, which had been transformed into a deep V shape, having previously collapsed. The driver was fortunate not to suffer injury, although his car was severely damaged. Investigation revealed that the stressing tendons were corroded, in some cases such that over 50 per cent of the cross-section had been lost, by the penetration of road salts down the joints between segments and beams. Further studies of elements of this bridge by Woodward and Wilson[11] have concluded that localized corrosion of tendons, and even fracture of some tendons, probably cannot be determined by deformation monitoring. An inspection system capable of detecting localized corrosion in tendons within mass concrete is urgently required.

A further instructive example of bridge failure through deterioration of material is the case of the Point Pleasant Bridge collapse.[12] This occurred on 15 December 1967 when the bridge in West Virginia, USA, collapsed into the Ohio River, without warning, resulting in the loss of 46 lives. The Point Pleasant Bridge, known locally as the Silver Bridge, was built in 1929 and carried US Route 35 across the Ohio River. It was an eyebar chain suspension bridge of unusual design, with chains functioning as the upper chord of the stiffening truss over portions of the length. Three task forces were established and one of them, the National Transportation Safety Board (NTSB), was newly created to determine the probable cause of failure.

The initial investigations concluded that the main cause of failure was the joint action of stress corrosion and corrosion fatigue which produced a crack in the head of an eyebar. The evidence supporting stress corrosion as the mechanism of crack growth was as follows:

1. A continuous high-stress intensity existed at the edge of the pin-hole at levels equal to or above the yield strength of the material.
2. The material near the surface of the holes showed evidence of having been 'cold worked', which increased its susceptibility to corrosion cracking.
3. An indicated range of nominal live load stress was small, probably about $15\,000\,\text{lb/in}^2$, although it may have been as high as $34\,000\,\text{lb/in}^2$ when stress concentration factors are taken into account.

The failure was triggered by the failure of a single eyebar. This threw all the load on to the remaining bar which was unable to resist it. Finally the stiffening truss, which might in a shorter span bridge have been able to sustain the load, gave way.

Csagoly and Jaeger[1] point out that if, say, 12 eyebars had been used, as is typical in much older European bridges of this type, there would have been no appreciable danger of collapse following an eyebar failure. They further point out that the nature of the cracking which almost certainly led to the collapse was such that it was unlikely to be discovered during inspection.

The Mianus River Bridge of the state road 95 of Connecticut, USA, collapsed suddenly at about 1 : 30 a.m. on 28 June 1983. Four cars on the bridge fell 21 m down into the Mianus River, resulting in the loss of four lives and three injuries. The bridge was constructed 25 years before for a service life of 50 years. An inspection was performed in September 1982 and the bridge had been evaluated using a scale of 1 (low) to 10 (high) with the following results: bridgedeck 3, superstructure 6, substructure 5, pin and hangers 6. The collapse was probably caused by failure of some of the pins from which the main girders were suspended. Some strange noises had been reported by local inhabitants before the disaster.

A final example from many case histories that are available is drawn from a review by Virlogeux[13] of the development of externally prestressed concrete bridges. He describes the failures of corrosion protection in early (1930 to 1955) German and French examples of such bridges. Despite these experiences bridges built in England and Belgium in the 1960s and 1970s still experienced corrosion problems. Part of the reason here is the lack of communication or experience across national boundaries.

The above examples indicate that a reserve of strength should be present in all bridges against material deterioration, even where regular inspection is assured. An alternative is for all key elements of bridges to be accessible for inspection. A precedent here is the provision in prestressed pressure vessels for nuclear containment for prestressing cables to be removed one by one for inspection.

Extreme Winds

Unloaded high-sided vehicles blow over in high winds, and can therefore lead to hanger or truss member fracture. For this reason suspension bridges in particular are normally closed to traffic when winds exceed a certain speed. Such bridges should, however, still be designed to survive should single hangers or members be destroyed.

In December 1986 a train was blown off an elevated bridge (the Amarube Bridge in Hyogo, Japan) of 40 m high and six lives were lost. Warning signals at both ends of the bridge to stop the train should have been switched on under the prevailing conditions (later it was found that the wind speed was nearly 30 m/s). The signal had not been switched on.

It is thought by many that the Tay bridge disaster was similarly caused by the passenger train on the bridge at the time being blown over.

Wind Oscillations

In 1939 and 1940 two most beautiful and graceful bridges were completed; the Bronx–Whitestone Bridge designed by Ammann and the Tacoma Narrows Bridge designed by Moisseiff. The first of these had a ratio of span to width of 2300 : 74 and the second 2800 : 39. Only a small amount of traffic was anticipated at first on the Tacoma Narrows Bridge; therefore a wide roadway was not required. Moreover economy was required since the tolls were not expected to produce much income. In both bridges the deck was stiffened by plate girders instead of trusses, the depths being only 11 and 8 feet, respectively. Thus they were less resistant to wind for two reasons. Firstly, they were more slender than any previous long span bridge and, secondly, the force on them was proportionately greater because the area presented by the solid plate girders in the deck was larger than that of the usual latticed stiffening trusses. The point must be stressed that both bridges had been most efficiently designed according to the usual exacting specifications. They appeared amply sufficient to withstand all of the customary forces and loads including the usual allowance for aerostatic forces on the roadway.

The Tacoma Narrows Bridge, which was the third longest span in the world in those days, was opened to traffic on 1 July 1940. Owing to its behaviour in wind it was promptly nicknamed 'Galloping Gertie'. Not only did the deck sway sideways but appreciable vertical waves appeared and the roadway oscillated up and down alarmingly under the action of quite moderate winds. Drivers of cars reported that, as they crossed the bridge, vehicles ahead of them completely disappeared from view and then reappeared, several times, owing to the undulations of the roadway. Before it was opened, hydraulic buffers were installed between the ends of the deck and the towers. An attempt was made, using diagonal ties, to reduce movements between the deck and the cables at mid-span. Three months later a further attempt was made to dampen out the oscillations of the main span by tying down the side spans to concrete blocks on the ground using cables. However, it was all to no avail. On 7 November, only four months after the bridge was completed, it collapsed under the action of a wind of only 42 mi/h (19 m/s). Bridges are usually designed to withstand gales of 120 mi/h (54 m/s). As the wind pressure varies according to the square of its velocity the wind force would have been only about one-ninth of the design pressure.

The storm which had been blowing up overnight reached this velocity by nine o'clock in the morning. By that time the deck of the bridge was heaving up and down in waves 10 m high and twisting around through an angle of nearly 45° to either side. A car trapped on the road was sliding about under movements of the bridge and was uncontrollable. Then suddenly just before 11 o'clock a number of the hangers connecting the deck to the cables snapped in succession and flew high into the air and a thousand feet of the deck crashed into the water. The violent twisting motion ceased and the bridge appeared to steady itself but quickly the movements were renewed and transmitted to the side spans; at once nearly the whole of the remainder of the deck of the main span collapsed; the side spans then sank down, slowly lost their motion and the wreck of the bridge became practically still.

There were similarities between the Tacoma Narrows Bridge and other bridges that had behaved in a similar fashion but no previous failures had been observed. Thus the collapse of the Tacoma Narrows Bridge after fifty years of immunity from failures of this kind came as a severe shock to the whole of the engineering profession. An immense amount of work has since been done testing models of bridges in wind tunnels and analysing the effects of wind on various shapes of structures.

The Washington Toll Bridge Authority started the reconstruction of the Tacoma Narrows Bridge in 1949. The original piers and approaches and parts of the anchorages were retained. The width of the bridge was increased from 39 to 60 feet and stiffening trusses 33 feet deep now carry four lanes of traffic. The trusses are four times as deep as the previous girders and have 37 times the stiffness. Moreover, the bridge is now considerably heavier and a number of slots have been left in the roadway between the traffic lanes to reduce the effect of wind. It opened to traffic in October 1950.

Even the mighty Golden Gate Bridge has not been completely immune from wind effects. In 1938 and again in 1941 under a wind velocity of 62 mi/h (29 m/s) a succession of waves or ripples 2 feet high was observed to run along the deck. On both of these occasions, however, the wind was from an unusual quarter and blowing at 45° to the axis of the bridge. Motion recording instruments were installed and in December 1951 during a 4-hour gale that reached a velocity of 69 mi/h (32 m/s), vertical movements up to 130 inches (3.3 m) were measured in the deck, which was swinging 12 feet (3.6 m) sideways in either direction. Since then 4700 tonnes of lateral bracing have been incorporated from end to end beneath the deck to give it more rigidity.

Two long-span cantilever truss bridges opened to traffic in the 1970s. One is the Chester Bridgeport of 501 m centre span at New Jersey Delaware River, USA, and the other is the Minato Bridge of 510 m centre span in Osaka, Japan. Both bridges had almost the same size of span length and same structure of cantilever truss. The difference is in the geometrical shape of the tensile members. The H-lettered tensile members of the Chester Bridgeport were the same aerodynamical shape as the stiffening girder of the Tacoma Narrows Bridge. They were therefore unstable with vortex-induced oscillations and cracks formed. No damage nor deterioration for the tensile members of the Minato Bridge has been found since the sections are closed and rectangular and hence so much more stable.[14]

Earthquakes

On 16 June 1964 the so-called Niigata earthquake occurred and caused severe damage to public and private structures in the city of Niigata in Japan. The earthquake (magnitude 7.5 on the Richter scale) had an epicentre located approximately 55 km from the city in a north-easterly direction and at a depth of about 40 km. A damage survey of 86 bridges (excluding timber bridges) was carried out in the north-west part of the mainland of Japan. No damage was found for 35 out of the 86 bridges and the remaining were damaged as follows: superstructure (expansion joints, main girders, etc.) 34.2 per cent; substructures (bearings, piers, etc.) 39.7 per cent; connections 26.1 per cent.

There were three bridges crossing the Shinano River in the city of Niigata, namely the Mandai Bridge, the Showa Bridge and the Yachiyo Bridge. The Mandai Bridge, built in 1929, was the oldest of these three to suffer from the earthquake and had not been designed seismically. It consisted of six spans of reinforced concrete arches. The left side pier settled down by 2.2 m and also moved horizontally. Many cracks appeared on the lower surfaces of the arches. However, the bridge was load tested and after the provision of some temporary supports the bridge was able to be used again.

Both the Yachiyo Bridge and the Showa Bridge were designed against earthquake. The Showa Bridge was built in 1964 and consisted of twelve spans of simply supported composite girders whilst the Yachiyo Bridge had ten similar spans. Five of the spans of the Showa Bridge fell down onto the river bed. The main reason for the failure was that the natural frequencies of the piers were different. This had the effect that there were excessive relative displacements between the piers and the girders and consequently the girders slipped off their bearings.

Until the Niigata earthquake, simple supports for multispan girder bridges were thought to perform satisfactorily in earthquakes. The reasoning was that no additional bending moments could be induced by, for example, vertical differential settlement of the piers. However, it is now realized that bridges are vulnerable to relative longitudinal displacements and so it is important that some connection between adjacent girders is provided to prevent the girders slipping off the piers.

Similar kinds of structural damage to bridges due to earthquakes were observed in the United States from the San Fernando earthquake of 1971. The California Department of Transportation (Caltrans) revised its design criteria and ordered modifications to existing structures. This entailed installing restraining tendons on existing bridges and viaducts so that an earthquake could not bring down a span. The powerful earthquake that struck in Northern California in November 1980 caused two spans of a large viaduct to drop and slightly damaged an adjacent structure. The 406-foot curved structures consisted of four simple spans of about equal length with a hinge over each bend. The superstructures consisted of multiple box girders with an integral deck of conventional reinforced concrete cast in place on falsework. It was thought that the collapse occurred simply because the movement was too large. The Salmon Creek fault runs right through the valley and the bridge was skewed right across the fault. The tendons required by Caltrans had not been installed.

On 26 May 1983, a powerful earthquake (7.7 on the Richter scale) struck in the northern part of the mainland of Japan. A number of ports suffered, piers collapsed and berths were knocked out; 62 persons were killed, 109 injured and 40 lost. The severe damage was due mainly to Tsunami (high tides) and liquefaction of the sand layer. In spite of such severe damage to public facilities, buildings and water and gas supply systems, little damage was caused to the bridge structures.

On 17 October 1989 a powerful earthquake (6.9 on the Richter scale) struck the San Francisco Bay area. Since 1971, construction codes had been tightened, buildings had been reinforced and emergency back-up water supplies and communication systems had been practised. In communities throughout the state, fire and police departments regularly practised earthquake evacuation and rescue responses and neighbourhood self-help groups had been organized. Nevertheless two major catastrophes occurred. A stretch of the Interstate 880 in Oakland collapsed and a 50-foot span of the Oakland Bay Bridge fell. I-880, known as the Nimitz Freeway, collapsed when dozens of its concrete vertical support columns shattered during the violent shaking of the earthquake. Steel reinforcing bars inside the columns snapped like dry sphaghetti under the weight of the four-lane upper highway. Some construction experts expressed the view that the steel bars were not sufficient to withstand a powerful earthquake.

There were reports that state officials had long known that the freeway, completed in 1957, was dangerously weak but had moved slowly to mount a major renovation programme. Governor George Deukmejian said, in calling for a state investigation, that a 1982 study had concluded that I-880 needed major reinforcement to prevent its collapse in a strong earthquake. Experts now say that simply wrapping the columns in steel sheathing—a common method used to shore up older bridges and highways—might have substantially reduced the damage.

There are suspicions that some initial reinforcement work, done in the 1970s, may have contributed to the collapse. In an attempt to strengthen the roadway, steel cables were used to connect the deck slabs. However, as sections of the highway began to collapse these cables may have produced a domino effect, pulling down one section after another.

In addition to the structural flaws in the highway, the condition of the ground on which it stood may have contributed to the collapse. Like the buildings that toppled in San Francisco's Marina District, parts of the freeway are built on landfill in an area that was once under the Bay. Under the enormous forces exerted by earthquakes, such landfill typically liquefies below its surface, turning into slush as the water is squeezed out. Because this quivering mixture amplifies the shaking motion of an earthquake, structures built on landfill are subjected to far more complex and powerful twisting and shaking than those that stand on bedrock.

Design flaws also seem to have contributed to the fall of part of the Bay Bridge, which consists of two differently engineered sections. Between San Francisco and Yerba Buena Island, the Bay Bridge is, like the Golden Gate Bridge, a suspension span built to withstand winds of 100 mi/h by swinging from side to side. Between the island and Oakland is the section that failed. It is of far less flexible, cantilevered design in which the roadway rests on vertical steel support towers. During the tremor, one such tower swayed, snapping off the 2-in bolts that attached it to the upper roadway and allowing a 50-foot section to crash down to the lower level.

Conclusions from Case Histories

The litany of failures presented in this chapter should not depress the reader into thinking that bridges are in some sense inherently unsafe. Bridges very often form links between communities and have very great economic and cultural importance. That they are so important is an indication of the safety and reliability that the general public has come to expect and is a great tribute to the engineers who have designed, built and maintained them.

In several countries, probabilistic risk analysis (PRA) is now being used to calibrate codes of practice and choose the partial factors adopted for limit state design. Codes and specifications give useful guidelines and set minimum standards. However, successful design requires attention also to many other factors which are more difficult to identify. Clearly it is possible to gain insights into the nature of these other factors from past failure and that is why a number of case histories have been presented in this chapter.

For example, the case of the Tjorn Bridge illustrated the importance of taking planning decisions on the basis of an appropriate amount of information. Obtaining information costs money and is often therefore skimped to save on direct costs. Decisions are then made on inadequate information and sometimes this leads to unfortunate consequences.

The Ohkumo Bridge failure, where the position of the shear centre was not considered properly, illustrates the need to understand the behaviour of a structure correctly. It emphasizes the importance of conceptual modelling in design which is the basis on which all probabilistic risk analysis depends and without which PRA is useless. Of course in most cases the engineer is reasonably expected to develop a good conceptual model within the current state of the technology. In other cases the situation might be more problematic and at the fringes of the technical understanding of the day.

The oscillations of the tensile members of the Chester Bridge and the resulting cracking was an example of the latter category.

Many bridge failures occur during construction since the structure is often at its most vulnerable during that period. The structural form of the bridge varies almost daily, the construction loads are difficult to control and the possibility for human error is always present. Some of the most famous failures have occurred at this stage; for example the complex story of the West Gate Bridge was described briefly.

The failure of the Point Pleasant Bridge is probably the best example of the need for alternative load paths to be available in cases where failure can be sudden and unexpected. The successful strengthening of the Golden Gate Bridge after some unacceptable oscillations occurred shows the way forward. However, even in an advanced society such as that of Southern California, it is difficult to overcome all possibilities for failure. The San Francisco earthquake of 1989, with the failure of the I-880 freeway, demonstrated to the world that recommendations made in 1957 had not been implemented. If they had, then lives might have been saved and extensive damage might not have occurred.

Finally it should be recognized that engineering is a human endeavour and is therefore always susceptible to error.

13.4 FUTURE DEVELOPMENTS

A number of key points are briefly identified below.

Control of Traffic Loads

This will become commonplace in developed countries, and will enable the design of new bridges to be further refined, and the capacities of existing bridges to be upgraded in many cases. More conservative approaches will probably need to be retained in the developing countries.

Robustness—Alternative Load Paths

The new American AASHTO Code is set to include alternative load path requirements as currently included in the Ontario Code. All national bridge codes should include similar provisions (and, it can be argued, so should all structural codes).

Robustness under Collision

It is now possible to model accurately the impact behaviour of vehicle bodies involved in collisions. This work should be extended to include bridge structure/vehicle interaction, in order that the effects of collisions can be accurately assessed and proper provision made for alternative load paths.

Recent work on the behaviour of loaded vehicles in collision with crash barriers shows that the actual loads on the vehicles can be shed in sideways impacts. Further studies of the potential effects of this on bridges should be made.

Design/Construction Interaction

The traditional separation of the design and construction functions is no longer appropriate (except perhaps for short-span bridges of a standard type). This must be tackled on two fronts. Firstly, it is essential that, from the earliest possible stages, engineers should receive education and training and then a minimum of actual experience in both design and construction. This demand for increased width of experience means some reduction in depth. Thus the second line of attack is that there must be education, training and experience in interpersonal skills and teamwork.

Availability of Information

A number of cases have been detailed above where collapses or serious deterioration has occurred because designers were unaware of well-documented experiences in other countries. Extensive databases have been developed and are being improved and updated in the legal, medical and chemical knowledge fields. American databases are now available in the bridge and structural areas, and it is to be hoped that it will not be long before the extensive work carried out in European countries, both East and West, as well as in Russia, China and Japan can be included with multilingual keyword lists and summaries.

The multilingual summaries are probably all that will be feasible over the next twenty years. It follows that a significant number of engineers in all countries will have to develop a language expertise, so that a project engineer in America, say, will be able to obtain an answer via an engineer fluent in Italian as to the relevance of a particular paper in Italian to an aspect of a particular project. While developing this language expertise and exploring issues identified in literature surveys will involve considerable expenditure, it will be a handsome investment when one considers the overall improvements in design and construction methods that will ensue, and the collapses and deterioration that will be avoided.

REFERENCES

1. Csagoly, P. F., and L. G. Jaeger: Multi-Load-Path Structures for Highway Bridges, Transportation Research Board report 711, Washington, pp. 34–39, 1979.

2. Hadiopriono, Fabian C.: Analysis of Events in Recent Structural Failures, ASCE paper ST7, pp. 1468–1481, July 1985.
3. Jaeger, L. G., and B. Bakht: Multiple Presence Reduction Factors for Bridges, *Proc. Bridge and Transmission Line Structures*, ASCE Structures Congress, Orlando, Fla., pp. 47–59, August 1987.
4. Bakht, B., and L. G. Jaeger: Bridge Testing—A Surprise Every Time, technical report SRR-88-04, Ministry of Transportation and Communications, Downsview, Ontario, pp. (i)–(iii), 1–26, 1988.
5. Bartlett, F. M., and R. G. Sexsmith, Bayesian Technique for Evaluation of Material Strengths in Existing Bridges, *ACI Mater. J.*, vol. 88, no. 2, pp. 164–169, March–April 1991.
6. Novak, A. S., A. E. Naaman, and S.-C. Ting: Reliability Analysis of Externally Prestressed Concrete Bridge Girders, special publication 120, *External Prestressing in Bridges*, ACI, Detroit, pp. 437–454, 1990.
7. Bylington, S. R.: On the Interchange Planning Considering Some Uncertainties, *Expressway and Automobile*, 1975 (in Japanese).
8. Paul, A. M.: 'The Day the Great Bridge Fell, *The Readers' Digest*, August 1972.
9. Ackermann, H.: Bruckeneinsturze—Ihre Folgen und Lehren, *Der Bauingenieur*, vol. 47, no. 1, pp. 9–13, 1972.
10. Frandsen, A. G.: Case Stories of Recent Ship Collision Accidents, *IABSE Colloquium*, Copenhagen, pp. 11–26, 1983.
11. Woodward, R. J., and D. L. S. Wilson: Deformation of Segmental Post-tensioned Precast Bridges as a Result of Corrosion of the Tendons, *Proc. Instn Civ. Engrs*, part 1, vol. 90, pp. 397–419, April 1991.
12. Scheffey, C. F.: Point Pleasant Bridge Collapse—Conclusions of a Federal Study, *Civil Eng.*, *ASCE*, pp. 41–45, July 1971.
Virlogeux, H.: External Prestressing: From Construction History to Modern Technique and Technology, special publication SP-120, ACI, Detroit, pp. 1–60, 1990.
14. Smith, H. S.: *The World's Greatest Bridges*, Harper and Row, New York, pp. 174–178, 1965.

FOURTEEN

RISK MANAGEMENT IN THE NUCLEAR POWER INDUSTRY

B. J. GARRICK

14.1 INTRODUCTION

There has never been a major industry that was developed from the ground up with the attention to safety that has been given to the nuclear power industry. The fear of atomic energy in the form of atomic bombs is the basis for considerable apprehension and concern about nuclear power safety by many people. While atomic bombs and nuclear power plants have nothing in common from a risk and safety standpoint, the fact that they are connected by the physical process of nuclear fission and radioactivity has always been a severe handicap to the total acceptance by the public of nuclear power plants for generating electricity.

In spite of the Three Mile Island and Chernobyl accidents, it is clear that the emphasis on safety at a very technical level has resulted in an industry with an unprecedented safety record when compared with other major industries that provide a basic need to our contemporary way of life. It is the purpose of this chapter to present an overview of the safety of nuclear power and the processes and methods employed to assure, assess and manage the risk from the operation of a nuclear power industry throughout the world.

The approach is to first establish the composition of the nuclear power industry in terms of plant types, locations and technologies involved. This is followed by a definition of safety issues that are peculiar to nuclear reactors and a discussion of nuclear plant safety performance, emphasizing the Three Mile Island and Chernobyl accidents. A brief description of the regulatory process is presented in reference to the major nuclear power plant nations, followed by some information on the technology of safety assessment and risk assessment. Finally, some opinions are given on the important lessons that have been learned about the safety and risk management of nuclear power plants. The chapter ends with some brief conclusions about risk management in the nuclear power plant field.

14.2 THE COMMERCIAL NUCLEAR POWER INDUSTRY

Nuclear Generating Station Designs

Commercial nuclear electric power generating stations exist in a variety of sizes and design concepts. However, all current nuclear power plants share two characteristics. Firstly, they all generate heat from nuclear fission with the primary fuel isotopes being U^{235} and Pu^{239}, the latter of which is made in the reactor from U^{238}. All commercial reactors then transform the kinetic energy of the slow or thermal neutrons released from the nuclear reactions into heat, which is applied to a standard water/steam thermal cycle to generate electricity. At this point, however, the similarities end. The major plant designs are described briefly below, and Table 14.1 provides a comparison of these designs. More comprehensive descriptions of the major nuclear plant designs can be found in Ref. 1.

Light water reactors (LWR) LWRs are cooled and moderated with light water and use slightly enriched uranium oxide pellets for fuel. There are two varieties of LWRs: pressurized water reactors (PWR) and boiling water reactors (BWR). In a PWR, the water used to cool the reactor is kept under pressure to prevent boiling and is circulated through secondary heat exchangers, called steam generators, to boil water in a separate circulation loop to produce steam for a standard steam turbine cycle. A simplified flow diagram of a PWR is presented as Fig. 14.1.

In a BWR, the water used to cool the reactor is allowed to boil in the reactor, and the resulting steam is routed directly to the steam turbine to produce electricity. Figure 14.2 is a simplified flow diagram of a BWR.

Heavy water reactors A reactor moderated with heavy water (D_2O) can be designed to use natural uranium (0.7% U^{235}) as fuel. This eliminates the need for costly fuel enrichment, which is required for other reactors. Canada has led the world in the development of commercial heavy water reactors with the CANDU (Canadium deuterium–uranium) reactor. The CANDU design is essentially a PWR using heavy water in the primary circulation loop to transfer heat from the reactor to the steam generators.

Table 14.1 Summary of major nuclear power plant design types

	Reactor type					
	PWR	BWR	CANDU	Magnox	AGR	RMBK
Moderator	H_2O	H_2O	D_2O	C	C	C
Coolant						
Fluid	H_2O	H_2O	D_2O	CO_2	CO_2	H_2O
Pressure (lb/in^2)	2250	1040	1602	278	488	1024
Temperature (°F)	617	551	594	590	1150	450
Fuel enrichment (%)	3.2	2.8	0.7	0.7	2.95	1.8
Fuel power density (kW/l)	98	54	12	0.8	2.76	
On-line refuelling	No	No	Yes	Yes	Yes	Yes
Steam generators	Yes	No	Yes	No	No	No
Vendors	Westinghouse Combustion Engineering Babcock and Wilcox Framatome Kraftwerk Union AG	GE Hitachi	AECL	Atomic Power Const.	Atomic Power Const. National Nuclear Corp.	Ministry of Nuclear Power

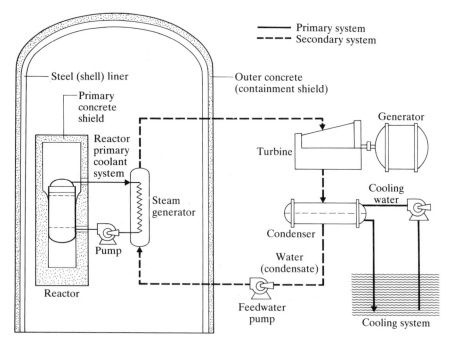

Figure 14.1 Schematic of pressurized water reactor power plant. *(Source: Nero.[1])*

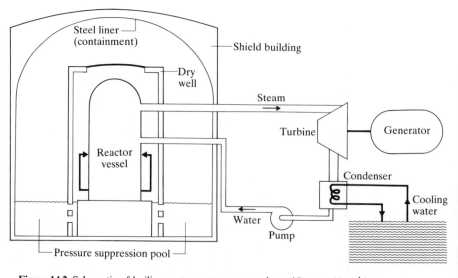

Figure 14.2 Schematic of boiling water reactor power plant. *(Source: Nero.[1])*

Graphite reactors Several types of reactors have been developed to use carbon (graphite) as a moderator, and carbon dioxide, helium gas or water to transfer the heat from the reactor to steam generators. Major varieties of graphite reactors include the Magnox, the advanced gas-cooled reactor (AGR) and the Soviet RMBK, which is water cooled.

Nuclear Power Industry Statistics

Table 14.2 presents a listing of the number of reactors and installed megawatts in service by country and reactor type. Figure 14.3 displays two pie charts made from the data in Table 14.2 that show the distribution of installed reactors by type and the countries with the most plants in service. As can be seen, light water reactors are the dominant design type, with PWRs making up about 54 per cent of the total population and BWRs adding another 20 per cent. The United States leads all nations with 114 reactors, followed by the Soviet Union with 57 and France with 55.

The degree to which nations rely on nuclear power rather than other conventional sources is illustrated in Fig. 14.4. The greatest reliance on nuclear power is found in countries that do not have large fossil fuel or hydropower resources. The United States, which has the largest number of reactors, obtains less than 20 per cent of its electricity needs from nuclear power.

Figures 14.5 and 14.6 chart the world-wide growth of the nuclear power industry. Figure 14.5 displays the cumulative number of reactors placed in service from 1956 to 1989. Figure 14.6 shows the number of plants placed in service in each year during the same period. The peak for nuclear plant completions was 36 in 1985 and has been steadily declining since then.

14.3 SAFETY ISSUES AND PRACTICES

The most distinguishing feature, from a safety viewpoint, of a nuclear reactor is its decay heat. Figure 14.7 tells the decay heat story. Simply put, it is not possible to totally shut down a nuclear reactor by simply stopping the nuclear chain reaction. To be sure, scramming the reactor stops the fission process and brings the reactor to a 'subcritical' shut-down state. Unfortunately, however, scramming the reactor does not stop all sources of heat generation.

If the reactor has been operating for a long time (approximately a year or more), the power generated immediately after shutdown will be approximately 7 per cent of the level before shutdown. This implies about 200 MW of heat from a typical 1000-MW_e nuclear power plant. This is sufficient heat to require heat removal systems for some time after the reactor has been shut down to protect the integrity of the fuel. The heat, of course, comes

Table 14.2 Operable reactors by type and country, July 1989

Country	PWR Units	PWR MWe	BWR Units	BWR MWe	Magnox Units	Magnox MWe	AGR Units	AGR MWe	CANDU Units	CANDU MWe	RMBK Units	RMBK MWe	Other Units	Other MWe	Total Units	Total MWe
Argentina	—	—	—	—	—	—	—	—	2	1 005	—	—	—	—	2	1 005
Belgium	7	5 749	—	—	—	—	—	—	—	—	—	—	—	—	7	5 749
Brazil	1	657	—	—	—	—	—	—	—	—	—	—	—	—	1	657
Bulgaria	5	2 760	—	—	—	—	—	—	—	—	—	—	—	—	5	2 760
Canada	—	—	—	—	—	—	—	—	18	12 603	—	—	—	—	18	12 603
Czechoslovakia	8	3 434	—	—	—	—	—	—	—	—	—	—	—	—	8	3 434
Finland	2	930	2	1 470	—	—	—	—	—	—	—	—	—	—	4	2 400
France	49	51 454	—	—	4	1 800	—	—	—	—	—	—	2	1 492	55	54 746
Germany DR	5	1 835	—	—	—	—	—	—	—	—	—	—	—	—	5	1 835
Germany FR	14	16 377	7	7 207	—	—	—	—	—	—	—	—	3	343	24	23 927
Hungary	4	1 760	—	—	—	—	—	—	—	—	—	—	—	—	4	1 760
India	—	—	2	320	1	166	—	—	5	1 145	—	—	2	178	9	1 478
Japan	17	13 177	19	15 937	—	—	—	—	—	—	—	—	—	—	38	29 445
Korea	8	7 037	—	—	—	—	—	—	1	679	—	—	—	—	9	7 716
Mexico	—	—	1	675	—	—	—	—	—	—	—	—	—	—	1	675
Netherlands	1	481	1	58	—	—	—	—	—	—	—	—	—	—	2	539
Pakistan	—	—	—	—	—	—	—	—	1	137	—	—	—	—	1	137
South Africa	2	1 930	—	—	—	—	—	—	—	—	—	—	—	—	2	1 930
Spain	7	5 902	2	1 454	1	496	—	—	—	—	—	—	—	—	10	7 852
Sweden	3	2 760	9	7 370	—	—	—	—	—	—	—	—	—	—	12	10 130
Switzerland	3	1 684	2	1 381	—	—	—	—	—	—	—	—	—	—	5	3 065
Taiwan	2	1 902	4	3 242	—	—	—	—	—	—	—	—	—	—	6	5 144
UK	—	—	—	—	24	5 468	14	9 264	—	—	—	—	2	370	40	15 102
USA	74	71 436	38	34 975	—	—	—	—	—	—	—	—	2	362	114	106 777
USSR	24	18 945	1	62	—	—	—	—	—	—	27	16 847	5	782	57	36 636
Yugoslavia	1	664	—	—	—	—	—	—	—	—	—	—	—	—	1	664
Total	237	210 874	88	74 151	30	7 930	14	9 264	27	15 569	27	16 847	16	3 527	440	338 162

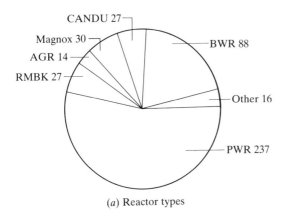

(a) Reactor types

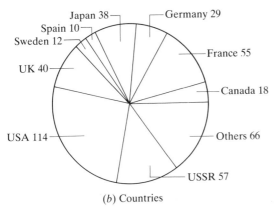

(b) Countries

Figure 14.3 Reactor population statistics (439 operable reactors world-wide). (a) Reactor types and (b) countries.

from the some 15 billion curies of fission products in the nuclear fuel. The particular source of the heat is the decay processes going on with the fission products.

The decay heat forces the requirement for post-shut-down heat removal capability. Without heat removal, the nuclear core will heat up and eventually melt, and may penetrate the reactor vessel and, under rare circumstances, the containment system. The result could be the release of large amounts of radioactive material into the atmosphere and a serious threat to the health and safety of the nearby public. Just what this threat is has been detailed in numerous risk assessments and will be discussed later.

Loss of decay heat removal capability during shut-down is not the only way a nuclear power plant can get into trouble; it is just a unique property of nuclear reactors that complicates the safety issue. During the operation of a nuclear reactor, there are basically two mechanisms that, if they were

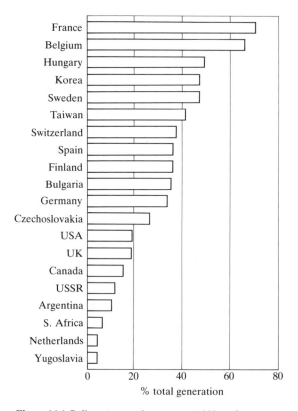

Figure 14.4 Reliance on nuclear power (1988 performance).

to occur without intervention, could eventually lead to damaging the nuclear fuel and releasing radioactive material. They are a nuclear transient involving excess reactivity[†] that outpaces the heat removal capability of the plant, and a loss of heat removal capability itself, such as might result from a failure of the reactor cooling systems. However, as will be discussed later, these are extremely low probability events and are the reasons for the excellent safety record of commercial nuclear power plants.

The safety of a nuclear power plant is assured as long as it retains its ability to remove sufficient heat to prevent overheating the fuel. Unless the fuel loses its integrity, it will not release sufficient radioactive material that could be a threat to public safety. This is the same for all nuclear reactor types. They are all subject to the same two basic mechanisms for having an accident, and all have afterheating as a result of the decay of fission products. To discuss the provisions for protecting against these accident mechanisms, we shall limit the balance of this discussion to light water reactors, which

---

† Reactivity relates to an excess of neutrons, usually brought about by an excess of fuel or a decrease in neutron adsorption.

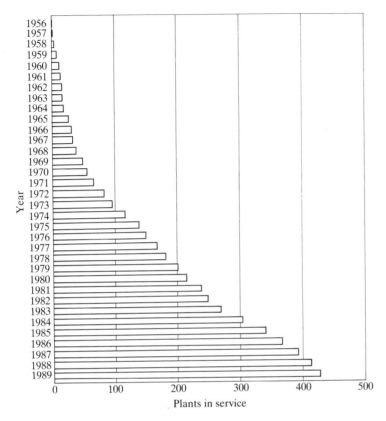

Figure 14.5 Growth of nuclear power.

constitute the bulk of the commercial plants throughout the world. Discussions of the safety features of the CANDU reactors can be found in Ref. 1.

It is clear from the above discussion that the underpin of protecting a nuclear power plant from an accident that can lead to the release of radioactive material is its heat removal systems. Usually, this means the availability of fluid systems and sources of electric power. Because large breaks in the cooling system are the most difficult to control and often constitute the design basis accident, this discussion will begin with them. Figure 14.8 is a schematic of the major features of a major break in the cold leg of a multiloop PWR. Of course, good safety design ensures a minimum of dependence on active systems. In fact, the first system to respond following a large break in the cold leg is the accumulator, a passive system. The accumulators provide a no-delay source of emergency cooling water to the reactor.

Since each accumulator exhausts its supply of about 7500 gallons of

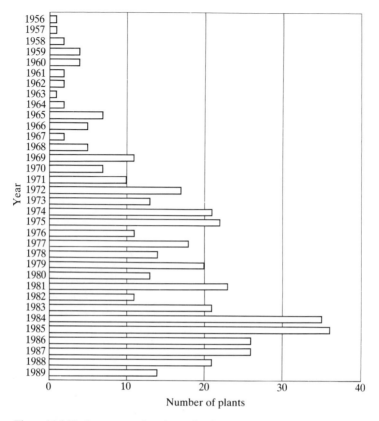

Figure 14.6 Nuclear power plant in-service date.

water very rapidly, there has to be another supply of water for sustained cooling. Sustained or long-term cooling is provided generally by 'active' low-pressure injection systems—low pressure because, by this time in the accident sequence, the pressure in the primary coolant system has been significantly relieved.

If the coolant line break is small and there is little or no pressure relief, then the safety systems that are called on are the so-called 'high-pressure injection systems'. The refuelling water storage tank and the volume control tanks are the usual sources of water for the injection systems. The water from these systems can be injected into either the hot or the cold legs of the primary coolant system.

To ensure very high reliability in such safeguards systems as emergency cooling systems, there is always redundancy. The design philosophy adopted in modern plants is to provide separate and independent safety trains to assure independent sources of both fluid and electric power systems. Most plants have two separate and independent safety system trains, but some

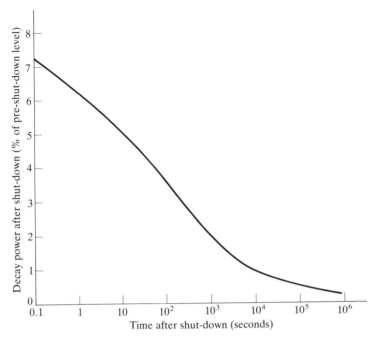

Figure 14.7 Thermal power after reactor shut-down. *(Source: Nero.[1])*

have even more trains. As will be discussed in Sec. 14.6, it is not always a plus to adopt the multiple safety system train concept too rigidly because of the impact such a design philosophy can have on the frequency of multiple failures.

With about a third of the light water reactors being of the BWR type, it is important to briefly discuss their engineered safety features. As its name implies, a boiling water reactor creates steam directly in the reactor vessel through boiling under a pressure of approximately 1000 pounds per square inch (lb/in²). The boiling temperature at 1000 lb/in² is 545°F (285°C). About 13 per cent of the water is vaporized as it passes through the reactor vessel; the remainder is circulated down an annulus formed between the core shroud and the reactor vessel to the plenum beneath the core. The fluid is then available for passing up through the core again. Thus, a distinguishing feature of a BWR from a PWR is that there is no external steam loop, and most of the action, from a thermal hydraulics standpoint, takes place inside the reactor vessel itself.

The lower pressure of operation, the direct steam cycle and the different containment concept result in BWRs having a very different emergency core cooling system from PWRs even though they perform the same basic function. The containment system is not the large dry type that is typical of most PWRs but instead involves a two-step system consisting of a dry well and

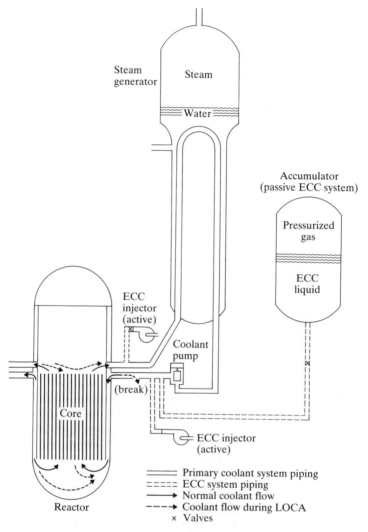

Figure 14.8 PWR emergency core cooling systems. *(Source: Nero.[1])*

a pressure suppression pool (wet well) that are connected to each other by way of horizontal vents. This design is a result of a substantial evolution of the pressure suppression system. This evolution is characterized by the labels of Mark I, Mark II and the present version, Mark III.

The idea of the pressure suppression containment system is that, following the blow-down of the reactor coolant into the dry well, the increasing pressure forces the fluid into the suppression pool through the connecting vent lines where steam condensing takes place to 'suppress' the

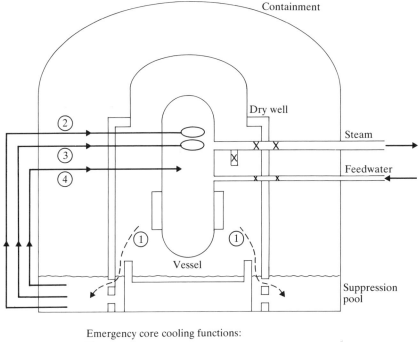

Emergency core cooling functions:

① Overpressure injection into pressure suppression pool

② High-pressure core spray

③ Low-pressure core spray

④ Low-pressure coolant injection

(**X** valves)

Figure 14.9 BWR emergency core cooling systems. *(Source: Nero.[1])*

pressure rise. The emergency core cooling systems are actuated on low water level in the reactor vessel, or high pressure in the dry well, or both. The specific safety systems include low-pressure injection, decay heat removal [residual heat removal (RHR)], and high- and low-pressure core spray systems. Figure 14.9 is a schematic of the BWR emergency core cooling functions.

The core spray system can be used to lower the pressure in the reactor vessels or, in the event that the core is uncovered, it can provide cooling directly to the fuel assemblies. The core spray system can also provide make-up water to the vessel. The sources of water are the condensate tanks and the suppression pool itself. It is possible to orchestrate the various safety systems by the selective valving of fluid control systems of the plant to accommodate a broad class of accident scenarios.

Both the PWR and the BWR engineered safety features have received extensive challenges from authorities, regulators, intervenors and numerous individual safety experts. These challenges have resulted in design modifications and many changes in operating procedures. However, on the whole, the systems have met most of the challenges and, based on the new wave of analysis accompanying the many probabilistic risk assessments that have been made, there is growing confidence in their ability to mitigate any of the accidents that are, in fact, likely to happen.

14.4 NUCLEAR PLANT ACCIDENT EXPERIENCE

There has probably never been a technology developed with as impressive a safety record as nuclear power. Ironically, there has probably never been a technology as feared, at least by a vocal segment of the population, as nuclear power. The root cause of the fear is radioactivity and nuclear power's unfortunate association with nuclear weapons. The result may be the compromise of an essential resource for a sustained quality of life on this planet.

The accident history of nuclear power is dominated by two accidents, one that did not result in acute injuries or deaths (the Three Mile Island Unit 2 accident in the United States), and the other much more serious Chernobyl accident in the Soviet Union where there were deaths and injuries. Both will be described.

Prior to describing the Three Mile Island and Chernobyl accidents, it is important to put the accident experience in context with the operating experience. There are some 114 nuclear power plants now operating in the United States with a cumulative experience of approximately 1500 in-service reactor-years. With the approximately 325 nuclear power plants operating outside the United States, the total cumulative operating experience as of January 1991 is estimated as 5600 in-service reactor-years. In addition, there is a very substantial experience base with other types of reactors, including submarine, weapons production, and research. It is not known what this translates into, but a rough estimate might be that the actual reactor operating experience is at least 8000 reactor-years. Over 65 per cent of this experience base involves water reactors for which there was only one accident involving a non-military operation, and no member of the public or the operating staff was killed or injured in that accident. This is by far the most spectacular safety story associated with the development of any major technology providing a basic need, namely energy, to mankind. This impressive safety record is by design, and it is necessary to keep it that way.

Three Mile Island, Unit 2, Middletown, Pennsylvania (28 March 1979)

Until the Chernobyl accident discussed below, the Three Mile Island Unit 2 (TMI-2) accident was a singularity in the history of nuclear power plant accidents around the world. It not only represented the worst accident to that time for a commercial nuclear power plant but also involved a step change in knowledge about the 'nitty gritty' process of accident management. Prior to providing a brief description of the accident, it is important to recall some of the main features of the TMI-2 plant itself. Figure 14.10 is a sketch of those features. The following discussion makes specific reference, by number, to equipment items in Fig. 14.10.

The plant involves a Babcock and Wilcox presurized water reactor ① to heat the primary coolant to approximately 600°F at a pressure of about 2100 lb/in². The primary coolant circulates through two steam generators ② that produce the steam to drive the turbines ③ that provide shaft power to the electric generators. Important auxiliary and safety systems are the auxiliary feedwater system ⑮, the emergency core cooling system of which the high pressure injection pump ㉒ is the key component, and various safety relief valves. While not a safety system as such, there is one other plant component, the pressurizer ⑥, that should be mentioned as it played a major role in influencing a number of accident management decisions.

The reactor core contains 177 fuel assemblies consisting of uranium oxide pellets stacked inside rods made of a zirconium alloy. The total amount of uranium is approximately 100 tons. The fuel assemblies each contain 208 rods and are about 12 ft in length. The assemblies contain space for cooling water to flow between the rods and tubes that may contain control rods or instruments to measure, among other things, core temperatures. The control rods used to shut down the chain reaction and to control the reactor are made of silver, indium, and cadmium.

The principal safety barriers of the plant are the fuel rods, which trap and hold radioactive materials, the reactor vessels and the large, dry outer containment vessel.

The TMI-2 accident started at 4:00 a.m. on Wednesday 28 March 1979, with a trip of the main feedwater pumps ⑭. What is not so clear is the time at which it can be considered that the accident was over. Perhaps, the milestone of making the transition to cooling by natural circulation can be considered a termination point of the accident. If so, the accident lasted for one month, as that transition was made on 27 April. Another possible endpoint for the accident was the time at which the block valve above the pressurizer was closed ⑯; that took place 2 hours and 20 minutes into the accident. Because of the importance of the accident and the extensive amount of documentation that it has received, only a few highlights will be provided here.

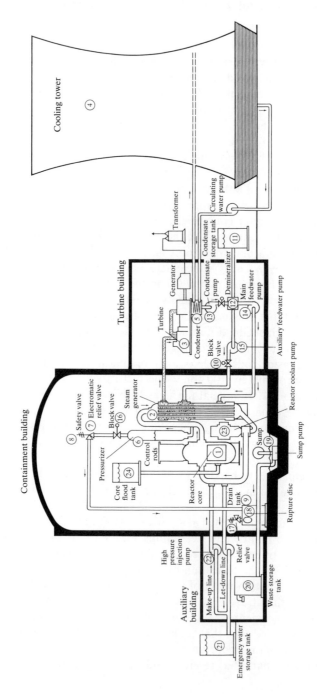

Figure 14.10 Three Mile Island Unit 2. (*Source: IEEE Spectrum, vol. 16, no. 11, November 1979.*)

Following the trip of the main feedwater pumps, several events took place as they were supposed to, such as the tripping of the turbine ③ and the dumping of steam to the condenser ⑤. As a result of the reduction of heat removal from the primary system, the reactor pressure began to rise until the power-operated relief valve ⑦ opened. This action did not provide sufficient immediate pressure relief and the control rods were automatically driven into the core ① to stop the fission reaction.

Normally, the accident might have terminated at this point had it not been for two important intervening conditions. Firstly, there was the problem of significant decay heat, which could have been handled straightforwardly had it not been for some later problems with cooling systems. The second, and turning point, event of of the accident (the event that most likely turned an incident into an accident) was that the relief valve failed to close and the operators failed to recognize it. The result was the initiation of the now-famous small loss of coolant accident, that is the small LOCA. The stuck-open valve, together with some valve closures that had not been corrected from previous maintenance activities, created a severe shortage of 'heat sinks' to control the thermal hydraulics of the plant. The events were further complicated by the failure of the operators to recognize the small LOCA condition that persisted.

What followed was automatic initiation of the high-pressure injection pumps ㉒, operator concern for losing pressure control capability over the primary system, shutting down of the injection pumps to maintain such control and the transfer of slightly radioactive water from the containment building to the auxiliary building. The water came from the reactor building sump and the reactor drain tank due to overpressurization. The water transfer was terminated before much radioactivity was involved.

High pump vibration and concern for pump seal failure resulted in the operators shutting down the main reactor coolant pumps ㉓ in one of two loops in the reactor. It was later learned that the pump vibration was due to the two-phase flow of steam and water that was taking place in the primary system. A short time later, the pumps in the other loop were shut down.

It was at this point that the severe damage to the core took place. In particular, the critical events were the overheating of the reactor and the release of fission products into the reactor coolant. The time interval for this most serious phase of the accident was 1 to 3 hours following the initial feedwater trip. What was happening during this time, and not recognized, was the separation of the water and steam phases and the uncovering and overheating of the core. Also, it was about 2 hours and 20 minutes into the accident that the block valve ⑯ over the pressurizer was closed, thus terminating the effect of the stuck-open relief valve.

What later happened, which is not discussed in detail, involved the problems associated with handling the by-products of an overheated core, such as non-condensable gases, including hydrogen. A central problem following the core damage events was the handling of these gases and the elimination of the resulting 'hydrogen bubble'. As indicated earlier, it took essentially a month before there was confidence that the plant was sufficiently stable to rely on natural circulation for continued cooling and protection against further fuel damage and possible releases of radioactive materials.

From the standpoint of public health, the consequences of the accident were quite minimal. There were measurable releases of radioactivity outside the containment, but not of sufficient magnitude to cause any immediate injuries. The latent effects are very speculative. Of course, the damage to the reactor was essentially total.

As far as the cause of the accident is concerned, the presidential commission concluded, among other factors, the following:

- Operator error
- Inadequate operator training, especially during conditions of emergency operation
- Poor control room design
- US Nuclear Regulatory Commission (NRC) attitude towards safety

Chernobyl Nuclear Power Station, Ukraine, USSR (26 April 1986)

The Chernobyl Nuclear Power Station accident was by far the most serious nuclear power plant accident ever to occur. The specific reactor involved in the accident was Unit 4 of the four-unit station. The reactor is a 1000 MW, boiling water, graphite-moderated, direct cycle, USSR RBMK type. Some of the important design features of the reactor are

- Vertical fuel channels that accommodate online refuelling.
- Fuel in the form of bundles of cylindrical fuel rods of uranium dioxide in zirconium tubes.
- Graphite moderator between fuel channels.
- A low boiling heat transfer medium with direct feeding of steam to the turbine.

Design advantages include the absence of reactor vessels and steam generators, online refuelling, flexible fuel cycle and high reliability. Disadvantages include a positive void coefficient[†] under certain conditions, high sensitivity to changes in reactivity, complex control problems to cope with the positive void coefficient, a complex piping system for reactor cooling, a susceptibility to contamination, the lack of a high-integrity containment system, and a slow response shut-down system.

The Chernobyl accident was initiated during a test of reactor coolant

[†] Meaning that increased boiling leads to increased power.

pump operability from the reactor's own turbine generators. The purpose of the test was to determine how long the reactor coolant pumps could be operated, using electric power from the reactor's own turbine generator under the condition of turbine coast-down and no steam supply from the reactor. Part of the motivation for the test was to better understand reactor coolant pump performance in the event of loss of load and the need to bypass the turbine to avoid turbine overspeed. The reactor should have been shut down during the test, but the experimenters wanted a continuous steam supply to enable them to repeat the experiment several times.

At the beginning of the test, half of the main coolant pumps slowed down, resulting in a coolant flow reduction in the core. Because of prior operations leaving the coolant in the core just below the boiling point, the reduced flow quickly led to extensive boiling. The boiling added reactivity to the core because of the positive void coefficient and caused a power transient. The negative reactivity coefficient of the fuel was insufficient to counteract the dominance of the positive void coefficient because of the conditions in the core at the time of the test. By the time the operators realized that the reactor was rapidly increasing in power, there was insufficient time to take the appropriate corrective action because of the slow response time of the control system. The power excursion caused the fuel to overheat, melt and disintegrate. Fuel fragments were ejected into the coolant, causing steam explosions and ruptured fuel channels with such force that the cover of the reactor was blown off.

While the off-site consequences of the Chernobyl accident are very much unresolved at this point, there were no acute injuries or fatalities, as best can be determined. The on-site consequences were a different matter. Reports are that some 300 people required hospital treatment for radiation and burn injuries, and 30 people are believed to have died from acute doses of radiation.

While there were no acute injuries or fatalities off-site, the accident certainly had its impact. For example, 45 000 residents of Pripyat were evacuated the day after the accident, and the remaining population within approximately 20 miles of the reactor were evacuated during the days that followed the accident. The ground contamination continues to be a problem, and it is not known when the nearby areas will be habitable again.

14.5 REGULATION OF NUCLEAR POWER SAFETY

Regulatory Practices

Today's commercial nuclear power industry can trace its origins directly from government-sponsored research and development programmes. The dominant light water reactor designs are direct descendants of reactors first developed for naval propulsion. As the commercial nuclear power industry grew away from its military roots, more comprehensive and publicly accountable controls were instituted. By the 1980s, a clear pattern of regulatory practice had evolved in most nuclear capable nations. The key principles behind this practice are codified in safety guides published by the International Atomic Energy Agency.

Key provisions of current nuclear regulatory practice include:

- The establishment of an independent government regulatory agency that is not responsible for the development or promotion of nuclear energy.
- The establishment, by the regulatory agency, of a formal licensing process to govern the siting and construction of new power reactors.
- Granting to the regulatory agency adequate powers for the inspection of nuclear facilities and the enforcement of regulations, including the power to order the curtailment of operations.

In most nations, a licensee must successfully complete the following tasks in order to build and operate a nuclear power plant:

1. Before construction can begin, a 'construction permit' must be obtained indicating that the site is acceptable for the proposed facility.
2. After construction is complete, an 'operating licence' must be obtained certifying that the plant has been constructed in accordance with specifications and that the operating staff is adequately prepared to operate the plant safely.
3. During operation, the plant must not experience significant operating incidents and must pass regular inspections of operating performance in order to retain the operating licence.

Safety Concepts in Regulation

The goal of regulation in the commercial nuclear power industry has always been to provide the highest achievable level of protection from radiological exposure for the plant workers and the general public in the vicinity of the plant. The way in which this protection is achieved has evolved and is still evolving.

The first nuclear facilities were developed for weapons production, and risks of accidental release or the consequential effects of a nuclear attack on the facility were minimized by locating the facilities in remote locations. Thus, the first safety concept was protection via isolation.

Isolation was impractical, however, for commercial power generation since it is desirable to have generation as close as practical to the electrical load to be served. To allow nuclear power plants to be located closer to population centres, the concept of isolation was replaced by the concept of 'defence in depth'. The basic idea behind this concept is to increase the number of barriers between radioactive materials and the environment so that the likelihood of breaching all barriers simultaneously is remote. Some of the more specific features of the defence-in-depth approach that have been applied to plant design are

1. *Containment*   The enclosure of the reactor and associated piping inside a sealed pressure vessel to retain any potential radioactive releases from the fuel and reactor. Figures 14.1 and 14.2 show the relationship of the containment to the other major plant components.
2. *Design basis accidents*   The requirement that plant designs incorporate the capability to withstand specific hypothetical piping or equipment failures without causing damage to the nuclear fuel.
3. *Single failure criteria*   The requirement that the plant be able to withstand the failure of any single component without fuel damage.

The defence-in-depth concept has generally been implemented through the promulgation of very specific deterministic regulations. Under this concept, a plant is judged to be adequately safe if the plant complies with the regulations.

A by-product of the application of the defence-in-depth concept has been a definite increase in the redundancy and complexity (and cost) of nuclear power plants. This trend has been especially severe in the United States.

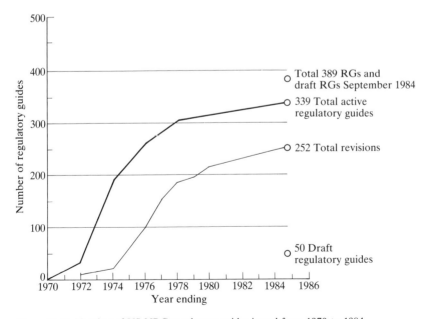

Figure 14.11 Number of US NRC regulatory guides issued from 1970 to 1984.

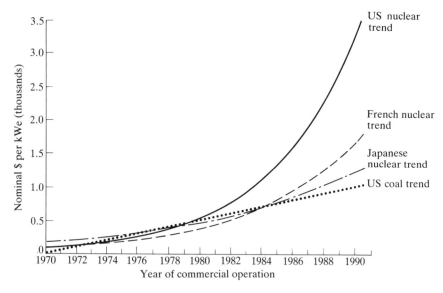

Figure 14.12 Comparison of nuclear and coal-fired plant construction cost.

Figure 14.11 illustrates the growth of regulatory documents in the United States, and Fig. 14.12 shows the accompanying rise in the cost of nuclear plant construction over the same general time period.

Indeed, many in the industry question whether some added safety features have been worth the required cost. Because of the acknowledged decline in the marginal safety benefit of continued increases in defence-in-depth, a new approach of quantitative risk management has increasingly been applied to ensure that resources invested for safety enhancements are spent in the most cost-beneficial areas. This approach is explored further in Sec. 14.6.

14.6 SAFETY ASSESSMENT AND RISK MANAGEMENT†

Safety, especially nuclear safety, has been a visible and fundamental concern in the development and commercialization of nuclear power. From the beginning of the nuclear industry, as indicated in the previous section, safety design philosophy has centred around the defence-in-depth, multiple-barrier concept. Early on, and in the absence of much operating experience, the analysis supporting the safety of the design was based on very conservative upper bound, deterministic calculations. With the growth of the nuclear power industry and the accumulation of experience data, safety analyses have

---

† This section is based, to a large extent, on material contained in numerous PRAs performed by PLG, Inc., under the general direction of the author. The principal authors of the material as it appeared in the PLG reports were B. J. Garrick and D. C. Bley, both of the PLG staff.

become more realistic. The most advanced form of safety analysis that is now employed world-wide is probabilistic risk assessment (PRA). The descriptor that has greater international acceptance is PSA, that is, probabilistic safety assessment. PSA is a rigorous and systematic identification of possible accident sequences (scenarios) that could lead to fuel damage and a quantitative assessment of the likelihood of such occurrences.

Until the recent change in severe accident policy, the US Nuclear Regulatory Commission had, for the most part, carried out its nuclear safety regulatory activities based on upper bound deterministic approaches for assessing nuclear power plant safety. The approach was based on the analysis of a fixed set of predefined accidents. The most severe of these accidents, the maximum hypothetical accidents, were originally selected to be studied in detail to establish required distance factors. The somewhat arbitrary nature of these distance factors began to stir interest in more logical and realistic approaches. In the early 1960s, F. R. Farmer of the United Kingdom proposed a new approach to power plant safety based on the reliability of consequence-limiting equipment.[2] The United Kingdom, faced with a need to bring nuclear power plants closer to large populations, began to move away from the vague idea of how safe such plants were to a more realistic and more quantitative definition of their potential public risk. Meanwhile, in the United States, a series of studies sponsored by the US Atomic Energy Commission was undertaken in the early and mid-1960s to probe the merits of using reliability techniques in the safety analysis of American nuclear power plants. These studies[3] identified the need for special data and analytical tools, such as fault tree analysis, to perform meaningful, quantitative risk analysis.

Interest in probabilistic risk assessment continued to grow during the 1960s. Analysis techniques were borrowed from statisticians and reliability engineers and were developed into tools suitable for predicting failure frequencies for large, complex nuclear power plant systems. The benefits in safety control and understanding were suggested in Ref. 4. (This reference was the first known study to propose specific steps for achieving an integrated and plant-wide probabilistic, i.e. quantitative, risk model.) As these tools evolved, investigators began to believe that it was possible to estimate the likelihood of low frequency, high consequence accidents at nuclear power plants.

In 1972, the US Atomic Energy Commission undertook the Reactor Safety Study (RSS) under the direction of Professor N. C. Rasmussen of the Massachusetts Institute of Technology.[5] This project, which took three years to complete, was a turning point in the way that people think about nuclear safety; in fact, as it has turned out, it has been a turning point in the way that we think about the safety of any engineered facility. It was the most thorough investigation of reactor safety conducted up to that time, and will influence analysis and understanding of safety for years to come.

WASH-1400, or the Reactor Safety Study, as it was called, calculated the risk from the operation of 100 current design light water reactor based nuclear power plants located in the United States. The report demonstrated that it is possible to derive and present results that are meaningful to both policy makers and analysts. The finished document formed a basis for thorough discussions of risk methodology, i.e. it focused criticism, review, and improvement. Two important findings of the study were that the risk associated with the operation of selected nuclear power plants is indeed small, and that the dominant contributor to risk is not the large LOCA previously emphasized in the US Code of Federal Regulations. Transients and small LOCAs often make up most of the contribution to risk.

Although it was a seminal work, the Reactor Safety Study was criticized. Between release of the draft report in August 1974 and the final version in October 1975, comments were received from 87 organizations and individuals representing government, industry, environmental groups and universities. Many of these comments had a significant impact on the final report; for example, the American Physical Society Study Group on Reactor Safety pointed out serious omissions in the consequence calculations. The Union of Concerned Scientists (UCS) released its review of the study in 1977. It criticized all aspects of the report: its objectivity, the accident analysis and the consequence analysis.

The most complete and even-handed review of WASH-1400 was conducted by the Risk Assessment Review Group chaired by Professor H. W. Lewis of the University of California, Santa Barbara. The group was organized by the the NRC on 1 July 1977, at the request of Congressman Morris K. Udall, Chairman of the Committee on Interior and Insular Affairs, who had held hearings on the Reactor Safety Study.

Following the release of the Lewis Report, the NRC issued a press release withdrawing the endorsement of WASH-1400. This announcement has caused great misunderstanding of the criticism offered by Lewis and others, and of the validity of WASH-1400 itself. It is important to observe that neither the Lewis Report nor the NRC disavowed the fault tree/event tree methodology.

The most astounding statement by the NRC was that 'the Commission does not regard as reliable the Reactor Safety Study's numerical estimate of the overall risk of reactor accidents'. This action was based on the Lewis Report conclusion that 'absolute values of the risks presented by WASH-1400 should not be used uncritically'. The leap from this cautious caveat to rejection is a large one indeed. The Lewis Report found that the RSS error bands are understated because of a sometimes inadequate database, occasionally weak statistical methods and calculational inconsistencies. In particular, the Lewis Report urges caution in the use of the numbers but does not reject them completely. In summary, the general methodology is strongly supported and recommended for future use. Care in stating the bounds of knowledge is necessary.

The accident that occurred at Three Mile Island Unit 2 (TMI-2) in March 1979 had a profound impact on the nuclear industry and on the concept of risk assessment. Portions of the TMI-2 sequence of events (especially the generation of significant hydrogen without core melt) were not included in detail in the RSS analysis, causing many to wonder if the analyses were valid.

In truth, the transient at TMI did fit the RSS sequences, albeit not exactly. It fits in the sense that a small LOCA with failure of high-pressure injection was included as one of the RSS sequences. However, it did not fit exactly because the numerical probabilities RSS placed on this scenario represented the probability that it would go all the way to core melt. The RSS did not estimate the likelihood that the operator would interrupt the core damage.

The initial reaction to the TMI accident was negative with respect to the value and role of probabilistic risk assessment; on reflection, the attitude soon changed. Two important post-TMI independent studies recommended greater use of probabilistic analysis techniques in assessing nuclear plant risks and in making decisions about nuclear safety. They were the report of the President's Commission on the TMI accident and the so-called Rogovin Report. Following the lead of the reports of these commissions, several post-TMI NRC reports also noted the value of quantitative risk analysis.

It is evident that the use of probabilistic methods in nuclear safety analysis received a singular boost from the RSS. However, as a result of all the controvery surrounding the RSS and the TMI-2 scenario, it became obvious that certain features would have to be added to the methodology used in the RSS in order for probabilistic risk assessment to be more 'scrutable'.

The first post-RSS study to capture some of these additional features was the industry-sponsored 'OSPA, Oyster Creek Probabilistic Safety Analysis', a draft report that was completed in 1979.[6] Among the 'additional features' in the Oyster Creek PSA was a significant step forward in the treatment of uncertainty (also see Ref. 7). The Zion[8] and Indian Point[9] probabilistic safety studies built on the Oyster Creek PRA methods and added the important new dimension of a comprehensive treatment of core melt phenomena and containment response. In addition to the advances made by these recent PRAs, a very significant sign of the developing maturity of risk assessment was the publication of a PRA Procedures Guide.[10] Developed by experienced practitioners in private industry and in government laboratories, this guide defines what is meant by a PRA and describes some of the alternative methods available for performing each of its aspects.

Meanwhile, the interest in PSA immediately following the publishing of

WASH-1400 was even greater in Europe. This was probably due to what was already the movement towards a risk-based approach to safety used in the United Kingdom by Farmer and his associates. In addition to the growing PSA activity in the United Kingdom, a risk analysis was performed in the Federal Republic of Germany for reactors in that country, based primarily on WASH-1400 methods. The results of the German studies were very similar to the RSS results but probably had a greater influence on the design of the German plants than did the US studies, especially during the years of scepticism immediately following the US Reactor Safety Study. PSA was also well received in Sweden and Japan and has had a marked influence on the design of their plants.

PSA has now been extended into many other industries, including chemical, space and defence. One of the best known early extensions of PSA to the chemical industry was performed in the United Kingdom on the industries on Canvey Island in the Thames estuary. This study had extensive influence on the safety practices there.

The number of PSAs that are being performed throughout the world has grown considerably. In fact, the US Nuclear Regulatory Commission now requires all nuclear plant licensees to conduct some level of a PSA on their plants. The result is that PSA is no longer just a risk management tool but also a regulatory requirement. The many benefits and lessons learned from this expanded activity are described and discussed in Sec. 14.7.

In view of the expanded use of PSA in the United States, the NRC has been actively updating the work of WASH-1400. The most significant activity is the so-called NUREG-1150 project.[11] Basically, NUREG-1150 updates, extends and improves on the work presented in WASH-1400. NUREG-1150 drew heavily from nuclear safety research and PSA work, including several major studies performed by industry, such as Refs 8 and 9, to assess the risk of five US nuclear power plants. NUREG-1150 is expected to play a major role in implementing the NRC's Severe Accident Policy.

In the previous section of this chapter, there was a discussion of the Chernobyl nuclear accident. It is important to note here the impact that accident had on safety assessment and risk management. The single biggest impact that the Chernobyl accident had on the safety assessment business was to greatly renew interest in source term and containment response analysis. The accident did not particularly reveal any new physical phenomena. In particular, the accident is understood by use of the physical models and experimental data available to the nations of the West.

Just prior to the Chernobyl accident, there was a diminishing interest in issues of containment response and consequence analysis. This declining interest was mostly created by the very favourable results that the PSAs were getting with respect to the likelihood of a release from a core damage event. The result was a heavy focus on core damage events on the thesis that these more likely events needed the greater attention. The Chernobyl accident has clearly put some focus back on issues affecting the likelihood and form of releases from core damage events.

14.7 LESSONS LEARNED AND FUTURE DIRECTIONS

In the 30 years that there have been commercial nuclear power plants, a great deal has been learned about their safety. Of course, the most valuable lessons have come from the actual operating experience accumulated around the world. Fortunately, except for Three Mile Island and Chernobyl, the experience base does not include any significant accidents that were a threat to public safety. The activity that has been most effective in putting in perspective lessons learned about safety is the probabilistic safety assessment work of the past 16 years. Thus, we will look to not only operating experience but also the results of these PSAs to identify and discuss the important lessons learned.

As before, since most of the commercial power reactors around the world involve light water reactors, the discussion will be with respect to pressurized water reactors and boiling water reactors.

Lessons learned

The roles of small LOCAs and transients in the safety of nuclear power plants and the importance ranking of contributors to risk Prior to WASH-1400, the focus of reactor safety was on large LOCAs as the design basis accident for the licensing and safety analysis of nuclear power plants. That focus resulted in designs that have proved to be highly resistant to such accidents and has been successful in eliminating them as a significant threat to public safety.

WASH-1400 was a giant step forward in putting into perspective just what is the nuclear plant risk and what are the major contributors to that risk. It was from WASH-1400 that we learned that large LOCAs had been successfully designed out as a safety threat and that, in fact, there were other contributors more important to safety. In particular, WASH-1400, together with the first major industry PRAs,[8,9] made it clear that the most frequently occurring initiators in the core damage sequences were small LOCAs; the loss of off-site power, the external event initiators of earthquakes and fires, the failure of critical support systems such as service water, ventilation and component cooling water, and the loss of main feedwater. These findings have been confirmed by PSA studies in the United Kingdom, Germany, France and Japan.

For boiling water reactors, transients are the dominant initiators in the core damage sequences. The most visible transients include loss of feedwater, turbine trip without bypass, closure of main steam isolation valves, loss of off-site power and the external events of fires and earthquakes. Sweden, with its extensive experience with BWRs, has reached similar conclusions.

It was also learned from the comprehensive safety studies and PSAs that the rank order of contributors to risk are very plant specific and very dependent on what damage index is under study. In particular, depending on the specific health effect, the rank order was different, and very different between health effects and core damage frequency. This was due principally to the capability of containment systems to contain most core damage scenarios.

The importance of a comprehensive treatment of dependent failures Comprehensive risk assessments have made it clear that equipment and personnel dependencies play a very important role in the risk of a nuclear plant. These studies have indicated that functional and shared equipment intersystem dependencies, spatially dependent physical interactions, common cause failures of components of the same design, construction and maintenance, and human action dependencies constitute important contributors to plant risk.

The importance of human response in recovering from degraded state of operation Human error is one of the most important contributors to the risk of nuclear power plants. Generally, this is the result of the dependences on operator actions for short-term response to abnormal conditions coupled with a relatively short time that is available to diagnose and take corrective action.

It is extremely important to be able to take credit for operator actions when assessing the safety of a plant. For example, the opportunities to recover a plant from a degraded state should be clearly exposed to enable the development of adequate emergency procedures. The types of operator actions that are now analysed as part of contemporary risk assessment practices are operator failures to take procedural actions, the likelihood of operators successfully restoring failed systems, the operator initiating a system when automatic initiation has failed, or other innovative recovery actions, depending on the specific circumstances of the accident.

The result of what has been learned by these human error studies is much better operating procedures and, most likely, safer plants.

The role of external events In the studies that have been performed, external events, mostly earthquakes and fires, are important contributors to risk.[12] This was especially true for older plants. In part, this is because, for older plants, the safety equipment, the associated support systems, and the buildings in which these components are housed were not designed and constructed to the same seismic qualification requirements as the newer plants. Similarly, separation and independence requirements for fire protection were not nearly as stringent when the older plants were designed and constructed.

The other reason for the high contribution from these external events is the considerable uncertainty associated with their occurrence frequency and the structural and component response to such events.

Depending on plant-specific factors, other external events such as flooding may also be important risk contributors.

The importance of understanding the risk from shutdown events The risk of a potential accident had been believed to be inherently greater at power operation than at cold shut-down. This is primarily supported by the following factors: during cold shut-down, the decay heat generation rate is lower, the stored energy in the core and the reactor coolant system is less, the fission product inventory is smaller, and a longer time is available for recovery actions. Recent experience and PSA findings have indicated, however, that the risk of a serious accident that is initiated during shut-down is not sufficiently small as to be neglected. This is due to:

● The existence of a degraded plant configuration and a more relaxed set of technical specifications for equipment operability.
● Lack of emergency procedures and guidelines for classifying emergency action levels for shut-down conditions.

It is evident from the analysis of shut-down risk that operator actions in response to abnormal shut-down conditions are very important. Procedures and training that cover abnormal conditions and alternative cooling schemes are also important. In addition, instrumentation and alarms to provide warning and to improve operator actions may also be needed.

The role of containment in controlling risk Until the Zion and Indian Point PSAs, all core melt scenarios were assumed to eventually involve containment failure. These landmark PSAs and others to follow made it clear that, for many plants, only a small percentage of the core melt scenarios actually result in early containment failure. The central basis for this important finding was a much more detailed analysis of the capacity of the containments to withstand loads. In particular, it was found that the pressure capacity for most containments was two to four times the design pressure. As a result, the frequencies of accidents with early overpressurization and large releases tend to be much lower than those for core damage.

Based on the results and findings of past PSAs, a number of containment design enhancements have been considered. For example, a containment design improvement that has been approved by the NRC is the implementation of a hardened vent capability for the BWRs with Mark 1

containments. To minimize the probability of dry well linear melt-through
for BWR Mark 1 containment, it was recommended to establish the capability
to provide fire water to the dry well spray sparger. In addition to the fission
product scrubbing function provided by the dry well spray operation, the
risk of dry well liner melt-through can also be decreased by the accumulation
of spray water on the dry well floor. Note that a similar enhancement has
also been considered for PWRs to reduce core concrete interaction. For
containments with ice condensers, it was proposed to use an uninterruptible
power supply for the hydrogen igniters.

The importance of evacuation as an element of emergency response In the
early full-scope PSAs that included consequence analysis, it was shown that
the public health risk from nuclear plant accidents is very small. Furthermore,
the results from more recent studies indicate that even under the assumption
of no immediate protective actions, the risks of early and latent health effects
are very low in relation to existing goals and standards of acceptable risk.
The result is that extensive evacuation is not necessary for purposes of public
safety. The reason is that risk studies indicate that, in general, 90 to 95 per
cent of the early fatalities and serious injuries resulting from exposure to the
immediate life threatening dose occur within 1 or 2 miles of the release point.

For the case of latent effects, evacuation is not an important factor
because, based on current models, most long-term health effects are predicted
to occur as a result of chronic exposure to radiation deposited on the ground
long after the prompt protective actions have been completed. The risk of
latent health effects is thus rather insensitive to the specific protective actions
adopted, such as evacuation and sheltering. It was shown in the Risk
Management and Emergency Planning Study for the United States' Seabrook
Station that between 70 and 95 per cent of the risk that can be avoided
through evacuation would be realized for an evacuation distance between
1 and 2 miles, respectively.

The extremely small additional risk reduction that is achieved with
evacuation from 2 to 10 miles is matched by sheltering the same population
segment. Similar results have been obtained from a major study of a BWR
plant.

Future Directions

The above achievements of risk management of nuclear power plants provide
a background to discuss future directions. The future direction of nuclear
plant risk management will most likely be driven by the following factors:

- Regulatory activities
- Involvement of nuclear plant/owner operator management
- Advancements in understanding accident phenomena

- Advancements in plant hardware, software and personnel training
- Upgrading of PSA application packages

Regulatory activities The nuclear power industry throughout the world is extremely regulatory oriented. Much of the risk management process is dictated by what the regulators and authorities establish in the way of requirements for licences. To be sure, industry can influence the regulatory process by taking the initiative on risk issues. An example of such an initiative is an aggresive use of PSA in the assessment and risk management of its plants. Obviously, if industry demonstrates excellent safety practices using PSA as the underpin of the risk management process, then most likely, the authorities are going to be much more inclined to adopt some of the same methods. On the other hand, if industry is passive in taking the lead on risk management practices, then the regulators will dominate the thinking and development of the risk management activity. Because risk is such a plant-specific phenomenon, it would clearly seem that the best course is for industry, indeed, to play an active role in the development of future risk management methods.

Involvement of nuclear plant owner/operator management Realizing the full potential of such modern risk management tools as PSA is very dependent on just how involved the management is in the overall risk management process. The potential will certainly not be realized if all the focus is just on complying with regulations. On the other hand, managements that seize the opportunity to use such progressive methods as PSA in the risk management and quality performance process should receive enormous benefits. Until such methods are incorporated into the fundamental decision-making process governing plant operations, management will fall short of taking the initiative to influence the future direction of regulations.

Advancements in understanding accident phenomena A better understanding of the physical processes that are involved during the progression of an accident is important to the quality of future risk management techniques and, thus, their general acceptance. For example, recent advances in experimental and analytical investigations into the physical and chemical processors of radionuclide transport during core melt accidents have provided a better basis for quantifying the uncertainty associated with the source term following an accident. Other issues that are associated with the understanding of accident progression include:

- Conditions under which there is failure of main coolant pump seals
- Arrest of core degradation before vessel breach
- Temperature-induced failure of the hot leg in high-pressure sequences in PWRs

- Basemat melt-through of PWR containments
- PWR containment loads during high-pressure melt ejection
- Hydrogen production in the in-vessel and ex-vessel phases in PWRs
- Drywell shell melt-through in BWR Mark I containments

All of these issues have been identified by NUREG-1150[11] as important to the future development of risk management. The main contribution from increasing our state of knowledge on accident phenomena is increased confidence in the risk models that are developed as a basis for risk management. It is particularly important to better understand the protection provided by passive systems, such as vessels, containment structures and basemat integrity, to decrease the uncertainty of the likelihood of a release. These insights will form the basis for accident management strategies such as severe accident mitigation procedures, calculational aids and accident progression monitoring instrumentation. Such knowledge is also fundamental to guiding advanced designs of future nuclear plants.

Advancements in plant hardware, software and personnel training The way these advancements affect the future of risk management is again to make risk models more realistic and accurate representations of the plants involved; that is, the uncertainty in the models can be greatly reduced through improvements in hardware, software and personnel training.

Hardware changes that can increase safety and decrease uncertainty, for example, are those in which accident mitigation becomes less dependent on active systems. Of course, this is the direction being taken in the advanced designs of nuclear plants and many of the modifications of existing plants. Other hardware changes receiving increasing attention include 'bunkered' cooling systems and back-up containment systems such as the filtered-vented containment idea. In these systems, the trend is towards passive, rather than active, components. None of these systems should be seriously considered without the use, for example, of a PSA-based risk model to quantify the impact on risk.

The software opportunities track increased monitoring and diagnostics capability very well. Improvements in software provide not only better real-time information on plant conditions but also a tremendous data resource that can greatly enhance the quality of the risk models developed.

The main point concerned with training is the way that such modern risk management techniques as PSA can influence it. PSAs are extremely valuable for providing visibility into what can go wrong at the plant. The key to recovering from a degraded state of the plant is to understand the context of any operator action that may be taken. Such information greatly minimizes the chance of doing the wrong thing as a result of not understanding the proper context of the accident involved. The scenarios that make up the risk model should be fundamental to the training process as they are, indeed, specific to the plant involved and represent the best possible picture of the nature and consequences of a degraded plant condition.

Upgrading of PSA application packages The opportunity exists to develop very powerful plant-specific risk management tools that can indeed be the foundation for meaningful accident management. These tools will require the modification and integration of existing software packages as well as the development of new ones. The path seems fairly clear on what needs to be done and how to do it. These advanced risk management packages should be able to answer such questions as: 'What is the core damage frequency?' 'What is the likelihood of release of different mixes and strengths of radioactive material?' and 'What are the health and cost effects to the public?' as well as:

1. What is the cost as well as the performance and the safety impact of proposed plant changes: e.g. hardware, software or procedures?
2. What is the risk from all causes, including external events, human errors of commission and sabotage?
3. What is the best strategy for emergency response?
4. Given a particular accident sequence, what are the best accident management options?

To facilitate the utility of the risk management software packages, they need to be structured for the specific user involved. For example, it is possible that they should be cast into three basic packages serving such distinct user groups as risk assessors, risk managers and those responsible for accident management and emergency response. The characterizing of the software packages or workstations in this manner would most likely be a major boost to the general acceptance of PSA as the underlying basis for quantitative risk management.

14.8 CONCLUSION

The risk management and safety engineering activities in the nuclear industry have been enormously effective in making electricity from nuclear power plants a very attractive energy option for societies throughout the world. While the general acceptance of nuclear power is more driven by political considerations than technical issues, it is believed that a good technical effort of operating plants safely will eventually overcome present anti-nuclear positions.

The safety engineering activities, stimulated by the work of such investigators as Farmer, Rasmussen and several key investigators in industry, have added much to bringing order and real meaning to the process of risk management. There now is a bona fide science of risk analysis and management that provides the owners and regulators of nuclear power plants with the insights and perspectives necessary to know with considerable confidence not only what the risk is but also, more importantly, what is contributing to it. The latter allows the effective use of resources to keep the risk levels under control.

A significant fall-out of the progress made in quantitative risk assessment in the nuclear power field, for example, is its adoption in other major industries including chemical, space and defence. It is clear that the logical principles applied in such disciplines as probabilistic risk assessment are fundamental to the engineering of quality products, whatever they may be.

ACKNOWLEDGEMENT

The author wishes to acknowledge the extensive effort of John P. Kindinger of the PLG staff who contributed valuable research and editorial assistance.

REFERENCES

1. Nero, A. V., Jr: *A Guidebook to Nuclear Reactors*, University of California Press, Berkeley, Los Angeles, London, 1979.
2. Farmer, F. R.: The Growth of Reactor Safety Criteria in the United Kingdom, Anglo-Spanish Nuclear Power Symposium, Madrid, November 1964.
3. Garrick, B. J., and W. C. Gekler: Reliability Analysis of Nuclear Power Plant Protective Systems, HN-190, US Atomic Energy Commission, May 1967.
4. Garrick, B. J.: *United Systems Safety Analysis for Nuclear Power Plants*, PhD thesis, University of California, Los Angeles, California, 1968.
5. US Nuclear Regulatory Commission: Reactor Safety Study: An Assessment of Accident Risks in US Commercial Nuclear Power Plants, report WASH-1400 (NUREG-75/014), October 1975.
6. Garrick, B. J., *et al.* at Pickard, Lowe and Garrick, Inc.: OPSA, Oyster Creek Probabilistic Safety Analysis, draft, prepared for Jersey Central Power and Light Company, August 1979.
7. Kaplan, S., and B. J. Garrick: On the Qualitative Definition of Risk, *Risk Analysis*, vol. 1, no. 1, 1981.
8. Pickard, Lowe and Garrick, Inc., Westinghouse Electric Corporation, and Fauske and Associates, Inc., *Zion Probabilistic Safety Study*, prepared for Commonwealth Edison Company, September 1981.
9. Pickard, Lowe and Garrick, Inc.: Westinghouse Electric Corporation, and Fauske and Associates, Inc., *Indian Point Probabilistic Safety Study*, prepared for Consolidated Edison Company of New York, Inc., and the New York Power Authority, March 1982.
10. PRA Procedures Guide—A Guide to the Performance of PRAs for Nuclear Power Plants, NUREG/CR-2300, January 1983.
11. US Nuclear Regulatory Commission: Severe Accident Risks: An Assessment for Five US Nuclear Power Plants, report NUREG-1150, draft, April 1989.
12. Garrick, B. J.: Lessons Learned from 21 Nuclear Plant PRAs, *Nuclear Technology*, February 1989.

FIFTEEN

PROCESS INDUSTRY SAFETY

T. A. KLETZ

15.1 THE MANAGEMENT OF SAFETY

In the process industries, as in other industries, there is a wide variation in performance. Hazard study procedures similar to those described below[1] are followed by many companies, but some small companies do not see the need for these systematic procedures and many companies, large and small, do not always follow in practice the procedures they advocate in theory.

Hazard Study 1

Safety studies should start at the earliest stage of design, the conceptual or business analysis stage, when we decide which product to make, by what route and where to locate the plant. At this stage it may be possible to *avoid* hazards by choosing alternative products that are less hazardous to manufacture, by choosing a route that avoids hazardous raw materials or intermediates or by locating the plant away from urban areas. Locating a plant near the source of raw materials may avoid the need to transport hazardous materials.[2]

Hazard Study 2

There is another opportunity to avoid hazards when the flowsheet is drawn up, that is when the drawing showing the main items of equipment and their principle interconnections, flow rates and operating conditions is produced. We may be able to specify designs of equipment that contain the minimum amount of hazardous material ('What you don't have, can't leak') and we may be able to use non-flammable or non-toxic auxiliary materials such as solvents, catalysts or heat-transfer media.[2]

Hazard Study 3

A third opportunity to identify hazards occurs when the line diagrams are complete. Hazard and operability studies (hazops) are widely used. Each line is examined in turn by a team of designers and the commissioning manager under an independent chairman. The team ask if no flow or reverse flow could occur in the line under examination. If it could, they ask if it would be hazardous or prevent efficient operation and, if so, what changes in design or method of operation would overcome the hazard or operating problem. The team then applies similar questioning to greater and lesser flows, temperature, pressure and any other important parameters. Finally, they ask about the effect of changes in concentration or the presence of additional materials or phases. These questions should be asked about all lines, including steam, water, drains and other service lines, for all modes of operation, start-up, shut-down and preparation for maintenance, as well as normal operation[3] (Fig. 15.1).

Hazop is a powerful technique for identifying potential problems but at this stage of design it is too late to avoid the hazards and all we can do is *control* them by *adding on* protective equipment. Unfortunately many companies who carry out hazops do not carry out the earlier studies. Their safety professionals do not get involved and their safety studies do not take place until late in design and safety then becomes an expensive (though necessary) addition to capital cost. If they carried out the two earlier studies they would be able, in many cases, to design plants that are both cheaper and safer.[2]

Of course, not all hazards can be avoided and many have to be controlled. The principle followed is defence in depth: if one line of defence fails there are others in reserve. Most of the materials handled, whether flammable, toxic or corrosive, are hazardous only when they escape from the plant and therefore the first line of defence is to minimize leaks by sound design, construction and operation and, in particular, by following any relevant codes of practice (see Sec. 15.2). The other lines of defence are:

1. Detecting leaks promptly, by automatic equipment and by regular tours of the plant.
2. Giving warning of leaks so that those people who are not required can leave the area and others can take any necessary action (see Sec. 15.5).
3. Isolating leaks by remotely operated emergency isolation valves. We cannot install them in every place where a leak might occur but we can

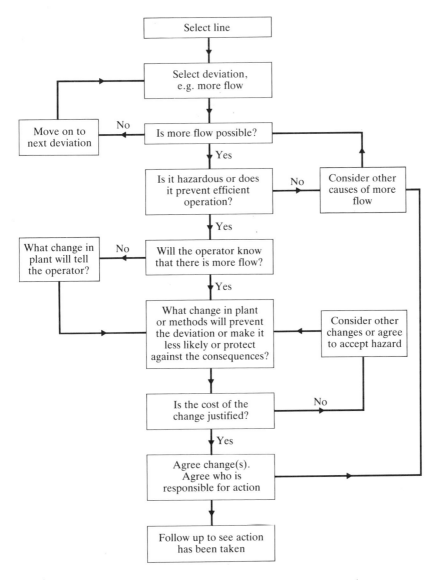

Figure 15.1 Hazop procedure. *(Source: Institution of Chemical Engineers.)*

install them where experience shows that the probability of a leak is higher than usual or the consequences of a leak are particularly serious.

4. Dispersing leaks of flammable gas by open construction; confining leaks of liquid by bunding and drainage; confining leaks of toxic gas (if possible) unless they can be dispersed before they reach places to which untrained people have access.

5. Preventing leaks of flammable gas or liquid from igniting by removing all known sources of ignition. This may seem to be one of the strongest lines of defence but is actually one of the weakest. So little energy is needed to ignite a leak that despite our attempts to remove known sources, many leaks do ignite (see Sec. 15.5).
6. Finally, minimizing fire damage by fire protection (with insulation or water spray) and by fire-fighting; minimizing the spread of fire by building plants in blocks with spaces between them, like the fire breaks in a forest; minimizing the damage caused by an explosion by a spacious layout and by building blast-resistant buildings.

A common failing is to rely on the inner lines of defence, that is those listed last, as they are considered impregnable, and neglect the outer ones. When the inner ones fail there is nothing to fall back on. Effective loss prevention lies far from the ultimate event (see Sec. 15.5).

Hazops often recommend many changes in design and checks should therefore be made to make sure that they have been carried out.

Hazard Study 4

Many incidents have occurred because construction teams did not follow the design in detail or did not do well, in accordance with good engineering practice (see below), details that were left to their discretion. One of the most effective actions that companies can take, to prevent serious incidents, is to specify designs in detail and then inspect thoroughly, during and after construction. The purpose is to make sure that the design has been followed and that details not specified in the design have been constructed in accordance with good engineering practice. The construction inspector should be on the lookout for errors that no one would dream of forbidding (for examples see Ref. 4, Chapter 16).

Hazard Study 5

After construction and before commissioning, a new plant should be inspected for everyday physical hazards such as means of escape, guarding, etc.

Hazard Study 6

Changes in design are often made during commissioning. They should be carefully considered to make sure they have no unforeseen effects[5] and, in addition, they should be systematically reviewed when the plant has settled down.

Ongoing Studies

Plants cannot be made safe by design alone. Although safety by design should always be our aim, it is often impossible or too expensive and we have to rely on procedures: training, instructions, audits, tests, inspections, learning the lessons of past accidents and so on. These procedures are subject to a form of corrosion more rapid than that which affects the steelwork and can vanish without trace in a few months once managers lose interest. A continuous management effort is needed to make sure that the procedures are maintained.

Areas of particular concern are the preparation of equipment for maintenance, the control of modifications and the testing of equipment such as trips and alarms, relief valves and pressure systems. Many accidents have occurred because these procedures were poor or non-existent or, more often, were not followed.

Legislation and Codes of Practice

The legislative control of plant design and operation varies from country to country. In the United Kingdom the regulations are mainly 'inductive', that is, they define an objective but do not say how it should be achieved, though advice is usually available in a code of practice or guidance note. There are also industry and company codes. Failure to follow a recognized code is *prima facie* evidence that the plant or method of working is not safe 'so far as is reasonably practicable', but the company can argue that the code is not applicable or that it is doing something else that is as safe or safer. In other countries, including the United States, there are many more detailed

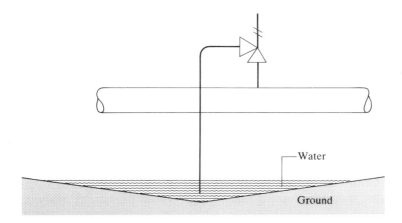

Figure 15.2 No code of practice says that relief valve tail pipes must not discharge into puddles. It is obvious; it is good engineering practice, but it happens.

regulations that have to be followed to the letter, whether or not they make the plant safer.

Many points are not written down in codes of practice or guidance notes as they are considered obvious—they are good engineering or operating practice—but accidents occur when they are ignored. We need to look out for errors no one has ever dreamt of prohibiting. For example, a pipeline carrying liquefied gas was protected by a small relief valve which discharged onto the ground. The ground was uneven and after rain the end of the tailpipe was below the surface of a puddle (Fig. 15.2). The puddle froze and the pipeline was overpressured. No code states that relief valve tailpipes should not discharge into puddles. It is obvious and it is good engineering practice, but no one noticed anything wrong when it occurred.

15.2 THE IDENTIFICATION AND ASSESSMENT OF HAZARDS

The traditional method of identifying hazards was to build the plant and see what happened. If an accident occurred, the design or method of operation was changed to prevent it happening again (or it was blamed on human error and someone was told to be more careful; see Sec. 15.3). This 'dog is allowed one bite' philosophy was defensible when the size of an accident was limited, but is no longer acceptable now that we keep dogs as big as Bhopal (over 2000 killed) or even Flixborough (28 killed) (see Sec. 15.5). We need to identify hazards before accidents occur. Hazard and operability studies (hazops), already described, are widely used for this purpose, particularly for studying new designs or plants that have been extensively modified.

On all existing plants safety audits should be carried out from time to time. They should look at technical hazards and procedures (for example the way in which protective equipment is tested or prepared for maintenance) as well as physical hazards.

Having identified the hazards on a new or existing plant we have to decide how far to go in removing them (or protecting people from the consequences). We cannot remove all hazards, however trivial or unlikely to occur, and in the United Kingdom the law does not require us to do so. We have to do only what is 'reasonably practicable', weighing in the balance the size of a risk and the cost, in money, time and trouble, of removing it. In the process industries hazard analysis [also called hazan, risk analysis, quantitative risk assessment (QRA) or probabilistic risk assessment (PRA)] has been widely used to help us decide whether a risk is so large that it should be reduced or so small that it can be ignored, at least for the time being.[3]

In applying hazard analysis we have to answer three questions:

1. How often will an accident occur? Experience can sometimes tell us the answer but often there is no experience and we have to estimate an answer from the known failure rates of the components of the system, using fault tree analysis.
2. How big will the consequences be, to employees, to members of the public and to the plant? Again, whenever possible experience should tell us the answer but often there is no experience and we have to use synthetic methods.[6]
3. Finally, we compare the answers to the first two questions with a target or criterion. Various criteria, usually based on the risk to life, have been proposed and recently the UK Health and Safety Executive have made proposals.[7]

Hazop is a technique that can (and should) be used on all new designs. Hazan, on the other hand, is a selective technique. There is no need, and we do not have the resources, to quantify every hazard on every plant. Having identified a hazard, our experience or a code of practice usually tells us how far we should go in removing it. Hazan should be used only when this case for and against action is finely balanced and there is no experience or code of practice to guide us.

Hazards cannot be assessed until they have been identified and therefore hazan comes after hazop. However, the major hazards on a plant are usually known by the time hazard study 2 is carried out and should be assessed at this stage. Whenever possible they should be removed by a change in design rather than controlled by added-on protective equipment, as already discussed.

The most frequent source of serious errors in hazard analysis is failing to identify all the hazards or all the ways in which they can occur. We quantify with ever greater accuracy the hazards we have identified and ignore others.

15.3 HUMAN ERROR

According to many accident statistics, most of the accidents that occur in the process industries are due to 'human error' or 'human failing', meaning by that the failings of the injured men or their workmates rather than the failings of the managers or designers. (They, apparently, are not human or do not fail.) This categorization is not very helpful as (1) it groups together accidents that differ widely in nature and in the action required to prevent them happening again and (2) it does not lead to constructive action. Instead it suggests that we should merely tell someone to be more careful.

It is more helpful to divide so-called human error accidents into the following four groups, though they merge into each other and sometimes more than one factor is at work:[8]

1. *Incidents preventable by better training or instruction*, sometimes called mistakes as the intention is wrong. Someone, operator, maintenance worker, designer, even a manager, did not know what to do. Sometimes he/she lacked elementary knowledge of the way equipment worked, of the properties of the materials handled, of company rules or procedures or of the nature of his/her duties; sometimes he/she lacked sophisticated knowledge or skills, such as those needed for fault diagnosis. Sometimes people are given contradictory instructions. For example, they may have been asked to complete an urgent batch or repair by a particular time and left with the impression, never clearly stated, that normal safety procedures could be relaxed. If a manager or supervisor goes on about the importance of output or repairs and never mentions safety the listeners are left with the impression that output or repairs are all that is required and they try to give what is required. What you do not say is as important as what you do say.

   To prevent these accidents we need better training or instructions, and clear instructions in ambiguous situations. However, if a task is difficult or error prone we may be more successful if we change the plant design or methods of working.

2. *Incidents that occur because someone knows what to do but decides not to do it*. These errors are sometimes called violations but often the person concerned genuinely believes that breaking the rule was justified. At other times, of course, someone breaks a rule to make the job easier. An operator may decide not to wear protective clothing or a manager may decide to keep a plant on line despite a leak.

   To prevent these incidents we need to convince those concerned that the rules are sound—we do not live in a society in which people will follow instructions blindly—and we need to monitor from time to time to check that they are being followed. We cannot convince people of the need for a rule by sending them a copy. We have to explain the rule and the reasons for it. We may then find out if the rule is unworkable. If the correct way of doing a job is difficult or time consuming it may be better to change the way the job is done.

3. *Incidents that occur because people are asked to undertake tasks beyond their physical or mental abilities*. For example, they may be asked to close a valve that is too stiff to operate or out of reach or they may be overloaded by too much information and become confused. To prevent these incidents we need to change the plant design or method of working.

4. *Incidents that occur as the result of a slip or lapse of attention*. For example, someone may forget to carry out a simple task such as closing a valve or

the wrong valve may be closed. The intention was correct but not the action. He/she knew what to do, intended to do it and was able to do it, but nevertheless forgot to do it or did it incorrectly. We cannot prevent these occasional slips and so we should try to avoid opportunities for them (or guard against their consequences or provide room for recovery) by changing the plant design or method of working.

Errors of this type do not occur because people are undertrained but because they are well trained. Routine tasks are delegated to the lower levels of the brain and are not continually monitored by the conscious mind. We would never get through the day if everything we do required our full attention so we put ourselves on auto-pilot. When something interrupts the smooth running of the programme, a slip occurs.

Senior managers often exhort their staff to do better but do not realize that their own actions, as distinct from exhortations, can directly influence the safety of the plant. When considering output, quality or efficiency they identify the problems, agree actions and ask for regular reports on progress. When considering safety they often think that exhortation is sufficient (see Sec. 15.5, An Accident Caused by Insularity).

15.4 LIVING WITH HUMAN ERROR AND EQUIPMENT FAILURE

Human beings are actually very reliable but there are many opportunities for error in the course of a day's work. Because so many hazardous materials are handled the lowest error rates obtainable—even when we have done what we can to reduce errors of the first two types by training and persuasion—may be too high. Automatic equipment is therefore widely used to replace operators or guard against the effects of their errors. It does not, however, eliminate the human element. If we automate an operation we no longer depend on the operator but we now depend on the people who design, install, test and maintain the automatic equipment and they also make mistakes. They may work under conditions of lower stress and may have time to check their work, so it may be right to use automatic equipment, but we should not kid ourselves that we have removed our dependence on people.

Equipment fails as well as people and, again, the lowest failure rates obtainable, at reasonable cost, may be too high. Increasingly, therefore, the process industries are trying to design plants that are user friendly, to borrow a computer phrase, that can withstand human error or equipment failure without serious effects on safety (and output). This can be done in the following ways, some of which have been mentioned already:

1. Use less hazardous material (intensification).
2. Use safer material instead (substitution) (see Sec. 15.5, Flixborough and Seveso).
3. Use hazardous material in the least hazardous form (attenuation).
4. Simplification: complexity means more opportunities for human error and more equipment that can fail (see Sec. 15.5, An Accident Caused by Insularity).
5. Limitation of effects, not by adding on protective equipment but by equipment design, by changing reaction conditions, by limiting the energy available (see Sec. 15.5, Seveso) or by eliminating hazardous phases, equipment or operations.
6. Avoid knock-on or domino effects.
7. Make incorrect assembly impossible.
8. Make the status of equipment (open or closed, on-line or off-line) clear.
9. Use equipment that can tolerate poor operation or maintenance.

These may seem obvious but until after Flixborough (Sec. 15.5) little or no thought was given to ways of reducing the inventory of hazardous material in a plant. People accepted whatever inventory was required by the design, confident of their ability to keep the lions under control. Flixborough weakened the public's confidence in that ability and Bhopal (Sec. 15.5) almost destroyed it. Now many companies are coming round to the view that they should see if they can keep lambs instead of lions: that is design more user-friendly plant. In many cases they can do so.[2] Such plants are often cheaper as well as safer as they contain less added-on protective equipment which is expensive to buy and maintain. In addition, if we can intensify, we need smaller equipment and the plant will be correspondingly cheaper.

15.5 CASE HISTORIES

The incidents discussed are mainly those that have hit the headlines but another is included to illustrate specific points.

Accident investigation is like peeling an onion. Beneath each layer of causes and recommendations lie other layers. The outer layers deal with the immediate technical causes, the middle layers with ways of avoiding the hazards and the inner layers with the underlying weaknesses in the management system.[3] The descriptions that follow try to bring out this layering effect.

Feyzin and Mexico City[9]

In 1966, at a refinery at Feyzin, France, a large ($1200\,m^3$) spherical pressure vessel containing liquefied propane burst on exposure to fire, killing 15 to 18 men (reports differ) and injuring about 80. It was at the time one of the worst incidents involving liquefied flammable gases (LFG) that had occurred and it made many, though not all, companies improve the designs of their LFG installations. It also led to a better understanding of the phenomena involved.

The incident started when an operator tried to drain water from the tank, a routine operation. There were two drain valves in series. He opened one valve fully and cracked open the second. There was no flow. He opened the second valve fully. The choke cleared suddenly; the handle came off one valve and the operator and his companions could not get it back on. The other valve was frozen solid. A cloud of vapour spread 150 m and after 25 minutes was ignited by a vehicle on a nearby road. The road had been closed by the police but the car approached down a side road. The fire flashed back to the sphere which was surrounded by flames. At this stage there was no explosion.

The sphere was fitted with water sprays but the water supply was inadequate. The firemen used most of the available water for cooling the neighbouring spheres, to prevent the fire spreading, in the belief that the relief valve would protect the vessel exposed to the fire. The ground under the sphere was level so any propane that did not evaporate or burn immediately accumulated under the sphere and burned later.

Ninety minutes after the fire started, the sphere burst. Men 140 m away were burned by a wave of propane that came over the compound wall. Flying debris broke the legs of an adjacent sphere which fell over and 45 minutes later this sphere also burst. Altogether, five spheres and two other pressure vessels burst and three were damaged. The fire spread to petrol and fuel oil tanks.

At first it was thought that as the vessels had burst their relief valves must have been too small. Later it was realized that the metal in the upper portions of the spheres had been softened by the heat and lost its strength. Below the liquid level the boiling liquid kept the metal cool.

Many detailed recommendations were made to improve the design of the draining systems on LFG vessels, including the fitting of remotely operated emergency isolation valves. Other recommendations were made to prevent fires escalating (Fig. 15.3):

1. Insulate vessels with fire-resistant insulation. It forms an immediate barrier to heat input and, unlike water spray, does not have to be commissioned. In some countries they now go further and cover LFG vessels with clean sand or gravel.

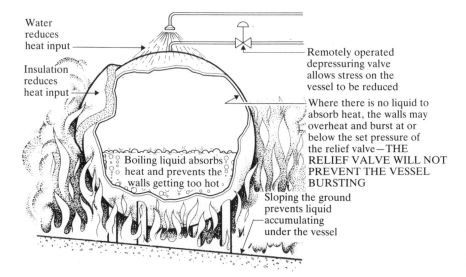

Water reduces heat input

Insulation reduces heat input

Remotely operated depressuring valve allows stress on the vessel to be reduced

Where there is no liquid to absorb heat, the walls may overheat and burst at or below the set pressure of the relief valve—THE RELIEF VALVE WILL NOT PREVENT THE VESSEL BURSTING

Boiling liquid absorbs heat and prevents the walls getting too hot

Sloping the ground prevents liquid accumulating under the vessel

Figure 15.3 How to protect pressure vessels from fire.

2. Provide an adequate supply of water for cooling the vessels.
3. Slope the ground so that spillages run off into a collection pit.
4. Fit an emergency depressuring valve so that the pressure in the vessel can be reduced, thus decreasing the strain on the metal.

There is some trade-off between these recommendations. If insulation is installed, less cooling water is needed and a smaller depressuring valve can be installed.

Feyzin was thus an incident that could have been prevented by better design, at the detailed level to prevent a similar leak and at another level to prevent a fire escalating. The former is not, of course, sufficient as leaks and fires can occur, and have occurred, for many different reasons.

It is difficult to avoid the hazard, if we wish to store fuel, but the quantities in store should be no greater than necessary. Today large quantities of propane are often stored refrigerated. The leak rate through a hole of a given size is less as the pressure is low (near atmospheric instead of about 10 bar) and the rate of evaporation is less as the temperature is lower ($-45°$C instead of ambient), an example of attenuation.

However, the fire would not have escalated if the firemen and the refinery staff had understood the limitations of the equipment and had used all the available water for cooling the vessel exposed to fire. They thought that the relief valve would prevent the vessel bursting. It will do so at ambient temperature but not if the metal gets too hot. Those concerned knew that metal softens when hot but they failed to apply their knowledge, a common failing. The accident could have been prevented by better training.

In the years following the fire I discussed it on many occasions with groups of design and operating staff, most of whom were professionally qualified. The reaction was usually the same. As the vessel burst the relief valve must have been too small or out of order or blocked. Only when they were assured that the relief was all right did they think of the correct cause. Another lesson of Feyzin is thus the need for some loss prevention training in undergraduate engineering courses. It should emphasize the importance of applying basic, not just advanced, knowledge.

Unfortunately not every company learned the lessons of Feyzin and in 1984 a similar, but far more serious, incident occurred in Mexico City in a plant for processing and distributing a butane/propane mixture. The incident started when a pipeline ruptured, for reasons which are not clear. The leak was ignited, 5 to 10 minutes later, probably by a ground level flare. Nineteen pressure vessels burst, some landing 1200 m away. According to official figures 542 people were killed, 4248 injured and about 10 000 made homeless, but unofficial estimates are higher. Many were living in a shanty town that had grown up next to the plant. If what we do not have, cannot leak, people who are not there cannot be killed and concentrations of people should not be allowed to grow next to a hazardous plant.

Although much of the plant was new the recommendations made after Feyzin had not been followed in its design. Unfortunately, the process industries do not always learn the lessons of the past and experience for which people have paid a high price is ignored or forgotten.

Flixborough[4,10]

The explosion at Flixborough, UK, in 1974 was a milestone in the history of the UK chemical industry. The destruction of the plant, the death of 28 men on site and extensive damage and injuries, though no deaths, in the surrounding villages showed that the hazards of the chemical industry were greater than had been generally believed by the public at large. In response to public concern the government set up an enquiry into the immediate causes and also an Advisory Committee on Major Hazards to consider wider questions. Their three reports[11] led to far-reaching changes in the procedures for the control of major industrial hazards. The long-term effects of the explosion thus extended far beyond the factory fence.

The plant on which the explosion occurred oxidized cyclohexane, a hydrocarbon similar to petrol in its physical properties, with air to a mixture of cyclohexanone and cyclohexanol, usually known as KA (ketone/alcohol) mixture and used for the manufacture of nylon. As the reaction was slow and the conversion had to be kept low to avoid the production of unwanted by-products, the inventory in the plant was large, many hundreds of tonnes. The reaction took place in the liquid phase in six reaction vessels, each holding about 20 tonnes. Unconverted raw material was recovered in a distillation section and recycled. Similar processes are operated, with variations in detail, in many plants throughout the world.

One of the reactors developed a crack and was removed for repair. In order to maintain production a temporary pipe was installed in its place. Because the reactors were mounted on a sort of staircase, so that liquid would overflow from one to another, this temporary pipe was not straight but contained two bends. Bellows, 28 inches in diameter, were installed between each reactor and these were left at each end of the temporary pipe.

The temporary pipe performed satisfactorily for two months until a slight rise in pressure occurred. The pressure was still well below the design pressure of the original equipment and the relief valve set point but nevertheless it caused the temporary pipe to twist. The bending moment was strong enough to tear the bellows and two 28-inch holes appeared in the plant. The cyclohexane was at a gauge pressure of about 10 bar (150 lb/in^2) and a temperature of about 150°C. It was thus under pressure above its normal boiling point (81°C) and a massive leak occurred, the liquid turning to vapour and spray. About 30 to 50 tonnes escaped in the 50 seconds that elapsed before ignition occurred. The source of ignition was probably a furnace some distance away.

The resulting vapour cloud explosion, one of the worst that has ever occurred, destroyed the oxidation unit and caused extensive damage to the rest of the site. In particular the company office block, about 100 m away, was destroyed and had the explosion occurred during office hours and not at 5 p.m. on a Saturday, the death toll might have been 128 instead of 28.

Following the explosion many recommendations were made for strengthening plant so that it can withstand an explosion, particularly control buildings, as most of the men killed were in such a building. However, the lessons to be learned from the disaster are mainly managerial. There should be a system for the control of plant modifications; their consequences should be assessed and they should be made to the same standard as the original plant.

One reason they were built to a lower standard is that there was no professionally qualified mechanical engineer on site. The works engineer had left and his replacement had not arrived. The men charged with the task of making and installing the temporary pipe had great practical experience and drive—they had the plant back on-line in a few days—but they did not realize that the pipe and its supports should have been designed by an expert in piping design. They did not know what they did not know. The only drawing was a full-size sketch in chalk on the workshop floor. The only support was a scaffolding structure on which the pipe rested.

As companies economize in staff, they should ensure that sufficient expertise is available. It is not sufficient to have experts on call if others do not know when to call them.

Perhaps the most important lesson to be drawn from Flixborough is the

need to avoid, whenever possible, large inventories of hazardous
The process operated was very inefficient, most of the raw mater
a 'free ride' and only about 5 per cent being converted per pass. Th
had become so used to such processes that it did not realize that
a reflection on the ability of its chemical engineers.[2] Other processes have
been intensified (redesigned so that the inventory in the process is smaller)
but not this one, partly because there is overcapacity in the industry and no
new plants have been built.

Flixborough started a debate on the extent to which and the means by
which government should control a hazardous industry. Detailed regulations
are obviously not appropriate for a complex, changing technology with only
a few plants in the country operating each process. The Advisory Committee
on Major Hazards[11] recommended that companies handling or storing more
than defined quantities of hazardous materials should prepare a 'safety case'
which identifies and assesses the hazards and shows how they are being
controlled. Emergency plans should be prepared and the public should be
informed. These proposals were accepted and were brought into force by the
CIMAH (Control of Industrial Major Accident Hazard) Regulations, 1984.
The ten years that elapsed before they came into force may seem long but
the procedure typifies the UK approach. There were extensive discussions
with industry and the resulting regulations were workable and generally
accepted. The same cannot be said of every country.

Seveso[4]

Seveso is a village near Milan, Italy, where, in 1976, a discharge from a
reactor (part of a process for manufacturing a herbicide) contaminated the
neighbourhood with dioxin, a highly toxic chemical. No one was killed but
250 people developed chloracne, a skin disease, and the area became
uninhabitable. No accident, even Bhopal (next subsection), has produced
greater 'legislative fall-out'. It led to the enactment by the European
Community of the Seveso Directive, which requires all companies that handle
more than defined quantities of hazardous materials to demonstrate that
they are capable of handling them safely. In the United Kingdom the Seveso
Directive was implemented by the CIMAH Regulations which were already
in the pipeline following Flixborough (last subsection).

The reactor at Seveso was heated by exhaust steam from a turbine and
the steam was normally too cool to overheat the reactor. However, the plant
was shutting down for the weekend, the turbine was on reduced load and
the steam was hotter than usual. The reactor was overheated, a runaway
reaction occurred and the contents of the reactor were discharged to
atmosphere through a bursting disc.

Italian law required the plant to shut down for the weekend, so Seveso
was due, in part, to well-meaning legislative interference.

There was no catchpot to collect the discharge from the bursting disc on the reactor. The catchpot may have been left out by the designers because they did not foresee that a runaway reaction might occur and they may have installed the bursting disc to guard against other sources of overpressure such as overfilling. However, there had been three runaways on earlier plants and it is not good practice to discharge any liquid to atmosphere.

Seveso could have been prevented by better design—by installing a catchpot—and by carrying out a hazard and operability study (Sec. 15.1) which would have forced the design team to ask what would happen if the steam temperature rose.

Bhopal[4]

This town in central India was the scene of the worst disaster in the history of the chemical industry. In 1984 a leak of a toxic chemical, methyl isocyanate (MIC), from a chemical plant, where it was used as an intermediate in the manufacture of the insecticide carbaryl, spread beyond the plant boundary, killing about 2000 people and injuring about 200 000. Most of the dead and injured were living in a shanty town that had grown up next to the plant.

The immediate cause of the disaster was the contamination of an MIC storage tank by several tonnes of water, probably a deliberate act of sabotage.[12] A runaway reaction occurred and the temperature and pressure rose. The relief valve lifted and MIC vapour was discharged to atmosphere. The protective equipment which should have prevented or minimized the release was out of order or not in full working order: the refrigeration system which should have cooled the storage tank was shut down, the scrubbing system which should have absorbed the vapour was not immediately available and the flare system which should have destroyed any vapour that got past the scrubbing system was out of use.

The first lesson to be learnt from the disaster is one of the lessons of Flixborough: 'What you do not have, cannot leak'. The material that leaked was not a product or raw material but an intermediate. It was convenient to store it, but it was not essential to do so. Following Bhopal, the company concerned, Union Carbide, and other companies greatly reduced their stocks of MIC and other hazardous intermediates. In many cases they eliminated the stocks entirely, using the intermediates as soon as they were produced. It is unfortunate that they did not heed the advice given after Flixborough.

If materials that are not there cannot leak, people who are not there cannot be killed. The death toll at Bhopal would have been lower if a shanty town had not been allowed to grow up near the plant (as at Mexico City; see the first subsection). It is, of course, much more difficult to prevent the spread of shanty towns than of permanent dwellings, but nevertheless companies should try to do so, buying and fencing land if necessary.

As already stated, the refrigeration, flare and scrubbing systems were not in full working order when the leak occurred. In addition the high temperature and pressure on the MIC tank were at first ignored as the instruments were known to be unreliable. The high-temperature alarm did not operate as the set-point had been raised and was too high. One of the main lessons of Bhopal is therefore the need to keep protective equipment in working order.

It is easy to buy safety equipment. All we need is money and if we make enough fuss we get it in the end. It is much more difficult to make sure that the equipment is kept in full working order when the initial enthusiasm has faded. All procedures, including testing and maintenance procedures, can vanish quickly once managers lose interest. A continuous management effort is needed to make sure that procedures are maintained (see Sec. 15.1).

The MIC storage tank was contaminated by substantial quantities of water and chloroform, up to a ton of water and $1\frac{1}{2}$ tons of chloroform, and this led to a complex series of runaway reactions. The precise route by which water entered the tank is unknown, but several theories have been put forward and sabotage seems the most likely.[12] If any of the suggested routes were possible then they should have been made impossible. Hazard and operability studies (see Sec. 15.1) are a powerful tool for identifying ways in which contamination and other unwanted deviations can occur. Since water was known to react violently with MIC, it should not have been allowed anywhere near it.

Note that contamination of the MIC was a triggering event rather than the underlying cause of the disaster. It would not have occurred if the MIC stock had been smaller, if there was no shanty town near the plant, if the protective equipment was in working order or if there was no water available near the stock tanks.

The Bhopal plant was half-owned by a US company and half-owned locally. The local company was responsible for the operation of the plant, as required by Indian law. In such joint ventures it is important to be clear who is responsible for safety, in design and operation. The technically more sophisticated partner has a special responsibility and should not go ahead unless they are sure that the operating partner has the knowledge, experience, commitment and resources necessary for handling hazardous materials. It cannot shrug off responsibility by saying that it is not in full control.

Did those who designed and operated the plant get sufficient training in loss prevention, as students and from their employers? In the United Kingdom all chemical engineering undergraduates get some training in loss prevention, but this is not the case in most other countries, including the United States.

At Bhopal there had been changes in staff and reductions in manning and the new recruits may not have been as experienced as the original team. However, the errors that were made, such as taking protective equipment out of commission, were basic ones that cannot be blamed on inexperience of a particular process.

Bhopal showed the need for companies to collaborate with local authorities and the emergency services in drawing up plans for handling emergencies.

Terrible though Bhopal was we should beware of overreaction such as suggestions that insecticides, or the whole chemical industry, are unnecessary. Insecticides, by increasing food production, have saved more lives than were lost at Bhopal. However, Bhopal was not an inevitable result of insecticide manufacture. By better design and operations, by learning from experience, further Bhopals can be prevented. As Bhopal shows, accidents are not due to lack of knowledge but failure to use the knowledge that is available. Bhopal (and Flixborough) remind us that one of the functions of management is to make sure that people, at all levels, have the skills and knowledge necessary for the job they have to perform.

An Accident Caused by Insularity[3]

Four men were killed, several injured and a compressor house was destroyed when a leak of ethylene—between 5 and 50 kg—inside a compressor house ignited. Examination of the wreckage showed that the source of the leak was a badly made joint on a small boreline.

The recommendations made to prevent similar explosions fell into four groups:

1. Ways of preventing leaks or making them less likely
2. Ways of minimizing their effects
3. Ways of reducing the probability of ignition
4. Underlying all these, ways of removing the managerial ignorance and incorrect beliefs that led to the accident

Most of the recommendations apply to other plants handling hazardous materials, particularly flammable liquids and gases, and many apply to all process plants.

Preventing leaks As already stated, the leak of ethylene occurred from a badly made joint on a small-diameter line, of about $\frac{1}{2}$ inch internal diameter. The joint was a special type, designed for use at high pressures, and assembling it needed more skill than assembling an ordinary flanged joint. At one time the assembly of these high-pressure joints was carried out by a few specially trained craftsmen, but this was resented by the others and so all craftsmen were trained to the necessary standard, or so it was thought. Unfortunately some of the newly trained men did not have the necessary skill, or perhaps did not understand the importance of using their skill to the full, and the standard of joint making deteriorated. Following the explosion a return was made to the original system.

In addition, a standard for the quality of joints was specified, an attempt was made to explain to the craftsmen why a high quality of joint making was necessary, a system of inspection was set up and better tools were developed. These actions reduced the leak frequency by a factor of about twenty.

Although leaks were quite common, about ten per month, mostly very small, nobody worried about them. They were often left until a convenient time for a shut-down. The attitude was, 'They can't ignite because we have eliminated all sources of ignition'. Unfortunately this view was incorrect. It is almost impossible to eliminate all sources of ignition and not everything that could have been done to eliminate them had in fact been done (see later).

Another reason for the large number of leaks was the large number of joints and valves. The plant consisted of several parallel streams, each containing three main items of equipment. Their reliability was not high and so, to maintain production, a vast number of cross-overs and isolation valves was installed so that any item could be used in any stream. The money spent in providing all this flexibility might have been better spent in investigating the reasons why on-line time was so poor. Later plants, built after the explosion, had fewer streams and fewer cross-overs.

Minimizing the effects of leaks The methods recommended are listed in the section on defence in depth (see Sec. 15.1, hazard study 3). In particular, three of the four men killed had ample time to leave the building, had they been warned, as the leak did not ignite until about 8 minutes after it was detected.

Reducing the probability of ignition Possible sources of ignition were faulty electrical equipment and loose unearthed metal objects on which a charge of static electricity from a leak could accumulate. There were no regular inspections of the special electrical equipment suitable for use in areas where leaks of flammable gas can occur and, as with joint making, the standard of workmanship had been allowed to deteriorate.

Managerial insularity The explosion would not have occurred if the people who designed and operated the plant had realized that sources of ignition can never be completely removed and so we should do everything possible to prevent and disperse leaks.

This was accepted on other plants on the same site. Explosions and fires had occurred on these plants in the past and this lesson (and others) had been learnt from them. However, these lessons had not been passed on to the plant where the explosion occurred or they were passed on but nobody listened. The plant staff believed that their problems were different. If you handle ethylene as a gas it is perhaps not obvious that you can learn anything from an explosion on, say, a plant handling propylene as liquid. An explosion on such a plant had occurred in the same company, a few miles away, about 10 years earlier. The recommendations made, and acted upon, were very similar to those outlined above. However, no one on the plant where the later explosion occurred took any notice. The plant was a monastery—a group of people isolating themselves by choice from the outside world—but fortunately the explosion blew down the monastery walls. Not only did the staff adopt many of the beliefs and practices current elsewhere, such as building open compressor houses so that leaks can disperse more easily, but they developed a new attitude of mind, a much greater willingness to learn from the outside world.

Individual parts of the company were allowed considerable autonomy in technical matters. It had been formed by an amalgamation of independent companies who still cherished their freedom of action and it was felt that attempts to impose uniform standards and practices would lead to resentment. The explosion did not produce a reexamination of this philosophy though perhaps it should have done. It probably never occurred to the senior managers of the company that their organizational structure had any bearing on the explosion—it was due to a badly made joint. Joints must be better made in future and no expense was spared to achieve this end. The management philosophy was not changed until many years later when recession caused different parts of the company to be merged.

Because the senior managers of the company might have prevented the accident by changing their organization and philosophy, we should not use this as an excuse for doing less than possible at other levels. The chain of causation could have been broken at any level from senior manager to craftsman. The accident might not have occurred if the organization had been different. Equally it would not have occurred if the joint had been properly made.

To sum up, the immediate technical recommendations were to improve joint making, install leak detectors and emergency isolation valves, warn people when a leak occurred and eliminate known sources of ignition. The hazard could be reduced by open construction and by simplification of the plant. However, all these recommendations will prevent the last accident rather than the next; to prevent that greater willingness to learn from others was needed.

Conclusion

Readers who have got this far may feel that the process industries have a poor safety record. In fact, the best companies have a safety record far better than industry as a whole and many plants go for months without a dangerous occurrence or even a minor injury, but this chapter has described failures, and the actions needed for further improvement, rather than successes.

When a plant was starting up after a shut-down for overhaul and repair there was a leak of hot, flammable liquid from a flanged joint. It did not ignite but nevertheless there was an inquiry. (All near misses should be investigated as well as injuries.) Afterwards the manager said, 'We broke and remade 2000 joints during the shut-down and got one wrong. That is the only one anyone has heard about'.

Unfortunately when handling flammable liquids we have to work to very high standards and one leaking joint in 2000 is one too many. Afterwards the gaskets in half the joints, those exposed to liquid rather than vapour, were replaced by a more user-friendly type—spiral wound ones which, if they do leak, do so at a lower rate.

Why were spiral wound gaskets not installed during construction? The company left the decision to the design contractor.

15.6 FURTHER READING

The standard work on the subject of this chapter is F. P. Lees, *Loss Prevention in the Process Industries*, Butterworths, Tonbridge, 1980 (2 volumes, 1316 pages). Shorter works are:

Fawcell, H. H., and W. S. Wood (eds): *Safety and Accident Prevention in Chemical Operations*, 2nd ed., John Wiley, New York, 1982, 910 pages (a collection of articles of variable length and quality by numerous authors).
Marshall, V. V.: *Major Chemical Hazards*, Ellis Horwood, Chichester, 1987, 200 pages.
Wells, G. L.: *An Introduction to Loss Prevention*, Godwin, Harlow, 1980.
King, R.: *Safety in the Process Industries*, Butterworth, Oxford, 1990, 762 pages.
See also Refs 2, 3, 4, 8 and 9.

REFERENCES

1. Hawksley, J. L.: *Plant/Operations Prog.*, vol. 7, no. 4, p. 265, October 1988.
2. Kletz, T. A.: *Plant Design for Safety—A User-friendly Approach*, Hemisphere, New York, 1991.
3. Kletz, T. A.: *Hazop and Hazan—Notes on the Identification and Assessment of Hazards*, 3rd ed., Institution of Chemical Engineers, Rugby, 1992.
4. Kletz, T. A.: *Learning from Accidents in Industry*, Butterworths, Oxford, 1988.
5. Kletz, T. A.: *Chem. Engng Prog.*, vol. 72, no. 11, p. 48, November 1976.
6. Lees, F. P.: *Loss Prevention in the Process Industries*, Butterworths, Oxford, 1980.
7. Health and Safety Executive: *Risk Criteria for Land-Use Planning in the Vicinity of Major Industrial Hazards*, HMSO, London, 1989.

8. Kletz, T. A.: *An Engineer's View of Human Error*, 2nd ed., Institution of Chemical Engineers, Rugby, 1991.
9. Kletz, T. A.: *What Went Wrong?—Case Histories of Process Plant Disasters*, 2nd edn., chap. 8, Gulf Publishing Co., Houston, Texas, 1988.
10. Parker, R. J. (Chairman): *The Flixborough Disaster—Report of the Court of Inquiry*, HMSO, London, 1975.
11. Advisory Committee on Major Hazards: *First, Second and Third Reports*, HMSO, London, 1976, 1979 and 1984.
12. Kalelkar, A.: *Preventing Major Chemical and Related Accidents*, Symposium Series 110, p. 553, Institution of Chemical Engineers, Rugby, 1988.

PART
FOUR

THE EPILOGUE

SIXTEEN

THE ROLE OF REGULATIONS AND CODES

D. E. ALLEN

Regulations and codes are instruments to protect the safety, health and welfare of people from events or conditions that can be controlled by man. This book is concerned with large man-made facilities such as buildings, bridges, dams, power stations and marine structures. This chapter on the role of regulations and codes concentrates primarily on buildings, bridges and offshore structures but the principles apply to other facilities.

Events or conditions affecting people that can be controlled through regulations and codes for large man-made facilities include structural collapse, the spread of fire or disease, air pollution, dangerous or disruptive working conditions, uncomfortable or annoying living conditions. Usually the event or condition affects only the occupants or owner of the facility in which it takes place, but sometimes it affects a whole community, as in the case of earthquake, spread of fire or collapse of a strategic communication structure. It is also now recognized that events or conditions that threaten the living environment must also be included. Regulations and codes are therefore used to protect people and the environment from losses of various kinds due to a wide variety of events and conditions that may occur.

In this chapter the term 'regulations and codes' includes a wide variety of documents used to protect people and the environment. They range from purely legal ones at one end of the spectrum to recommendations at the other end—legal acts, by-laws, regulations, codes, specifications, standards, codes of practice, recommendations and guidelines. This chapter concerns itself with any of these documents because, although their legal status varies, they all may be used in litigation for malpractice. The term 'code' will generally be used to cover all of them.

This book concerns itself not only with what is physically required by regulations and codes (the technical criteria) but also with how the regulations are implemented (quality control) and how regulations and codes directly affect people. Because building codes provide the most direct link between society and the technology of large facilities and because building codes have the longest recorded history, their development will be briefly reviewed.

16.1 HISTORY OF BUILDING CODES

Building codes came with the growth of cities in ancient civilizations. The Code of Hammurabi, dating from about 1750 B.C., is paraphrased in Table 16.1.[1] It defines what happens to a builder if the building collapses causing death, injury or loss of property. This is a purely legal instrument with no technical criteria. The Roman and other civilizations probably had building regulations but we know little about them.

A model for the development of modern building codes is the history of building regulations in the city of London.[2] It starts in 1189 with the technical requirement that party walls between adjoining occupancies (mostly houses) must be made of stone, 3 feet thick and 16 feet high. This regulation arose primarily as a result of fire spread (devastating fires occurred frequently) and, although it has since been technically generalized, it remains as a central requirement of building codes today. Other requirements introduced at that time included the fixing of joists in walls and the right to natural light. Requirements introduced later included non-combustible materials for roofing (tiles instead of thatch) and a minimum height of 9 feet to a building projection over a street to allow the passage of people on horses.

During Elizabethan times regulations were introduced to control the density of people within the city by the prevention of infill and subletting. This regulation was introduced due to concern about the spread of plagues

Table 16.1 The Code of Hammurabi (1750 B.C.)[1]

If a builder build a house for a man and do not make its construction firm and the house which he has built collapse and cause the death of the owner of the house—that builder shall be put to death.

If it causes the death of the son of the owner of the house—they shall put to death a son of that builder.

If it cause the death of a slave of the owner of the house—he shall give to the owner of the house a slave of equal value.

If it destroy property, he shall restore whatever it destroyed, and because he did not make the house which he built firm and it collapsed, he shall rebuild the house which collapsed at his own expense.

If a builder build a house for a man and do not make its construction meet the requirements and a wall fall in, that builder shall strengthen the wall at his own expense.

(a very real concern) but wording such as 'tenements harbouring idle, vagrant and wicked persons' also suggests the type of people as well.

The great fire of London, 1666, initiated the development of comprehensive regulations for the rebuilding of London that provided the basis for modern building codes. The primary concern was again the spread of fire resulting in undue loss. Structural requirements on the thickness of masonry walls and the sizing of wood framing were also included. During the eighteenth century a number of collapses killing or injuring bystanders (falling bricks, etc.) resulted in regulations concerning the protection (by timber hoarding) of people from unsafe buildings. Such hoardings are now required to protect people from accidents during construction. During the seventeenth to nineteenth centuries specifications were introduced concerning the making of bricks and mortar, early technical requirements for quality control of building products.

The nineteenth century saw the development of new building materials— steel and reinforced concrete—which, along with scientific principles culminated in allowable stresses being introduced into building codes at the beginning of the twentieth century. The development of allowable stress design, recently generalized to limit states design, will be discussed in more detail later in this chapter (see also Chapter 3). Many technical building requirements, however, have been generated by bad experiences, with very little scientific research.

It is interesting to look into the relationship between cause and effect behind some past requirements. As cities grew in size the dangers of contagious disease became more and more to be dreaded. During the nineteenth century two measures were introduced in the United Kingdom to combat this: one was an insistence on fresh air and ventilation which came out of a fear of 'putrid emanations' believed to be carriers of infectious fevers, the other was an improved drainage and water supply (sanitation) based on advancing medical knowledge about how disease does in fact spread. Experience proved the latter to be crucial and the former ineffective in controlling the spread of disease. A lack of understanding of the relationship between cause and effect (through scientific verification) is also evident in the Elizabethan regulations concerning density of people within the city of London.

Just as interesting as the development of technical requirements is how the building regulations were implemented. During medieval times they were usually not implemented at all and, even later, they were often ignored. The great fire of London in 1666 was largely attributed to this neglect. During medieval times irregularities (called nuisances) were dealt with at ward meetings presided over by the alderman. Irregularities were reported to the alderman by 'scavengers' who also had a number of other duties, including search to collect duty on imported goods and the condition of streets (refuse, etc.). Later 'City Viewers', master masons or carpenters, were appointed to watch building operations and report on irregularities to the alderman and help resolve disagreements. Apparently this arrangement was not very effective, probably because the fees for inspection were insufficient to combat corruption. This problem still remains in some countries.

After the great fire of 1666 district surveyors were appointed to ensure that the new regulations were enforced during the rebuilding of London. District surveyors were appointed on a permanent basis in 1774 to ensure the application of the building regulations. District surveyors were practising architects, surveyors or builders with proven abilities for the application of the building regulations. They generally combined inspection duties, for which they were paid from building permit fees, with private practice. With the coming of steel and reinforced concrete, engineers began to replace architects. Also the district surveyors were paid by salary to eliminate conflict of interest. Helpers or building inspectors would carry out much of the routine work. Only in recent times have the building regulations been rigorously implemented.

Although building codes are continuously changing in the technical detail, as a sociotechnical instrument to protect people they are mature. In addition, building codes are the most complex of codes for large structural facilities because they are concerned with the widest variety of hazards affecting the safety, health, comfort and economic welfare of people.

16.2 CONTENTS AND OBJECTIVES OF CODES

Codes contain the technical requirements, including quality control requirements, to protect people from the many hazards described above, as well as to protect the environment of which we are a part. Codes also contain requirements concerning duties and obligations of persons to ensure that the code is implemented; these are generally separated from the technical requirements. Codes may also provide useful technical information in appendices or commentaries to help code users carry out their tasks.

Human safety and health have traditionally been the primary concern of building codes but more recently access (especially for the handicapped), comfort, building functionality, energy consumption and durability of components are issues of increasing concern which are being reflected in codes themselves or in referenced guidelines. New materials and products to build structures are also being developed. The situation is continually changing and so, of course, must the codes.

In addition to protecting people and the environment, codes must not result in unfair competition in the market-place. In fact this may be a strong reason for writing a code or standard in the first place. Unfair competition can occur between products as a result of specification-type requirements within a code or as a result of differences between codes that address essentially similar products or facilities.

Finally codes must be understandable to those that use or enforce them—designers and builders of the facilities, regulators, manufacturers of component products of the facilities and, when trouble comes, lawyers.

16.3 CODE DEVELOPMENT

These objectives determine the criteria for code development. To ensure that all concerns relevant to the objectives are addressed each code is written and approved by a committee. The code committee includes the people who will use the code (e.g. the designers and builders), the regulators and the manufacturers, as well as experts who understand the technical requirements and the need for them. Lawyers are not involved in writing code technical requirements because the legal process relies on expert interpretation of technical requirements. Code development is therefore a consensus process.

Sometimes difficulties arise when the consensus process is not working (see Fig. 16.1). For example, if there is too much influence from experts, the codes may become difficult to use (difficult to understand, difficult to build, etc.). If there is too much influence from a manufacturing segment, the codes may result in unfair competition or may not adequately protect people. The latter is generally not a difficulty in structural codes for large facilities because most requirements are performance-based rather than based on specifying materials or systems. Differences between codes addressing similar facilities related to the protection of people and the environment should be identified and controlled by an umbrella committee for all such facilities.

Who should pay for code development? The answer is again determined by the code objectives. The health, safety and welfare of people and protection of the environment should be supported by government. It is also in the interests of the manufacturing and building industries to support code development in order to provide facilities people are satisfied with without excessive cost (due to excessive protection) and to ensure fair competition in the market place. Finally the professions (engineers, architects) have professional obligations to protect people and to provide good service to their clients. Better codes mean better service by the profession as a whole.

The cost of code development is high and much of it is borne, in one way or another, by government. There has been a tendency, however, to rely too much on volunteer work which, ultimately, can lead to the continuance of codes which are either unsatisfactory or out of date. Because of the important role they play, both for people and for the industry, their development should not be left to 'volunteer' support.

The consensus process provides the proper checks and balances but also retards code development, especially if it relies entirely on 'volunteer' support. This difficulty appears to be greater for international standards and for certain countries such as the United States.

Figure 16.1 Code Committee—lack of consensus. *(Source: Drawing by Booth; © 1977, The New Yorker Magazine, Inc.)*

16.4 CODE COMPARISONS

Codes for different facilities have similarities but they also have differences. For example, a building code has a very broad category of users (from owners to technical specialists) whereas a code for offshore structures has a narrow, specialized category of users. In addition, the category of structures covered by an offshore code is much narrower than for buildings and, because of their cost, the specialist effort (such as the design) is orders of magnitude greater. As a result an offshore code is more of a performance code and less of a specification code. The loads, for example, are not specified, only the maximum probability of their exceedance (return period). Thus the nature and contents of a code depends both on the category of facilities covered and the category of code users. In fact some codes such as a building code are generally divided up into sections addressed to different categories of users.

Codes for large facilities, such as buildings or bridges, are similar in principle to codes for other technologies, such as aeroplanes, mechanical systems, chemical manufacturing processes and electrical systems. They are similar with regard to the identification of specific hazards and the technical means for protection against them. One special feature of large-scale structures that often does not occur in other technologies is that most large-scale structures are one of a kind and each design must be based on experience, calculations and materials testing without prototype testing. The other feature is that large-scale structures are essentially static objects as compared to essentially dynamic systems or chemical processes for other systems. The latter tend to have a greater variety of specific hazards affecting life safety and the environment, and a wider variety of technical measures to control them. The concepts, however, are similar, for example structural redundancy being similar to pressure relief systems.

16.5 WHAT IS WRONG WITH CODES?

Codes are written for the future but are based, to a considerable extent, on past experience. This often works well, for example where nailing requirements for wood-frame housing in building codes have remained essentially unchanged for many years. When materials, systems and environmental conditions change, however, the code requirements may no longer provide protection.

An example is the disintegration of concrete bridge decks and parking garages due to corrosion of the reinforcement—a problem that costs billions of dollars in repair every year. It arose from two changes, the introduction of salt as a deicer for roads and the introduction of multistorey parking garages. This problem took years to reveal itself, and more years to agree on its cause and prevention by code requirements. Similar phase lags resulting in epidemics such as this occurred with the introduction of high alumina cement in concrete and the lack of consideration of differential movement between brick veneer in high-rise buildings and the concrete structure.

Codes also create difficulties when applied to existing facilities. The difficulty arises because the code is written for the future (design of new facilities using current systems) and does not adequately address old systems and how to upgrade them; by implication they tend to require that the old system be replaced by a new one. For heritage buildings, the old structure is often completely replaced by a new one supporting heritage components as artefacts, rather than making use of the existing materials by tying them together to make the system perform effectively. This problem is most apparent for heritage masonry buildings in seismic areas.

Codes, written for the design of new facilities, also ignore some important design considerations such as maintenance of the facility (inspection and repair) and future alterations. This is partly because codes emphasize safety, not life-cycle cost.

Finally codes are sometimes difficult to read. Sometimes requirements for a specific thing or question are scattered throughout the document and referenced documents. The computer will improve this. Complexity is also a problem that will be discussed later with regard to limit states design.

16.6 CAN TECHNICAL CRITERIA BE IMPROVED?

As stated in the last section, the greatest problem is that codes are written for the future but the criteria are based on the past. This, of course, is a fundamental problem of human prediction not restricted to codes. When changes were slow, as they were before the industrial revolution, the traditional empirical criteria of proportion based on experience worked sufficiently well. Modern science cannot improve on the design of Roman aqueducts and Gothic cathedrals using the materials and construction equipment available at that time. Nevertheless, disastrous collapses occurred during the long development stage of these magnificent structures.

When changes became more rapid this process broke down. The industrial revolution brought rapid changes, especially new materials, and, as a result, the method of design by experience only had to be replaced. To meet this need more generalized methods were developed based on scientific principles. The following describes the development of the limit states method, a generalized method now used as the basis for all structural criteria in codes and standards.

In 1741 someone investigated damage to the dome of St Peter's Cathedral, carried out calculations based on Newton's law of statics, determined the cause of damage to be yielding of the circular tie at the base of the dome and recommended adding more ties. The report caused a tremendous reaction because, until that time, all structures had been designed and evaluated by experience only. Design by experience only continued until the nineteenth century because changes in construction materials and procedures were still very gradual. The first iron bridge built in 1789, for example, was essentially a replica of a masonry arch bridge. Rapid changes brought on by the industrial revolution, including the development of iron and steel and the sudden need for railway bridges, meant that design by experience only was no longer possible. To answer this need, structural engineers combined testing of materials with Newton's law of statics and the theory of elasticity (Hooke's law) to develop the allowable stress method. The allowable stress method provided engineers with a powerful tool to successfully design and build structures undreamed of before, including long-span bridges and tall buildings. As a result allowable stresses became the basis of all structural criteria in codes and standards. Due to limitations in the allowable stress method, allowable stresses have recently been generalized into limit states.

The limit states method, described in Chapter 3, is a marriage between scientific principles, experience and practical thinking. The basic biological purpose of practical thinking is to survive by getting the things that we need (structures for different purposes) and to avoid the things that are dangerous or make life difficult (failures of various kinds). The limit states define the things that are dangerous (ultimate limit states) and the things that make life difficult (serviceability limit states). Newton's laws of statics and dynamics, testing and theories of structural behaviour provide the means of calculating whether the structure will fail and how. This gives the engineer an understanding useful for practice. Safety factors are incorporated to keep the risk due to the uncertainty in the calculation assumptions sufficiently low.

The effectiveness of the limit states method, as well as the allowable stress method, is verified by the fact that structural failures in practice are rare and almost all are due to human error. The causes of structural failure, once determined, are usually easily understood by professionals. Furthermore, there is no restriction in the application of the limit states method provided the properties of materials and components have been determined. The limit states method provides a tool for practice which, for changing situations, avoids the big mistake of using experience only, such as described above with regard to bridge decks and parking garages. Furthermore, by the understanding it conveys on how structures work, it promotes innovative development.

The problem with the limit states method is that it is too narrow-minded. It concerns itself only with structural mechanics, that is strength, deflection, vibration and local damage such as cracking or spalling. It ignores all other considerations. To illustrate this narrow perspective Table 16.2 reviews the contents of a typical structural design standard to see how well it addresses the problems that occur in practice. The first conclusion of Table 16.2 is that

Table 16.2 Typical structural standard

Limit states	Length	Requirements	Problems	Recommendation
Ultimate	100 pages	Many	Few	Simplify
Serviceability	1 page	Few or none	More	Pull together
Durability	1 sentence	Vague	Most	Improve understanding

structural designers know more about ultimate limit states and therefore there are fewer problems (collapses). The second conclusion is that more should be done about serviceability and deterioration.

Deterioration is the most serious concern of structural facilities today. With increasing carbon dioxide and industrial chemicals in the air (e.g. acid rain), the outside environment is becoming worse, not better, and this means more trouble—corrosion, disintegrating mortar and sandstone, etc. Deterioration has not been a problem for most building interiors in the past but the situation has changed; parking structures exposed to road salt and swimming pools exposed to a chlorinated damp atmosphere are major problem areas.

Deterioration is generally assumed to be a materials problem, the experts being materials scientists and corrosion engineers. However, most of the problems that occur are caused at the design stage or as a result of changes during construction or poor workmanship. Furthermore, structural engineers are called upon to assess deterioration and recommend repairs, which may or may not work. It is therefore clear that structural engineers must be able to understand deterioration with a higher level of professional competence than they do now. This will require education and, along with this, the development of limit states criteria for durability in structural standards. Introduction of deterioration and estimated life into structural design will mean that maintenance and repair will become a greater factor in the design of large facilities. These concepts are already being introduced for some major bridge and tunnel projects.

Codes and standards must also rely on experience because it is not possible to prevent something unforeseen from going wrong, even if it is covered by the limit states method. Figure 16.2 shows, for a new problem such as the bridge deck/parking garage epidemic, incidence versus time. The top curve shows the present situation. The bottom curve shows the situation as it should be with better feedback from experience. The shaded area is the

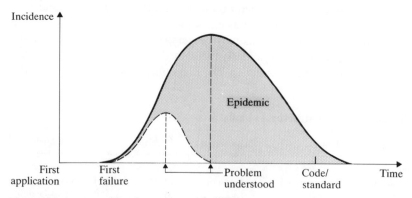

Figure 16.2 A new problem in constructed facilities.

loss that could have been prevented. Figure 16.2 shows that a more effective and rapid system is required to feed back information on the problems that occur and to carry out the research required to provide solutions. This is especially important for problems related to changing environmental conditions. Such a feedback system is central to quality assurance in the manufacturing industry but has not yet been adequately developed within the construction industry. Initial attempts have been made in a number of countries, but it will only succeed when all participants in the construction process actively support it (Chapter 4).

16.7 ROLE OF PROBABILISTIC RISK ANALYSIS

The technical criteria in regulations and codes are based on risk. Risk concerns events or conditions that result in dangerous, disruptive or annoying consequences, i.e. hazards. Hazards include the spread of fire in a city, leakage of a toxic substance from a processing plant, the collapse of a building during an earthquake or the annoying vibration of a new floor. For each hazard, risk can be defined as the probability that the event will occur times the expected consequences of the event or loss. Risk used for determining code criteria has been based mostly on bad experiences and not probabilistic analysis of events and measured losses.

Only in recent years has probability analysis been used to develop criteria for codes. Structural reliability theory, a particular application of probability analysis, has been used to develop limit states criteria in structural codes and standards. Load factors, load combinations and resistance factors have been determined to give consistent reliability (probability of failure) for a wide variety of applications. Some adjustments have been made to the criteria to take into account the consequences of failure. An importance factor for buildings takes into account the consequences of failure related to use (e.g. postdisaster services) and occupancy (e.g. low human occupancy). Greater reliability is also incorporated for failure of some components rather than others (e.g. connectors versus members).

Reliability theory, however, has its limitations. This can be simply stated as follows—if the mechanisms of failure are not understood, reliability theory is not meaningful. In the case of a simply supported bridge girder loaded by trucks the mechanisms of failure are fairly well understood. In the case of a building subjected to earthquake we know a lot less. This ignorance about modelling the real world means that reliability theory can be used only as a relative measure, not an absolute measure. For example, reliability studies[3] have shown that the calculated probability of failure for code earthquake criteria is 1/25 (reliability index of 1.75) compared to 1/1000 (reliability index of 3) for other loads. A probability of failure of 1/25 is unacceptably high. However, is 1/25 real or is it distorted because of our ignorance? Earthquake damage experience strongly indicates that 1/25 is distorted. One reason for this is that earthquake motion is represented by a static lateral load equal to the maximum acceleration perceived by the structure times its mass, without consideration of the displacement of the structure required for failure to occur. Calibration to existing experience is therefore necessary in using reliability methods, and the reliability index provides a useful measure only when the circumstances under which it is compared are essentially similar.

When treated with care, however, reliability theory will be a useful tool in the future to help determine technical criteria for codes. It has recently been used to develop two sets of load factors for two safety classes in the preliminary Canadian code for fixed offshore structures.[4] The lower safety class is used for members whose failure does not result in widespread collapse or for loads such as ice if emergency measures are implemented to avoid severe consequences of failure.

Reliability theory has also been recently used to develop reduced load factors for the evaluation of existing structures. The need arises out of the severe economic penalty where an existing structure does not meet the code and yet is safe enough for use. Reduced load factors have been developed for the evaluation of existing bridges in the Canadian bridge code.[5] The new requirement makes use of a reliability index which is determined by the engineer depending on the type of failure, redundancy, inspection programme and satisfactory experience of the bridge. Each of these factors affects the risk to life, given failure or recognition of impending failure.

16.8 QUALITY CONTROL AND HUMAN ERROR

It is well known that over 90 per cent of structural failures of a structural mechanical type are caused by human error, including accidents, not inadequate technical criteria. Can codes be improved to avoid such failures? This question is addressed from three aspects—legal requirements, technical requirements and feedback.

The legal requirements (e.g. the building act) provide an instrument to ensure compliance with the codes. Legal requirements include the issuing of permits to ensure code compliance before construction and occupation of the facility and the issuing of protection or evacuation orders to safeguard people from an unsafe condition in or near an existing facility. These legal requirements are implemented by government regulatory authorities such as building inspectors. Sometimes technical agencies carry out this function for insurance companies. Access to the site and documentation (drawings, specifications, test results, etc.) must be provided to the regulatory authority to check code compliance. For unusual structures outside the scope of the code technical requirements or outside the expertise of the regulatory officials, the regulatory authority may require a peer review. Similarly, new materials and systems not addressed by the code will require special evaluation reports to verify compliance with the intent of the code.

The way technical requirements are formulated and presented also affects human error and quality control. Human error relates to practical thinking. Practical thinking is motivated by obtaining the things we need and avoiding the things that are dangerous or make life difficult or unpleasant i.e. the failures. Codes address the things that we need (buildings, bridges, etc.) but the technical requirements address the things that are dangerous or make life difficult. The technical requirements are essentially a check-list of failures with criteria to prevent them. Existing requirements that are not directly related to identifiable potential failures should be removed. The technical requirements must therefore be cohesive, clear, easy to find and as few as possible. For example, Table 16.2 indicates that the criteria for the ultimate limit states have become too complex. The requirements must also be practical to implement, verifiable and yet not restrict innovation. An example where such difficulties were encountered was during the introduction of code requirements against progressive collapse following the collapse of part of the Ronan Point apartment building in London in 1966. This is why so much care must go into the preparation and revision of technical codes and standards and why it takes time. More research is needed on how to best write a technical code or standard for the people who must use them. The goal of this research is to reduce human error.

Because codes take time to write and revise, however, they cannot keep pace with the changes that are taking place (see Fig. 16.2). Besides, many requirements apply to a broad variety of applications and, consequently, they may be forgotten or ignored for new and different applications. For this reason it is important to have feedback indicating particular problems that are either covered by the code and not implemented or are not adequately covered by the code. This information might be in the form of practice sheets, flagging problems and indicating tentative recommendations until the code is revised. This would provide quality control in the construction industry that was more like that in the manufacturing industries.

16.9 THE FUTURE OF CODES

Codes are here to stay. Along with education and training, codes provide the most effective mechanism of technology transfer that is available. They will, however, change. Codes will change in response to the changing requirements of people who use the structures and in response to new materials, systems and applications and changing environmental conditions.

Some codes will change more than others. The building code, for example, is expected to change considerably. This is because people spend most of their lives inside buildings and therefore quality, not just safety, is an increasing concern. Access for the handicapped has only recently been included in the building code. Noise is a problem for many building occupants not adequately addressed by the code. Air quality is another. Energy conservation, durability and maintenance are only partially addressed by the building code. Future codes of broader scope will require a wider scope of training, not only for practitioners but for regulatory officials as well. Risk analysis will be used more widely as a tool for code development as the variety of hazards and applications continue to increase.

Structural standards such as for bridges, towers and marine structures will not change as much as the building code, although new codes will be written for new applications. Table 16.2 indicates that future structural standards will simplify strength criteria, pull together serviceability criteria and develop durability criteria. These changes are already starting to happen.

REFERENCES

1. Feld, J.: Lessons from Failures of Concrete Structures, American Concrete Institute Monograph 1, PO Box 4754, Redford Station, Detroit, Mich., 1964, 179 pp.
2. Knowles, C. C., and P. H. Pitt: *The History of Building Regulations in London 1189–1972*, Architectural Press, London, 1972, 164 pp.
3. Ellingwood, B., T. V. Galambos, J. G. MacGregor, and C. A. Cornell: Development of a Probability Based Load Criterion for American National Standard A58, NBS Special Publication 577, US Department of Commerce, Washington, D.C., 1980, 222 pp.
4. Canadian Standards Association: CSA Preliminary Standard S471—M1989. General Requirements, Design Criteria, the Environment and Loads. Part 1 of *The Code for the Design, Construction and Installation of Fixed Offshore Structures*, Canadian Standards Association, Rexdale, Ont., 1989, 51 pp.
5. Canadian Standards Association: Existing Bridge Evaluation, Supplement No. 1–1990 to CSA Standard CAN/CSA S6–1988, *Design of Highway Bridges*, Canadian Standards Association, Rexdale, Ont., 1990, 51 pp.

SEVENTEEN

RELIABILITY AND THE LAW

17.1 INTRODUCTION

This chapter is the only chapter in the book written by a lawyer. Although
the problems of engineering reliability and of dealing with the consequences
of failure to achieve it will occur in all countries and in a very similar ways
in all developed countries, the legal solutions to the problems will not be
identical. What follows in this chapter is an account of the relevant English
law. English law is part of a family called the common law world, which
embraces the United States and most but not all of the countries of the
Commonwealth. At the level of generality of this chapter it can be assumed
that what is true of England will be very largely true of all the other members
of this family. Most of the other great industrialized countries belong to the
civil law family whose legal systems have been heavily influenced either by
the French Code Napoleon or by the German Civil Code of 1900. These
systems do have a largely different conceptual structure. This does not
necessarily mean that different results are reached. One of the curiosities of
law is that it is often possible to reach the same result by a wide range of
different routes. One might summarize this by saying that an English lawyer
and an Australian lawyer would start by assuming that their law on the
matters discussed in this chapter was very likely to be identical; an English
lawyer and a New York lawyer would assume that there might be differences
in detail but would be using the same conceptual structure and would find
it fairly easy to work out what the detailed differences were; an English
lawyer and a German lawyer would start by assuming that the conceptual

structure was different though they would be likely to find that a good many of the final solutions turned out to produce the same results.

We shall start by giving an account of the present system. English law deals with the results of unsafe operations in two principal ways. One is through the operation of the tort system, that is that part of the civil law which is designed to compensate those who suffer injuries. We shall also consider the operation of the criminal law, that is those rules that operate to punish people for behaviour that is prohibited by the state. As we shall see, neither of these methods is primarily concerned to establish the factual reasons for disasters. We need to say something therefore about the practice of holding public inquiries to investigate the reasons for disasters. Having given this account of the present law in practice we shall then go on to consider what light this throws on the relationship between law and engineering in relation to questions of safety, reliability and so on.

17.2 TORT

The primary tort remedy for someone who suffers personal injury or death is an action in negligence. Such actions are traditionally said to require proof of three elements: duty of care, breach of the duty of care and damage. Each of these elements requires some discussion.

The duty of care is a conceptual technique used by judges to distinguish cases of careless behaviour that give rise to liability from those that do not. Historically English law has distinguished between careless acts and careless words. At one time it was thought that careless words did not give rise to liability at all. For the last 25 years it has been clear that they may give rise to liability but that liability does not depend on simply showing that there has been carelessness. Thus, for instance, if a firm of accountants carelessly audits a company's books and signs a report that gives a misleading account of the company's financial position, they have been said by the House of Lords not to be under a duty of care to potential buyers of shares in the company. This represents in effect a policy decision that although accountants should be careful, there should be limits to the scope of their liability. In the case of physical injuries resulting from careless acts we come across these policy limitations much less often and it can usually be assumed that someone who does an act that is liable to cause injury to someone else will have difficulty in persuading the court that he/she owned no duty of care to those who were likely to be injured by his/her behaviour. So if a motorist drives a car at great speed down a crowded street the court is not likely to waste much time deciding that he/she was under a duty of care to those in the street. Nevertheless, even in this situation, questions will arise. Suppose the driver of the vehicle was not an ordinary motorist but an ambulance driver trying desperately to reach the scene of a disaster. Is this position to be treated in exactly the same way? The answer is clearly no. The motorist had no adequate reason for driving so fast; the ambulance driver did have a reason for driving faster than the ordinary motorist. On the other hand, even ambulance drivers need to have regard for the safety of the public. Therefore a balancing exercise has to take place in which one takes into account the urgency of the situation, the real degrees of risk, the fact that the ambulance driver is signalling rapid approach with a siren and lights and so on. A classic example of this balancing exercise is the case of *Bolton v Stone*.[1] In this case a cricket club played cricket on a ground where the evidence was that a few times each year balls were hit out of the ground. The plaintiff was injured when a ball came out of the ground and hit him. The plaintiff argued that since it was clear that balls did regularly though not frequently come out of the ground, it was statistically certain that sooner or later somebody would be hit and therefore it was negligent to play cricket on this ground in these circumstances. The House of Lords held that although it was statistically certain that an injury would eventually take place, this had to be balanced against the social usefulness of playing cricket and the benefit that members of the community, both players and spectators, derived from this. We can be certain that the result of the case would have been different if the activity that had been taking place was one that was not central to the English way of life and had lacked redeeming merit. Similarly, the result would have been different if there had been simple steps that the cricket club could have taken to minimize or eliminate the risk of balls getting out of the ground. The evidence was that there were no such simple steps and that the only way to avoid the risk of injury was to give up playing cricket on the ground. The House of Lords did not consider that in the circumstances a desire for safety required this.

One could describe this process as a kind of cost–benefit analysis. It is clear that the legal theory does require a balancing exercise but the balancing is basically intuitive and not based on any refined mathematical considerations. One cannot carry out a serious cost–benefit analysis without some idea of the costs but this is the sort of information that would seldom if ever be presented to a court in the litigation of a personal injury case. A good illustration of this is that English courts have been markedly reluctant to hold that road accidents arise from faulty design of vehicles (American courts have been much less reluctant). It is clear that all motor cars manufactured today have many safety features that were not present in motors cars manufactured thirty years ago. Some of these features had not then been developed but others were known but were regarded as too expensive to put into volume car production. Car manufacturers were no doubt indulging in cost–benefit analysis and considering whether making a car safer was likely to increase sales in a way that would reflect the extra cost of improving the safety of the car. For reasons that we will come on to later a court would be an unsatisfactory mechanism for resolving questions of this kind.

The second stage is establishing that a defendant who is under a duty of care has been in breach of that duty. In straightforward cases like motor accidents this is said to depend on whether the defendant has displayed the care and skill of the reasonable man. The reasonable man represents an objective standard and so it is not enough for the defendant to show that he did as well as he could be expected to do; he must achieve the standard of the reasonable man. The reasonable man test is also a flexible test since it allows the judge (in England, unlike the United States, tort cases are virtually always tried without juries by the judge alone) considerable flexibility in raising or lowering this standard to fit the facts of a particular case. In driving cases, for instance, the reasonable man is a paragon of virtue. He never loses concentration; he is not distracted; he is meticulous in giving the appropriate signals and obeying all road signs; and he is careful to think ahead and plan defensive action against the faults of other drivers. So the reasonable man achieves a standard far above that of the average driver. This means that although the court is stating the law on a basis that appears to be fault based it is reducing the element of fault to a minimum. Thus, in a motor crash between two drivers who can be identified, it would be very unusual for the court not to conclude that at least one of the drivers was at fault. (In theory the accident might have been caused by the layout and condition of the roads or by the design and manufacture of the cars, but it would be a very surprising and exceptional case in which a court decided that an accident was caused by one of these factors and that neither of the drivers was to blame.)

In deciding how a reasonable driver behaves, the court would normally not entertain evidence as to the behaviour of the average driver but would proceed in a largely intuitive fashion based on its own experience. This would not be appropriate when considering whether a professional had behaved like a reasonable professional. The leading statement of the appropriate test for a professional is that stated by McNair J in *Bolam* v *Friern Hospital Management Committee*.[2] He said:

> Where you get a situation which involves the use of some special skill or competence, then the test whether there has been negligence or not is not the test of the man on top of the Clapham omnibus, because he has not got this special skill. The test is the standard of the ordinary skilled man exercising and professing to have that special skill. A man need not possess the highest expert skill at the risk of being found negligent. It is well established law that it is sufficient if he exercises the ordinary skill of an ordinary competent man exercising that particular art.... A mere personal belief that a particular technique is best is no defence unless that belief is based on reasonable grounds.... A doctor is not negligent if he is acting in accordance with ... a practice (accepted as proper by a responsible body of medical men skilled in that particular art), merely because there is a body of opinion that takes a contrary view. At the same time, that does not mean that a medical man can obstinately and pig-headedly carry on with some old technique if it has been proved to be contrary to what is really substantially the whole of informed medical opinion.

This test has been repeatedly approved by higher courts.

Although the reasonable expert test is in a sense an adaptation of the reasonable man test, there are revealed in the *Bolam* test significant differences. One is that courts are markedly more reluctant to hold professionals negligent than to hold drivers negligent. This is no doubt closely related to a feeling that it is a much more serious matter to declare that a doctor or lawyer or an engineer has been professionally negligent than to say that a driver has been negligent. Nevertheless, actions against professionals have grown at a rapid rate in recent years and by no means all fail.

The second difference between professional negligence and ordinary negligence cases is that professional negligence will in virtually all cases require the court to be assisted by evidence as to what competent and experienced professionals would do in a given situation. In practice, except for those cases that are so clear that they seldom if ever reach court, such as the patient who has the wrong leg removed in hospital, a competent lawyer would not advise a client to start proceedings for professional negligence unless he had found other members of the same profession who were willing to testify that what the defendant did was negligent. Cases of professional negligence turn therefore very largely on the evaluation of the expert evidence.

A classic example in an engineering context is the Abbeystead disaster, *Eckersley* v *Binnie*.[3] In this case a link was designed and built between the rivers Lune and Wyre at Abbeystead between 1972 and 1979. The link was designed by Binnie and Partners, a firm of consulting engineers, constructed by Nuttalls, a firm of tunnelling contractors, and operated by the North West Water Authority. There had been complaints from members of the community about the environmental aspect of the link and on 23 May 1984 a party of 38 people from the village of St Michaels-on-Wyre went on a visit to the pumping works at Abbeystead. While they were in the pumping works there was an explosion in the valve house, All those who were in the valve house were injured and 16 people died. The reason for the explosion was in a sense clear. A dangerous accumulation of methane had been pumped into the wet room of the valve house and there ignited probably by a match or cigarette lighter. The methane had accumulated because there was a void in the tunnel because the washout valve was partly open and there had been no pumping for 16 days because of a period of drought. Therefore the amount of water entering the tunnel was less than the amount going out through the walls and the washout valve. Methane had accumulated in this void, having entered the tunnel partly as gas and partly in solution in the water. When the pump was switched on to demonstrate its operation, the methane was pumped up through the valve and into the valve house.

The victims of the accident sued Binnies, Nuttalls and the Water Authority. The trial judge held all three defendants to be negligent. In the Court of Appeal, all three judges concluded that Nuttalls and the Water Authority were not negligent. It was clear that Nuttalls' testing for methane during the construction process has been perfunctory and below an acceptable standard, but, as tunnelling contractors, their obligation to test for methane during tunnelling was so as to protect their work-force against a dangerous accumulation in the tunnel during construction. No accident had taken place in the tunnel during construction and therefore Nuttalls, though negligent in this respect, had caused no damage. The Court of Appeal thought that Nuttalls were not under a duty to test for methane in order to guard against an accident of the kind that happened. Similarly, all the judges in the Court of Appeal thought that the Water Authority were entitled to rely on careful design and supervision of the works by Binnies and that there was nothing in the circumstances to alert them to the risk of the kind of accumulation of methane that had taken place.

The critical division of opinion was in relation to Binnies, which is the most interesting for the present purposes. The question was whether they should have been alert to the possibility of an accumulation of methane in the tunnel once it was operational. It is clear that Binnies are a large, highly experienced and generally competent partnership of consulting engineers. It is clear that no one involved at Binnies in the work did in fact foresee the possibility of methane being in the tunnel. Methane can occur biologically through the decay of organic material but there was no reason to suspect that either before or after the event in the Lune valley. The probable source of the methane was a reservoir which had been trapped for centuries under some non-permeable rocks that had been cracked during construction of the tunnel. The methane then seeped through the crack and in increasing quantities into the tunnel.

Whether Binnies should have guarded against this depended on what state of geological knowledge a competent civil engineer should have had at the time of the tunnelling and whether a competent civil engineer would have sought further advice that might have revealed the possibility of methane trapped in this way. The trial judge and two members of the Court of Appeal thought that Binnies should have pursued their enquiries this far; Bingham L J disagreed. He did not think an ordinarily competent engineer in the position of Binnies would have foreseen the danger to life and health of methane leaking into the tunnel from the reservoir. The difference of opinion is striking since all four judges were analysing exactly the same evidence. No fewer than 11 experts were called by the four parties in the case and the experts were not of course fully agreed. In applying the *Bolam* test it should have been sufficient for Binnies to show that some competent engineers would have contented themselves with the sort of geological survey that Binnies undertook even though others might have gone further. Bingham L J clearly thought that the evidence went at least this far. The majority must have thought that the evidence showed that no competent engineer could have stopped where Binnies did.

It is worth saying a little more about professional negligence in general. There are a number of ways in which it may manifest itself. An important source is failures in management, particularly failure to exercise sufficient supervision over inexperienced staff. A professional man is also under a duty to identify problems and warn his client of risks. In the engineering field it is particularly important to consider whether sufficient investigatory or research work has been carried out.

An interesting example is the case of *Vacwell Engineering Co. Ltd* v *BDH Chemicals Ltd*.[4] In this case the defendants decided to use the chemical boron tribromide instead of boron trichloride which they had previously used. In fact boron tirbromide is very dangerous since it is liable to explode if it comes into contact with even small quantities of water. The defendants did not know this and the information was not to be found in a number of modern books that they had looked at. On the other hand, older books, which were in the defendants' library but which had not been consulted, did reveal the danger. When an accident eventually took place because of a mixture of boron tribromide and water which destroyed a laboratory the defendants were held to be negligent. This is to impose a very high standard of research since most of us undoubtedly assume that the best state of knowledge is in the most recent books and expect authors to have carefully read and carried forward the lessons of the research of the past. That the case was a borderline one is shown by the fact that an appeal was abandoned at the doors of the Court of Appeal. It is believed that the plaintiffs agreed to accept, in return for the defendants abandoning their appeal, a substantially smaller sum than they had been awarded by the judge. This no doubt reflects advice from their lawyers that there was a significant chance that the Court of Appeal would reverse the trial judge's finding.

To what extent does the tort of negligence help to promote safety? Clearly there is some contribution since a defendant is more likely to be held liable the more he/she falls below an acceptable standard of conduct. However, it is clear that the system is not designed to promote safety in general but to decide whether a particular defendant should compensate a particular plaintiff for injuries. Any objective enquiry into the true causes of disaster is affected by the fact that in the common law world the courts in such cases employ what is called the adversary system, that is that the judge's function is simply to decide on those questions that the parties choose to argue. The lines of argument put forward by the contending parties will be heavily influenced by tactical forensic considerations and by the difficulties of proof. Therefore in a car accident it is much easier and cheaper to argue that the other driver is to blame than to seek to show that an accident was due to the configuration of the road. Setting out to show that would involve a leap into the dark both as to proving the facts and as to the relevant law. In most cases a prudent lawyer is going to lean against such an adventurous course. On the other hand, we need to remind ourselves constantly that cases are only decided after the event and that it is all too easy once a disaster has taken place to persuade oneself that it was foreseeable.

There has been considerable theoretical discussion as to whether the tort rules discussed above operate to provide incentives to safe conduct and thereby to increase safety.[5] It can be argued that if people know that they will have to bear the costs of their actions, this provides them with an incentive to avoid those sorts of action that will carry costs, at least if the costs of prevention are less than the costs of not avoiding the action. This argument has considerable force where it is possible to identify the danger with reasonable clarity. Thus newspaper editors and proprietors know that they are liable to be sued for defamation if they print untrue stories about people and so editors and proprietors are likely to take steps to make sure that papers are read carefully to eliminate such stories as far as possible or at least only to print them when the likely increased sales make this an acceptable commercial risk. The deterrent effect is markedly less strong when applied to an activity like driving a car. Many drivers drive carelessly when they fondly imagine they are driving carefully. The deterrent effect does not bite on them at all. In relation to professional negligence the argument is rather different. Undoubtedly professionals are worried about being held to be professionally negligent and the vast majority are likely to take steps to minimize the risk of this. However, the defensive measures may involve avoiding conduct of a kind that is thought to carry a high risk of being sued, even if one is not negligent. It is this which leads doctors, or so it is said, to desert high-risk specialities like obstetrics in favour of low-risk specialities like ear, nose and throat surgery.

Another factor that is clearly of great importance in relation to deterrence is insurance. Car drivers are required to be insured and in the United Kingdom the insurance has to be unlimited in amount so the car driver knows that the only financial effect of an accident for which he/she is liable is an increase in the premium in the following year. It seems fanciful to suppose that this is likely to be a major deterrent. Professionals are not legally required to be insured though some professional bodies require this as part of their code of professional practice. Most professionals are no doubt in practice insured but it would be very unusual for the amount of the insurance to be unlimited. Since most professions do not permit practice in a limited liability form the threat of damages awards above the insurance threshold is a very real one and this is undoubtedly a factor that affects judgments of the courts in the field of professional liability (as, for instance, in the case of the accountants discussed above).

The thrust of this discussion is that the tort system is far from effective as a means of deterring unsafe behaviour. It is also widely regarded as ineffective as a means of achieving compensation. At least two major alternatives have been canvassed in the last 25 years. One is to shift to a system that does not require the plaintiff to prove that the defendant has been at fault. Undoubtedly in practice much of the difficulty of operating the existing system is that although it is clear that something has gone wrong it may be very difficult and expensive to prove that anyone is at fault. Good examples of this are the thalidomide disaster and the recent case of haemophiliac victims infected by AIDS through faulty blood transfusions. In both these cases the victims had overwhelmingly strong moral claims for financial support but very great difficulties in establishing that there was negligence. A shift to a system that does not depend on proof of fault also has attractions for professionals because it divorces the question 'Should the plantiff be compensated?' from the question 'Is the defendant negligent?'. A shift to such a system was brought about by the *Consumer Protection Act 1987* which instituted a strict liability for unsafe products that caused personal injury or death. This was designed to implement a European Community Directive requiring member states to adopt such a policy though permitting them, as the United Kingdom has done, to qualify the strict liability by the so-called development risk defence under which a manufacturer of a product could escape liability if it could be shown that the product was as safe as the state of knowledge of producers of the product would permit at the time of production. (This is in effect to introduce a question of negligence by the back door but only over a limited field.)

An even more radical reform which was adopted in New Zealand would be to abandon the tort system altogether. The tort system is extremely expensive in that nearly half of the money that it generates for compensation, typically from insurance funds, is consumed by the fees of lawyers and the administrative expenses of insurance companies. If one could introduce a much simpler system then a much higher percentage, say 90 per cent of the money, could be devoted to victims. In New Zealand this has been effected by the introduction of a state-based compensation system which operates via the social security mechanism. Everyone who suffers injuries of the prescribed classes is entitled to state benefits irrespective of proof of fault. So, instead of the present situation where some accident victims get paid large sums and others get nothing at all, you would have a system in which all accident victims would receive some compensation. Such a system has attracted much enthusiasm among academic lawyers and many hoped that the Royal Commission chaired by Lord Pearson set up in the 1970s in the wake of the thalidomide disaster would recommend such a system. In effect, these hopes were dashed and that Commission produced instead a very careful but rather cautious report suggesting substantial extensions of the strict liability regime. Even this has so far only been adopted in the field of product liability.

It will be seen that a shift to a state-funded social security compensation scheme for injuries would not have deterrent effects. What is more problematic is the difference that a change from a fault-based system to a strict liability system would produce. Would it make any difference to the manufacturer of an aeroplane if it were to be liable for injuries caused by the plane being unsafe only if it could be proved to have been negligent or if mere proof of unsafety would suffice? It could be argued that deterrence cannot force anyone to be more careful than he/she knows how to be. This may be true of a relatively simple activity like driving a car but it is not necessarily true in the same way about a complex corporate activity like building an aeroplane. In the latter case safety depends not only on individual decisions but on a complex structure of responsibilities and it is conceivable that imposing a higher standard of liability would provide incentives towards the development of tighter and more effective structures. An important additional point is that the shift to a strict liability system has great forensic importance. In a fault-based system the plaintiff has to prove that the defendant was negligent. When dealing with complex activities like building an aeroplane or developing a new drug the plaintiff has enormous practical difficulties in showing that the defendants' conduct was negligent, particularly where questions of design are concerned, since so much depends on the effectiveness of testing which will be entirely within the defendants' own knowledge. If all the plaintiff has to do is to show that the finished product was unsafe and caused injury the task is much easier. This means that those errors that the defendant might previously have hoped to cover up in a fault-based system will now give rise to liability. It is likely that this change will have some deterrent effect but sufficient will have been said by now to make it clear that deterrence is not the primary thrust of the relevant rules.

17.3 CRIMINAL LAW

In general the criminal law does not attach liability to careless behaviour. The most obvious exception to this principle is the crime of manslaughter, that is unlawful homicide falling short of murder. One of the ways in which manslaughter may be committed is killing as a result of gross negligence. Although gross negligence has been described as nothing more than negligence with the addition of a vituperative epithet and is certainly difficult to define precisely it appears to require a particularly large departure from the standard of care expected of the reasonable man. In principle there is no reason why a defendant who has been very careless and as a result has been responsible for someone's death cannot be prosecuted for manslaughter. In practice, however, there appear to be substantial limitations. It is notoriously difficult to persuade British juries to convict of manslaughter arising from particularly dangerous driving which leads to death. This is so much so that Parliament introduced by statute an offence of killing by dangerous driving which would appear to have a substantial degree of overlap with manslaughter arising from the use of a motor vehicle. There are quite often cries for prosecutions for manslaughter arising from major disasters, but the collapse of the prosecution in the case of *The Herald of Free Enterprise* (a disaster arising from the sinking of a ship in Zeebrugge harbour) showed the substantial practical difficulties in getting convictions in cases of this kind.

In practice, however, the general rule has been abandoned by statute in most of those situations where accidents are particularly liable to happen. Thus in relation to road accidents there is a complex hierarchy of offences ranging from causing death by dangerous driving and careless driving to exceeding the speed limit. It is worth stopping to ask why the state has adopted this approach. Most of the conduct that would give rise to criminal liability would also amount to negligence for the purposes of the law of tort. One important difference is that the law of tort only comes into play when someone has been injured, whereas the criminal law can be invoked simply because the rules have been broken though no one has been hurt. Therefore the driver of a high-powered car may believe that it can be driven with complete safety on a motorway at 100 mi/h and is very unlikely to be deterred from doing so by the thought that an accident may arise and that he/she may be sued in tort; he/she may well, however, be deterred from driving at this speed if he/she thinks there is a significant risk of being caught by the police and prosecuted. Common-sense observation on the motorway indicates that virtually all drivers are exceeding 70 mi/h but that a large number are not exceeding it by more than about 10 mi/h. It is possible to explain this on the basis that many drivers believe that they are unlikely to be stopped by the police if they are breaking the law in the same way as all the other surrounding drivers and that if they are stopped they are not likely to be prosecuted if they were only doing 80 mi/h if the limit is 70 mi/h. Deterrence here may work in a somewhat oblique way. If the legislator thinks that the safe speed on a motorway in ordinary conditions is 80 mi/h, it might well be decided to set the speed limit at 70 mi/h on the basis that many drivers will exceed the speed limit but not by much. The deterrent effect of criminal law in relation to driving a motor vehicle is of course greatly reinforced by the fact that there is a publicly funded body responsible for enforcing the system, that is the police. This means that in practice careless driving is much more likely to give rise to a criminal prosecution than to a civil action in court. Someone injured in a motor accident has to decide whether it is worth while to sue and the cost of engaging a lawyer (unless this cost is covered by insurance) is likely to be a very important factor in the calculations. No such calculation will enter into the mind of a traffic policeman who sees a motorist driving too fast or without adequate care. Of course the operational decisions of the police force arising from the amount of resources that can be put into traffic control do affect the likely success of the deterrent system.

The two preponderant locations for injury-causing accidents are on the road and in the work-place. Just as criminal law has been used to try to restrict the number of accidents on the road so it has also been used to seek to control accidents in the work-place. Legislation requiring employers to take specified safety steps, for example to fence dangerous machinery, goes well back into the nineteenth century. In England there was a fundamental change of course brought about by the *Health and Safety at Work Act 1974* which was based on a Committee of Enquiry under Lord Robens set up in 1970. This Committee stated that: 'The primary responsibility for doing something about the present levels of occupational accidents and disease lies with those who create the risks and those who work with them.' It is an essential feature of the regime set up under the 1974 Act that there should be a major shift from state regulation to personal responsibility on the part of management and employees. Therefore regulations made under the Act in 1977 established a right of trade unions to appoint safety representatives who could request employers to establish safety committees. This gave those who were exposed to the major risks a more effective voice in drawing attention to the risks. The Act also requires a company to make a statement of company safety policy. Such statements do serve to emphasize that safety is a major management responsibility. Some managements will be lax and incompetent and some work-places will be ununionized or have inadequate unions. There are good reasons to suspect that there is a close correlation between these factors and the safety record in a particular industry. For instance, the safety record of the construction industry is among the worst with an average of three deaths per day throughout the year and many hundreds of injuries each day. It is reasonable to relate this to the fact that the industry is extremely heterogeneous. Many contracts now involve the use of very large numbers of subcontractors since even the largest construction firms find it convenient to operate through large networks of subcontractors rather than to employ many workers directly. Work is spread over a large number of sites and employees therefore are going to different sites at different times; there is much use of casual labour and the unions are for the most part absent or ill organized. (A further important factor is that the construction industry at the work-force level, particularly among unskilled workers, has a risk-taking ethos since taking risks is thought in the short run to maximize earnings.)

It would be imprudent in view of these factors to leave safety wholly to individual employers and employees. The Act set up two bodies designed to promote safety. One is the Health and Safety Commission which consists of representatives of employers, employees and local authorities, with a Chairman appointed by the Secretary of State for Employment, which is primarily a body for formulating policy. The second is the Health and Safety Executive which is a professionally staffed body operating on behalf of the Commission and employing a body of inspectors for this purpose. One of the major ways in which the Executive has promoted safety is through the development of codes of practice. Some of these codes are in relation to particular substances, for instance dangerous substances; the control of substances hazardous to health; lead, asbestos and others in relation to employment generally, for example safety representatives committees; and first aid. The Health and Safety Inspectorate is entitled to monitor what happens in the work-place and it can issue either an improvement notice requiring an employer to remedy a contravention within a specified period of time or a prohibition notice where there is a risk of serious personal injury. In the latter case the activity that contravenes the relevant provision or code of practice cannot be carried on until the necessary remedial action has been taken. In practice the Inspectorate is often able to get remedial action simply by the threat of issuing one of these notices.

It will be seen that the systems used to promote safety on the roads and in the work-place are not the same. The system in the work-place relies in the first instance on cooperation between employer and employee. Such a system would not make sense on the roads since drivers do not have continuing relationships with other drivers. Road safety might be improved by steps designed to raise driving standards, but this course has been largely neglected (it is noticeable that the driving test does not require a candidate to drive in the dark or to drive on motorways, both of which are very different from driving on ordinary roads during the day). Both systems suffer from two significant limitations. One is that the effectiveness of the system must depend on the resources that the government allocates to it. Thus the number of police cars to be seen outside pubs at closing time is likely to affect the numbers of those who drink and drive. Similarly, if the Health and Safety Inspectorate was larger and better staffed it is reasonable to suppose that the number of accidents would be reduced.

The second limiting factor is that both systems work best in relation to the issuing of commands that can easily be understood and obeyed (for example don't drive at more than 50 mi/h and wear a hard hat when on this site) and less well with those that require an element of judgement before they can be obeyed (for example don't drive carelessly). This difficulty is better accommodated within the health and safety framework because of the constant possibility of updating codes of practice and regulations and of dealing at the level of the individual factory or office. The criminal law does little to deal with road accidents that arise out of faulty road construction and configuration.

17.4 INQUIRIES

Many disasters take place because of relatively simple causes. *The Herald of Free Enterprise* sank in Zeebrugge Harbour because it attempted to leave harbour with the bow doors open. Recently a plane crashed on the M1 motorway because the pilot and co-pilot thought that one of the two engines was on fire and turned off the wrong engine. In retrospect at least it is easy to see how these accidents could have been avoided. The allocation of responsibility is more difficult. Was it the fault of the Captain of *The Herald of Free Enterprise* that he attempted to leave harbour with the bow doors open, granted that from the bridge he could not see whether they were open or not? Was it the fault of management in not having installed a mechanical means of preventing this happening, for example by having a warning light on the bridge which would be red if the doors were open or by installing closed circuit television so that the Captain on the bridge could see that the doors were open? Were the pilots who switched off the wrong engine at fault or were the indicators in the cabin misleading? In other cases it will be much more difficult to tell what the reason for the disaster was. It has already been suggested that neither the law of tort nor the criminal law will necessarily provide appropriate machinery for discovering the true causes of the accident. The primary reason for this is that discovering the true cause of the accident is not the primary purpose of the court proceedings in either civil or criminal cases. To a non-lawyer this may seem puzzling and indeed defeatist. To expect anything else would be to misunderstand the system. In trials conducted under the adversary system the ambit of the evidence will be determined by the forensic decisions taken by the Counsel on each side. Of course, Counsel may make decisions that make an inquiry into what actually happened necessary, but this will very often not be the case. To take a simple example, a barrister defending a man accused of murder will simply be concerned to raise in the minds of the jury reasonable doubt as to whether the client is guilty. The barrister will not be concerned to demonstrate that somebody else committed the murder. It would usually be an act of folly for an advocate to seek to show not only that there was doubt whether the client was guilty but affirmatively that somebody else was guilty.

In civil proceedings many cases involving disasters do not get to court. There are a number of reasons for this. Litigation is extremely expensive and lawyers in England will expect to be kept in funds by the plaintiff as the case goes on. Only the very rich and those who are so poor as to qualify for legal aid can regard a major action as anything other than a gamble. There are important differences in procedure here between England and the United States. In the United States lawyers will take a case on the basis that they will be paid a percentage if they win and nothing if they lose. Such cases are also typically tried by juries who are notoriously more generous with other people's money than judges. Thus lawyers will take on accident cases as a speculative venture. The rules of professional conduct as to the institution of class actions also make it much easier for a lawyer to gather together a large number of similar cases as will typically arise in a major accident. Therefore it would be worth while for an American lawyer to become an expert on asbestosis in order to try to corner the market in asbestosis claims, whereas the economics of this would be much more doubtful for an English lawyer. All of this means that both plaintiff and defendant are constrained to put their cases in the most attractive light, though doing so very often will not lead to an in-depth inquiry as to the true reasons for a disaster. We have therefore a substantial tradition in English practice of setting up inquiries into disasters designed not to punish or to award compensation but to discover as far as possible the true cause of the accident. In some cases there are standing bodies in charge of this, as on the railways and the airlines; in other cases bodies are set up specially for this purpose. In the 1970s, for example, a one-man royal commission was set up to enquire into the reasons for the collapse of box girder bridges and Sir Alec Merrison produced a report that established both the reasons for the collapses and the safety parameters that should be observed.

A very recent example is the inquiry held in Scotland into the disaster on the *Piper Alpha* oil rig where 167 people were killed in a series of fires and explosions on 6 July 1988. In this case the Chairman, a Scottish Judge, Lord Cullen, sat for 180 days, heard evidence from 260 witnesses who gave over 6 million words of evidence and produced a 488-page report. These figures alone show why it is unlikely that the litigation system will provide a thorough investigation of the causes of a complex accident. In litigation the cost would be borne by the parties, primarily by the loser, and would be so large as to encourage out-of-court settlements, which would be largely based on the capacity of the parties to face expenditure of this colossal amount. The inquiry framework permitted the investigation of a wide range of possible culprits. Lord Cullen's report contains criticisms of the Department of Energy, of the Offshore Management and of detailed mistakes by the management on the rig. There were faults in training of most levels of management to cope with crises of this kind and significant defects in much of the safety and fire-fighting equipment. It would be particularly difficult to achieve this even-handed analysis in a contested trial since it would be unlikely that all the possible defendants would be parties and it is often the case that the best forensic course for each defendant in such a situation is to argue that it is somebody else's fault (as indeed it often plausibly is). In a trial the judge might make some general comments but would be unlikely to spend time going in detail into possible future action which would not be part of his function.

The holding of an inquiry does not bar the way to either civil or criminal litigation. On the whole if the inquiry produces a clear answer, it is likely that the potential parties to civil litigation will settle their disputes on the basis of the inquiry report (though the inquiry will not of course normally address the question of how much individual claimants are entitled to). In the case of the *Piper Alpha* disaster it is understood that 166 of the 167 families have settled their claims but that one family has decided to pursue a claim in the United States. Criminal proceedings sometimes follow but here the defendant is entitled to fight the matter all over again. In *The Herald of Free Enterprise* case the judge who conducted the inquiry was critical of the corporate defendants. When the prosecution for manslaughter was brought against a number of Directors and the Captain it rather quickly collapsed. An important factor here is that the desire to protect those who are accused of crime is so strong that guilt has to be proved beyond reasonable doubt and in some cases evidence that would be admissible before an inquiry can be excluded in a criminal trial.

17.5 EVALUATION

The engineer who is interested in questions of safety may well have found the discussion so far confusing or dispiriting. This response is understandable but at least to a substantial extent it may underestimate the importance of the structure of the system. For a lawyer a critical question is, 'Who is trying to do what to whom?'. Neither in civil nor in criminal proceedings is an abstract inquiry into the historical causes of an accident the primary concern. It may be a secondary concern, but the primary concern will be either whether a particular defendant should compensate a particular plaintiff for injury or whether a particular defendant should be convicted of a criminal offence and punished. It is not that lawyers are incapable of conducting a dispassionate inquiry into causes of an accident, as is shown by Lord Cullen's report in the *Piper Alpha* case; it is that the structure of the litigation system does not require or even encourage a disinterested pursuit of an inquiry of the fundamental causes of the accident. Recourse to the law may have valuable benefits for those who have been involved in disasters since they or their families may welcome some public ventilation of their resentment against those who have caused the accident. However, this is not the primary purpose of either civil or criminal litigation and it is not surprising that once the matter gets into the hands of lawyers the inquiry takes on a very different appearance. This suggests strongly that if one wants to increase the seriousness with which safety is pursued, it is necessary to set up a mechanism, such as the Health and Safety at Work Executive, which will be able to maximize the use of resources in the relevant area. From this point of view the recommendations of the Robens Report and the mechanism of the Health and Safety at Work Executive undoubtedly present a more fruitful model than the law courts.

Law courts have not only to decide individual cases but to propound general principles for the solution of other cases in the future. It has been suggested already that this process works best where it is possible to identify some simple and clearly defined steps which can be taken to improve safety. It works least well when the cause of the accident is complex and sophisticated. It is difficult to propound in advance general principles which are very helpful in achieving safety in such contexts. The *Bolam* test of 'the ordinary skill of an ordinary competent person' is perhaps an acceptable standard for engineering professionals. Much turns in practice on how the standard is interpreted and applied. This depends in turn on the willingness of expert witnesses to testify that what was done was (or was not) within the range of things that an ordinary competent person might have done. It might be thought that if the defendant produces credible experts to testify that they would have done the same this would be sufficient to establish that duty had not been broken, but the system does not necessarily work in that way. If the plaintiff has produced other credible experts who testify to the opposite effect the judge will decide which set of experts are preferred. In litigation judges normally sit in such cases by themselves without the assistance of expert assessors. In an inquiry, if a judge is appointed to conduct the inquiry, he would be likely to be assisted by technical assessors of high competence who would be able to help in the assessment of the evidence. This shows that what is important is not so much the abstract standard, which is probably perfectly acceptable, as the mechanism to be used for proving it. This leads to the conclusion that the law as it is administered in the courts can make only a limited contribution to safety. This should not surprise us since the law as administered in the courts affects only a very small fraction of human dealings directly. If businessmen had to go to court every time another businessman did not keep his word, this could give rise to equally serious problems. In the case of agreements, however, businessmen can usually be told by their lawyers whether the agreements are likely to be enforced by the courts. In the case of safety, this is much less clearly the case unless the factors that produce unsafety are particularly clear-cut. Unfortunately, the most difficult cases are those where all the law offers is an open-textured rule such as what the reasonably competent engineer would do. A lawyer would tend to regard the use of such residuary rules as inevitable since it is difficult to imagine that one could ever comprehend in advance all possible sources of unsafety inside simple instructions. The way to safety in the future surely involves developing mechanisms from learning from the disasters of the past and incorporating them into the practice of the future as quickly and cheaply as possible. In this respect the model provided by the Health and Safety Executive and by the practice of holding dispassionate inquiries into major disasters seems more likely to be fruitful than battles in the court.

REFERENCES

1. *Bolton* v *Stone* [1951], AC 850.
2. *Bolam* v *Friern Hospital Management Committee* [1957], 2 All ER 118 at 121–2; [1957], 1 WLR 582 at 586–7. The leading account is in Dugdale and Stanton, *Professional Negligence*, 2nd ed., 1989.
3. *Eckersley* v *Binnie* [1988], 18 Con LR 1.
4. *Vacwill Engineering Co. Ltd* v *BDH Chemicals Ltd* [1971], 1 QB 88.
5. Cane, Peter: *Atiyah's Accidents, Compensation and the Law*, 4th ed., Chap. 24, 1987.

EIGHTEEN

AI IN RISK CONTROL

J. B. COMERFORD and J. R. STONE

18.1 INTRODUCTION

It is intended here not to give a detailed account of techniques and tools of artificial intelligence (AI) but to provide an introduction to the ideas and philosophies underlying their development and use, and to highlight how these may assist engineers in dealing with problems of risk and safety in engineering. The reader requiring a deeper study of AI is referred to the many books now available (e.g. see Refs 1 and 2) for a more detailed account of the underlying principles and methods than can be presented here. For a definition of the nature of AI and its goals, perhaps the most general is that by Minsky who states that 'artificial intelligence is the science of making machines do things that would require intelligence if done by men'.

In the following discussion, the basic philosophies and techniques will first be presented from the point of view of building and using models, and then illustrated through descriptions of a small number of existing and proposed applications. It is hoped that through the discussion below, engineers will be stimulated to investigate the possibilities of these new methods for dealing with their problems of managing safety in engineering.

18.2 NATURE OF LARGE ENGINEERING FACILITIES

It was stated in Chapter 1 that the problems of safety associated with large facilities such as dams, buildings, bridges and marine structures should be viewed as a problem of management of risk. These engineering facilities have certain characteristics which are pertinent to the problem of risk management and which make the problems associated with their safety differ from those of the manufacturing industry:

1. They are generally situated in the natural environment.
2. They are usually one-off products.
3. It is usually difficult to distinguish individual components of the facilities with well-defined interactions.
4. They are difficult if not impossible to test (at full scale) against design load conditions in order to verify (or falsify) the design model.
5. The behaviours of the materials used are by no means fully understood.
6. The control of the construction process is variable.
7. The construction and operation of these projects is at the sociotechnical interface.

These facilities are subject to uncontrolled and to some extent unpredictable inputs (for example earthquakes and floods), in addition to changes in the properties of the constituent materials (for example corrosion, alkali–aggregate reaction). It follows that issues of safety and risk management continue after design and construction has finished and require feedback of information from the facility over the period of operation.

The industry is made of diverse entities between which communications are not always ideal. The organizations that design, construct and operate systems may often be different. This may be one reason why the feedback of information from constructed projects through *a posteriori* analysis and monitoring has not been as common in the past as one might wish.

Monitoring provides a path for examining the behaviour of the systems and comparison with predicted behaviour based on the theories used in design. This feedback path is essential to the control of risk for identifying departures from expected behaviour. In large engineering projects this path can be too long or even non-existent. At present data returned by monitoring systems must be interpreted by engineers who have knowledge of the behaviour of the system.

Some of the techniques and developments in the field of AI will be described, to give some idea of how they can assist engineers with some of the problems and requirements described above.

18.3 THE USE OF COMPUTERS IN THE MANAGEMENT OF RISK

The problem of safety in complex systems is seen here as one of management of risk rather than quantitative assessment of risk for the reasons given earlier (see Chapters 1 and 10).

Fundamental to the continuing management of risk is the reduction in uncertainty about the state of the system and its behaviour. One method of achieving this goal is through comparison of observed behaviour with expected behaviour. This requires, firstly, modelling of the system in question in order to make predictions of expected behaviour and, secondly, feedback of information concerning the performance of the system for comparison with the predictions.

Computer programmes have been used in the past in the management of risk. These programmes have proved successful in many tasks where a procedural execution of an algorithm for analysis, prediction or simulation is required. However, they are less well suited to the task of risk management in a more general sense for a number of reasons. Firstly, the models of the behaviour of the system used in the calculations are represented implicitly in the code; therefore, the model is usually neither easily accessible nor changed in the light of new information. Secondly, there is no explicit representation of the uncertainty associated with the model used in the calculations. Thirdly, the boundaries of the model, that is the limits to what is represented and what is not, are not obvious. Finally, the operation of the model is a fixed concept to produce certain types of outputs given certain types of inputs.

In management of risk there is a need for models where the complexity of the system can be modelled explicitly and the model explored to reveal behaviours of the system. The uncertainty associated with the model and the extent of the boundaries of the model represented need to be expressed. There may be a need to use more than one model arising from different 'views' (see the next subsection) of the systems and then resolve conflicts between the predictions or explanations given by these models.

Research in the field of AI has provided new approaches to modelling which allows some of these issues and requirements introduced above to be addressed.

Modelling

Models may be viewed as representations of our theories about the system. They represent a particular world view (or 'weltanschauung') in that we choose a particular set of entities and relationships between them to represent in the model. In conventional programmes used in engineering, the model represented is some form of mathematical model which expresses some understanding of the behaviour of the system. The model transforms input variables into output variables through some procedure to give predictions. If there is a desire to express the uncertainty associated with these variables it is generally expressed in the form of probability theory using stochastic variables.

However, the factors pertinent to the safety of a large engineering structure cannot all be represented by mathematical variables. Large engineering projects operate at the sociotechnical interface; hence many concepts are not measurable in engineering terms—they are qualitative. These factors may be measurable in a qualitative sense, as is done in social sciences, but generally cannot be represented by the variables of a mathematical model.

One of the most powerful and useful developments in the field of AI has been the development of methods of representing models of qualitative concepts and the relationships between them. In parallel has been the development of methods of reasoning with these models.

The basis of these models is symbolic representation of the concepts as opposed to numeric representation in conventional programmes. Variables in a qualitative model can take on values that are a string of symbols or a name that stands for some concept in the modelled domain. Reasoning with this model involves manipulation of these symbol structures. There are various formalisms that can be used for building these models; these will be described later.

18.4 ARTIFICIAL INTELLIGENCE

AI is considered here to be a collection of philosophies and techniques based on models of human cognitive processes which have enabled new ways of programming and using computers to be made. These philosophies and techniques have been developed through research in the principal areas of interest such as:

Representation of knowledge
Methods of reasoning
Qualitative physics
Machine learning
Neural networks
Vision
Language understanding

The first five subjects listed above have some relevance to the problem of management of risk and will be discussed below; the other two are beyond the scope of this discussion. Developments in the first three of these have led to the emergence of what have been called knowledge-based systems or expert systems. These systems are increasingly being used in industry and commerce.

The traditional roles for such systems have been in the role of decision-support systems which offer advice to decision makers or assist them in managing complex data and problems.

Knowledge-Based Systems

The terms 'knowledge-based systems' and 'expert systems' are both in some sense misleading in that all engineering computer programmes generally represent some degree of knowledge and expertise. The difference between these and conventional programmes lies in the nature of the models and how they are used.

Knowledge-based systems derive their name from the fact that the model consists of representations of knowledge about some domain and the system has techniques of reasoning, that is drawing inferences from this knowledge. The knowledge may be represented in a number of formalisms, the most simple being a set of facts about the domain and of rules relating these facts. The different formalisms will be discussed later but in essence they are a qualitative model, as described in Sec. 18.3, of relationships between concepts. Expert systems derive their name from the fact that knowledge about a particular domain may be gathered from experts in that field.

The term 'expert systems' is unfortunate because these systems are not experts in any sense. They lack many of the abilities of human experts such as self-awareness of their own expertise, the ability to communicate effectively and most importantly to take responsibility. They represent a model of some expert knowledge in a particular field. The engineer may use the system as an aid and tool in decision making but the responsibility always remains with him/her. The term 'knowledge-based system' is preferred here (though some would argue that they are in fact different).

An important aspect of such knowledge-based systems is what is called meta-reasoning, that is the ability to reason about the nature and operation of the problem-solving process itself. Meta-reasoning is on a level above the operation of the system in performing its tasks and enables such processes as examining the consistency and completeness of the model and generating explanations for the conclusions or advice it offers.

This form of meta-reasoning is essential in cases where the models have a high degree of uncertainty associated with them. For example, models of behaviour established through observation of past behaviour may be invalidated as external conditions change. The monitoring of the dependability of the model may be as important as the monitoring of differences between observed behaviour and that predicted by the model. The explanation of the line of reasoning and presentation of the base data leading up to a given conclusion are essential parts of such systems if they are to allow the operators to explore the problem domain of the model.

The use of such systems in management of risk has some obvious benefits. Such systems enable reasoning about the nature of and the sources of risk in a given problem and the uncertainties inherent in it, rather then simply attempting to calculate its value, that is to come up with an 'answer'.

The components and techniques incorporated in these systems will be discussed under the headings of domain knowledge, reasoning, building knowledge-based systems and representation of uncertainty. There are other issues involved in the development of these systems, such as software engineering issues and knowledge acquisition, but they are of less importance for the present purpose.

Domain knowledge Different aspects of the knowledge about the domain can be distinguished.

Model of the domain structure That is knowledge about the entities in the domain and the relationships between these entities. Figure 18.1 gives a simple example of a model of the structure of a domain which is some type of family. The entities, FATHER, MOTHER, FIRST SON and SECOND SON are contained in boxes and the family relationships between these entities are given in circles. This model of a family structure is a representation of some knowledge of a typical family. It is a 'frame' or 'template' for particular families that fit this structure.

Reasoning in the domain This is knowledge about how to reason in the problem domain in order to solve particular forms of problems. For example,

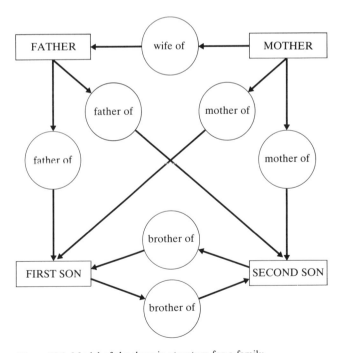

Figure 18.1 Model of the domain structure for a family.

if the problem to be solved is to establish whether two given boys are brothers, given some information about their parents, then the following reasoning strategy might be useful:

Check whether both boys have the same father

and then,

Check whether both boys have the same mother

If these two checks are affirmed by the information available then we know that the two boys are brothers.

Meta-knowledge That is knowledge about the competence, effectiveness, relevance and limits of the model and reasoning strategies described above. In the example given above the model of Fig. 18.1 takes no account of the possibility of divorce. Two children may have the same parents, but the parents may in fact be no longer married. In such circumstances the model breaks down. This is a limit on the competence of the model and reasoning.

Reasoning Research in philosophy, the cognitive sciences, psychology and AI has led to models being developed of methods of reasoning used by humans. Two aspects to these models can be distinguished which are often lumped together in knowledge-based system literature: strategies of reasoning or problem solving and methods of inference. In general, in order to build a knowledge-based system both methods of inference and strategies of reasoning have to be implemented in the system to reason about the problem domain structure model.

The strategies of reasoning are the methods or procedures used to solve the particular problems in the domain and represent domain specific knowledge as discussed above.

Deduction, induction and abduction are methods of inference. Deduction is where conclusions are derived from axioms through logical inference. For example, from the axioms

All engineers are underpaid

and

Joe is an engineer

the conclusion

Joe is underpaid

is a locally valid conclusion.

Induction is the generalization of a rule or principle from a set of facts. Hence, if we are given that:

John is an engineer and is underpaid
Joe is an engineer and is underpaid

we might form the conclusion

All engineers are underpaid

Abduction is a process that generates explanations. From the statements:

All engineers are underpaid
Joe is underpaid

the explanation might be given that:

Joe is an engineer

These methods of inference may be used to manipulate the model in the knowledge base.

Building knowledge-based systems Knowledge-based systems have been built using a variety of software tools, ranging from programming languages to complex integrated development environments. The following types of development tools will be discussed:

Rule-based systems
Frame-based systems
Programming languages
Knowledge-based system toolkits

Rule-based systems In these systems the knowledge about the problem domain is expressed as a set of rules called production rules. These rules take the form:

IF (set of conditions are true)
THEN (perform a set of actions)

or

IF (set of conditions are true)
THEN (set of conclusions are true)

The knowledge base consists of a set of such rules which express the domain knowledge. The rule-based system operates on these rules given a base set of data using what is commonly called an 'inference engine' (which performs some form of inference) to explore what conclusions can be drawn from the base data on the basis of the rule-base. Let us examine a simple example. Consider the knowledge base:

Rule 1
IF (engineer is competent)
THEN (design is good)

Rule 2
IF (design is good)
THEN (building is safe)

If we were then to assert, that is give the system as base data, the fact:

engineer is competent

then the inference system would draw the conclusion

building is safe

The basic operation of this inferencing system is of matching patterns of symbols or concepts. The system matches the fact:

engineer is competent

with the head (conditions) of rule 1 and then asserts that:

design is good

The system is then able to match this fact with the conditions of rule 2 to assert that:

building is safe

Hence from the base data of the fact:

engineer is competent

we have the two facts:

design is good
building is safe

The system should be able to explain this path of reasoning.

An obvious fact about the example knowledge base given above is that it is unfortunately not true to common experience. Life for engineers would be much simpler if it were. However, there is some truth in these rules and they are obviously not false. The fact that an engineer is competent does not make certain that the building is safe, but it obviously helps. The uncertainty associated with conclusions such as those given above arise from the uncertainty in the rules making up the model and in the incompleteness of the model itself. Dealing with this problem of representation of uncertainty will be discussed later.

Frame-based systems There has been a convergence between developments in software engineering for complex programmes and in AI for methods of representing knowledge. Both have been driven by the desire for better structuring of the software systems. This has led to the emergence of object-oriented methods in software engineering and frame-based systems in AI. The two paradigms are very similar and since frame-based methodology has emerged from AI it will be discussed rather than object-oriented methods.

Frames are the basic structure of knowledge representation in frame-based systems. A frame is used to represent the knowledge concerning a particular type of concept, for example some type of object or event. It consists of a set of slots where attributes related to the concept can be stored. When the slots are filled the frame is said to be 'instantiated' and then represents a particular concept or entity. These frames allow a modularizing and structuring of the knowledge in a domain that is not possible using the rule-based formalism.

Frames can be arranged in classes with class members sharing attributes they have in common. A model of some domain can be constructed using these frame structures expressing the relationships between concepts of the problem domain using linkages between the frames.

Figure 18.2 shows an example of a frame representing the family structure shown in Fig. 18.1. The frame is a 'family' frame and the slots of the frame given the structure of the family. This frame is instantiated with particular values for the slots so the frame represents a particular family.

FRAME	FAMILY
SLOTS	VALUES
Name	Comerford
Father	Bernard
Mother	Elizabeth
Sons	Michael, Joseph

Figure 18.2 Frame representation of family structure from Fig. 18.1.

Programming languages Knowledge-based systems have been written using conventional programming languages such as FORTRAN or Pascal. However, their procedural nature renders them particularly unsuitable for the declarative nature of building knowledge-based systems. Symbol-manipulation languages such as LISP or PROLOG are widely used in knowledge-based system development. Their power of symbol manipulation and pattern matching enable them to perform the required manipulation of knowledge represented in symbolic form. These languages can be used to build frame-based and rule-based systems or other paradigms for knowledge structuring and representation. They are the most flexible method of building systems but require a high level of expertise and effort. PROLOG and LISP and similar languages have a built-in inference system or theorem prover, which facilitates the development of reasoning procedures.

Object-oriented languages such as C++ are becoming increasingly popular due to their combination of frame-like structuring and flexibility. This enables a flexible approach to system development while providing the means for structuring the knowledge base.

Knowledge-based system toolkits Knowledge-based systems toolkits generally allow more than one method of representing knowledge, usually rules and frames. In addition it is often possible to use them in conjunction with programming languages, either procedural languages or symbol-processing languages.

These toolkits allow conventional procedural programming using mathematical reasoning and also declarative programming using qualitative reasoning to be combined. They often allow access to databases and spreadsheets as well as calls to external programmes. This represents a flexible and powerful modelling environment for representation and problem solving. New tools are emerging constantly, enabling applications to be developed more easily and quickly.

Representation of uncertainty In engineering it has been usual practice to study and represent the uncertainty associated with the values of parameters in engineering models (using probability theory) but less common to express the uncertainty associated with the models that are used.

Methods have been developed of representing these uncertainties in the form of numerical uncertainty measures attached to the relationships in the qualitative models. The ability to manipulate qualitative models of knowledge-based systems also allows the manipulation of the uncertainty measures using some form of calculus to combine and propagate them through chains of reasoning.

If we were to attach some measure of the uncertainty to the rule in the knowledge base given earlier, then

IF (engineer is competent)
THEN (design is good)   (certainty = 0.6)

The uncertainty measure given above represents the uncertainty associated with the relationship in the model between competent engineers and good designs. We might interpret this factor, 0.6, as the probability that any given design engineer who is competent will produce a good design, or the measure of general belief that a competent engineer will produce a good design, or a reflection of the evidence available which suggests that competent engineers have produced good designs in the past.

There are different aspects to the uncertainty associated with theories, models, explanations and reasoning; changes of events occurring, vagueness in definition of concepts, uncertainty in cause and effect linkages, incompleteness in information and understanding, and uncertainty in mapping between the observations we make of a continuous world and the discrete set of concepts available to describe this diversity.

Qualitative Physics

Qualitative physics is a recent development in AI. Research in this aspect of AI has been prompted by a desire to reason about the behaviour of physical systems. The essence of qualitative physics is the formulation of qualitative models of the behaviour of devices or structures and the use of these to reason in a qualitative way about their behaviour.

In following the discussion given below, readers may like to consider the following question. In modelling the behaviour of physical systems why should we be constrained to represent the quantities or variables of the system on the real number scale, and why should the only language we use to describe the behaviour be that of mathematics?

Consider a model of the load deflection behaviour of a centrally loaded, simply supported beam with modulus of elasticity E, inertia I and length L subjected to a central point load P. The mid-span deflection d may be calculated from the relationship:

$$d = \frac{PL^3}{48EI}$$

This is sometimes considered as being *the* description of the behaviour and in some way the truth. Here, it is considered as one possible model of the beam's behaviour which is dependable (see Chapter 1) within certain conditions. The parameters of the model: P, D, E, I, L take values defined on the real number scale, which may be described as the 'quantity space' for the model. We could, however, construct another model which reflects the load–deflection behaviour of the same beam B in a qualitative sense:

IF (load is low),
THEN (deflection is minimal)

IF (load is medium)
THEN (deflection is moderate)

IF (load is high)
THEN (deflection is severe)

Such a model might be seen to reflect the way engineers or non-engineers reason about the behaviour of a beam in a common-sense way. The quantity space for the deflection is the ordered set {minimal, moderate, severe} and for the load is {low, medium, high}.

One might ask why one should use such a model when the mathematical model given by the equation is adequate and has served us well in the past. Is the mathematical model better in some way in that it is in some sense more 'accurate' or 'true'?.

The argument for using such a qualitative model is that of *appropriate modelling*, that is in essence that the models used in problem solving should have a level of detail and precision that is appropriate to the type of questions we wish to answer and to the precision of the data available.

Firstly, the two models appear to accord with observational evidence and are then both dependable (within the constraints of their range of applicability). Secondly, accuracy in the sense of precision is not an end in itself. In science, precision is often an essential goal, but in engineering one might consider appropriateness of the model to the data available and the type of decisions to be made to be more important (one does not require a finite element model of soil behaviour to decide to avoid driving heavy plant near unsupported trenches).

Finally, there are some areas of engineering knowledge, particularly associated with complex systems, where it is not possible to identify dependable engineering models of the behaviour of the phenomena either due to the absence of underlying theories, the inability to test theories that exist or the inability to quantify the variables involved. However, it is often possible to give some qualitative description of the behaviour. For example, one could say that the collapse of underground structures leads to settlement of the ground surface above and collapse of large structures will lead to significant settlements, but it is questionable whether a dependable model could be formed of the precise physical movements of the soil structures.

18.5 APPLICATIONS

How can the philosophy and methods of AI be used to assist engineers in the control of risk? The remainder of this chapter first examines some current achievements and then speculates about future developments.

Problem solving using artificial intelligence techniques must prove itself to be both useful and dependable if it is to become widely accepted by engineers. The emphasis in practice is necessarily on the degree to which the available tools can assist in the making of decisions, rather than on any theoretical appeal of particular computational approaches. The final products are simply computer programmes with the same scope and limitations as any others. Until recently, most developments in this field have been in the form of small-scale 'expert system' demonstration and feasibility studies rather than commercially useful applications. This is beginning to change with the emergence of a growing number of systems which are being used in practice to help solve problems. Applications are appearing across the whole spectrum of business, in the public, private and service sectors. A selection of detailed case studies of the process of initiation, development and implementation of expert systems in a number of major companies[3] illustrates the significant financial savings that may accrue through the use of this new technology. According to this study, one computer manufacturer expects to reduce costs by $1.5 million per year for each hour saved following the introduction of a $100 000 asset control system.

The construction industry, for example, is becoming increasingly aware of the potential benefits of the use of AI. The development of investment and attitudes in this sector in the United Kingdom has been surveyed recently,[4] highlighting factors such as an increase in the use of networking to link computers in order to simplify the collection and distribution of information and an expected 50 per cent increase in expenditure on 'information technology' (IT) by contractors in the next two years. An earlier exercise[5] attempted to predict the impact of expert systems on the UK construction industry, and noted that their low investment in IT compared with that of Japanese companies was likely to have a long-term adverse effect on the ability of UK companies to gain overseas contracts. While both of these surveys relate specifically to the UK construction industry, which is notorious for its low investment in research and development, many of their broader findings would be applicable to other branches of engineering.

A recent and extensive list of over four hundred references to applications of AI in civil and structural engineering[6] shows the extent to which a previously esoteric research topic is beginning to find practical uses. The same growth may be seen in other branches of engineering.

This section examines a small number of expert systems that have been developed to assist in the management of different problems. The continuing growth in the popularity of the expert system approach to decision support is such that any such selection is necessarily very restricted and rapidly outdated. The following examples are therefore intended to illustrate some of the basic features of such systems rather than to form an exhaustive survey of the most recent developments.

Existing Knowledge-Based Systems

One of the first intrusions of artificial intelligence into engineering has been in the field of knowledge-based, or 'expert', systems. This may reflect the nature of many low-level engineering decisions—for example the sizing of a structural member subjected to a range of forces—which are governed by codified rules and standard procedures. Such rules are often readily represented in a form that can be manipulated within a knowledge-based system (KBS), as described in Sec. 18.4. Table 18.1 shows only a small selection of the many KBSs that have been developed within civil/structural

Table 18.1 Some knowledge-based systems in civil and structural engineering

Name	Usage	Developer	State
AUTONAP	Surveying and land records	Rensselaer Polytechnic	Commercial
CONE	Interpretation of cone penetrometer	Carnegie-Mellon University	Prototype
DAMP	Diagnosis of moisture in buildings	New Zealand Building Association	Commercial
HOWSAFE	Safety of construction project	Stanford University	Operational
IBDA	Evaluation of bridge deck damage	MIT	Prototype
SAFEQUAL	Evaluation of contractors for safety	Stanford University	Operational
SACON	Finite element operation	Stanford University	Operational
SEISMIC RISK	Safety of buildings for seismic risk	Stanford University	Commercial
SPERIL	Earthquake damage assessment for buildings	Purdue University	Operational
TRAL1	Traffic signal design	Carnegie-Mellon University	Prototype
WELDING ADVISOR	Weld procedure selection	Stone and Webster	Commercial
WSRP	Water shortage response plan	University of Washington-Seattle	Operational

engineering. The examples have been chosen to reflect the range of applications rather than to be a complete collection—an impossibility in a time of rapid change—and indicate what is believed to be their current state of development.

In studying the KBSs currently in use, it is clear that many of them act essentially as 'check-lists'—that is they guide the user to a decision based upon a number of deterministic rules. Check-lists are readily programmed in KBS form and serve an important function in helping to ensure that essential tasks are completed in the correct sequence, and as such are widely used (for example by airline pilots or by designers wishing to achieve compliance with all the requirements of a code of practice). They therefore have an important role to play in the quest for safety.

One commercially available example of this class of KBS is WELDING ADVISOR,[7] which assists with the sometimes complex problem of ensuring that the welders assigned to a particular task are fully qualified by virtue of having passed the correct tests. A typical rule from WELDING ADVISOR is:

IF	The qualification code is ASME IX
AND	The process combination is SMAW
AND	The configuration is pipe
AND	The filler metal is an F-34 electrode
AND	The root pass conditions will not apply
AND	Multiple process conditions are satisfied
THEN	Select Welder Qualification test #071

where ASME IX is the appropriate code of practice from which a test is to be selected and the individual rule clauses relate to the details of the weld type and environment. The knowledge encapsulated within the rules was provided by an expert available within the company, and the system is understood to be in general use.

The check-list approach to problem solving cannot be considered as particularly 'intelligent', although it may be the most appropriate method for a small and completely defined domain. It addresses only a part of the problems faced in engineering. The kind of complex 'real world' (see Chapter 1) problems relating to risk are commonly characterized by uncertain, incomplete and contradictory information. It is possible, for example, that eliciting knowledge from two human experts regarding a particular problem will produce two quite different responses. Any system that is designed to be of significant help in solving real-world problems should therefore be capable of handling information of this form in a natural manner.

One KBS which embodies a means of modelling uncertainty is HOWSAFE,[8] which is common with many others was developed as a university research project. HOWSAFE was designed to assist with the evaluation of the safety of construction companies by considering aspects of the prevailing attitudes and management practices—aspects of what might nowadays be referred to as the company 'safety culture' (see Chapters 8 and 9). The overall goal of HOWSAFE is to evaluate the degree of belief in the 'top-level' hypothesis: 'This construction firm has the required organization and procedures to promote safe construction'. This it does through examining the belief in intermediate goals such as 'Top management truly cares about safety' and 'Managers at each level are held accountable for the safety of all their subordinates'. Each intermediate goal is then viewed as a hypothesis with evidence from lower-level goals. For example, the belief in the hypothesis that 'Top management truly cares about safety' is derived from such statements as 'Top management knows all workers and their families personally' and 'Clients weight the company's safety record as a factor in negotiating contracts'. Uncertainty is represented by using certainty factors (Sec. 18.4), where all questions are answered on a scale from $+5$ (definitely true) through 0 (don't know) to -5 (definitely false). The explicit inclusion of uncertainty in this example reflects the increased complexity of the problem domain.

Current Research and Development

In order to speculate about future developments in AI it is useful to consider which factors contribute to 'intelligence'. Clearly the attributes engineers often associate with computers—speed, arithmetic capability and accuracy—are not of themselves sufficient for the machines to be called intelligent. Much current research in AI is directed towards modelling other aspects of human intelligence such as pattern recognition and learning. This section will examine two promising areas in which new research may allow improved control of risk.

Signal interpretation Many engineering decisions are based upon the interpretation of readings from instruments—for example temperature as measured by a thermocouple or pressure given by a piezometer. The safety of a dam may, for example, be inferred partly from evidence provided by a large number of instruments continually recording parameters such as settlement, inclination, water level and internal pore pressure. The process under investigation may be required to operate subject to certain specified boundary conditions ('limit states'), and actions may be taken to prevent or to alleviate the effects of transgressions of the boundaries. In some situations the monitoring of a process may be straightforward, for example where a thermocouple gives clear and unambiguous readings of temperature. However, many occasions arise in engineering where instrument readings are not so readily interpreted. These may include situations where readings are changing rapidly, are imprecise, or are of questionable accuracy. Many processes, such as that of monitoring dam safety noted above, can generate considerable quantities of data, leading to a possible 'information overload' in which it is difficult to get a clear picture of what is happening.

The interpretation of complex signals is a difficult process commonly carried out by engineers with considerable experience in the problem domain. While individual approaches may differ, two common aspects of interpretation are the compression of the data by some means of extracting features of interest from the background 'noise' and, secondly, the classification of these features according to some measure of their similarity to examples that have occurred before. This naturally requires the possession of an appropriate model of the behaviour of the process (whether mathematical, physical or mental) in order to be able to recognize characteristic features.

The tasks of data compression and feature classification may both be assisted by the use of AI. Indeed, feature classification depends upon pattern recognition, an area of considerable current development within AI.

The following two examples relate to the problems of determining the integrity of concrete foundation piles and the safety of dams, and reflect some of the current research into the use of AI in the interpretation of signals.

Pile integrity testing Many structures are supported upon cast *in situ* piles, in which concrete is placed in prebored holes in the ground. Some of the problems that can arise with this approach are localized necking, bulging or the inclusion of debris due to disturbance of the surrounding soil during concrete placement. While it is common practice to load test a sample of the piles on a particular project, this can prove expensive and time-consuming. A number of quick and simple non-destructive tests have been developed in order to reduce the risk of defective piles remaining undetected. One such method records the propagation of sound waves within a pile caused by striking a blow on the pile-head with a hammer. The resulting signal trace of pile displacement with time can be examined, and certain distinctive features may allow a practised observer to diagnose specific defects. The interpretation of these signals is clearly a problem of pattern recognition, and research[9] at Bristol University has shown how an AI approach can assist.

Figure 18.3 shows a typical test result from a pile with no significant defects. The horizontal axis of Fig. 18.3 is expressed in terms of distance rather than time, using the known velocity of sound waves in hardened concrete, and the vertical axis is plotted at an arbitrary scale to accommodate the three different plots. The three lines represent the raw data of the decaying stress wave and the *median line* and *log plot*. The median line joins the average values of consecutive maxima and minima in the raw data and the log plot represents the natural logarithm of the peak-to-peak values. When interpreting pile test results the expert looks at the median line and log plot for evidence of disturbance, or *events*. In the log plot these events take the form of changes of gradient and in the median line they take the form of

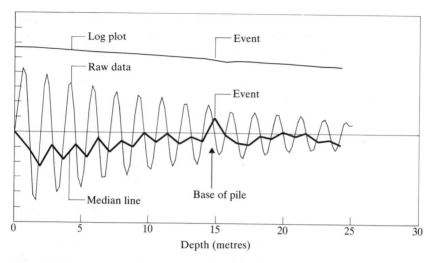

Figure 18.3 Typical test result from pile with no defect.

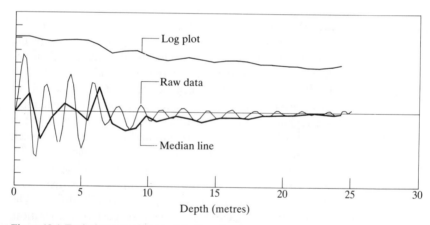

Figure 18.4 Typical test result from defective pile.

peaks. Figure 18.4 shows the trace resulting from a 6.0 m long pile with a suspected inclusion at 3.0 m from the top.

The skill of the expert lies in the reliable interpretation of the meaning of these events from their type and position in a trace. This is a problem of pattern recognition, in which similarities are sought between the current trace and those resulting from known defects. SIPIT (System for Interpreting Pile Integrity Tests) has been developed to assist in this task. SIPIT contains a knowledge base, elicited from an expert, of rules about the meaning of particular events. The rules, expressed as PROLOG clauses, are based upon a generalized hierarchical description of signal features, such as 'upslope', 'downslope' and 'plateau'. This representation is based upon the observation that the expert's interpretation depends less upon the fine detailed features of the trace than on its broader characteristics. For example, a sharp peak may be defined as the sequences [upslope, downslope] and a flat peak as [upslope, plateau, downslope]. Each of these features is further defined in terms of more detailed features such as 'flat', 'upstep' and 'downstep', which are in turn related to the time interval into which the signal is divided.

The SIPIT rules include an uncertainty measure, and the system will quantify the degree of belief in the advice it gives. For example, the result of analysing the trace of Fig. 18.4 is to suggest that there is strong evidence for an inclusion at a depth of 3 m and weak evidence for a crack at the same depth.

The system at present has a success rate of approximately 80 per cent when compared with interpretations made by an experienced engineer. It is expected that this may be improved by refining the knowledge base and, perhaps more importantly, by pursuing a deeper understanding of the process used by the expert. It is nevertheless clear that many of the routine event recognition tasks may be performed reliably by computer, thus releasing the expert to concentrate on the more complex or uncertain cases.

Safety of dams The design and safety of dams has been discussed in Chapter 10. Although the chances of failure of a particular dam may be small, the consequences are often potentially catastrophic. It is therefore important that those responsible for the operation and maintenance of these structures are kept reliably informed of factors that may effect safety. This information is commonly obtained from continuous readings of a variety of instruments such as piezometers, inclinometers and strain gauges and, as noted above, this can result in considerable quantities of data.

The second signal interpretation project[9] is a simulation designed to give a pictorial representation of the overall 'cause for concern' for each of eight instruments in the core of an embankment dam. It differs from the pile test problem in that now it is necessary to interpret a number of signals from different sources rather than a single trace, and the approach of the human expert carrying out the task is to attempt to detect deviations from a norm instead of searching for similarities.

Instrument data is compressed according to three global statistical measures of behaviour. These are standard deviation, a 'uniformity' measure of discontinuities and 'extremeness' which gives an indication of the dwell of the signal at maximum excursions from the mean.

Dam engineers were asked to characterize a number of graphs of instrument signals according to their rarity and cause for concern and to create two knowledge bases. The first relates compressed data to expected rarity of occurrence and the second is used to determine an overall cause for concern for each instrument. The pilot scheme may be presented with a set of simulated signals, which are compared with the information in the knowledge bases, and a picture of the dam cross-section displayed with a shading pattern representing the level of concern at each position.

An AI-based approach to monitoring dam safety in Italy is currently being developed by ENEL (Italian National Power Agency) and ISMES (an engineering consultancy). An object-oriented system employing a causal model of failure modes is intended to allow an improved level of continuous safety appraisal.

Machine learning from failures Engineers have a professional and social duty to learn from failures that occur and to apply those lessons in the future. Many of the results of this learning process emerge as alterations to the codes of practice and regulations which provide guidance and control. Unfortunately, a number of factors hinder the efficient operation of such a failure/investigation/learning/improvement cycle. In the construction industry, for example, there is very little feedback. This is partly due to the particularly fragmented nature of the industry, in which a small number of very large companies (consultants and contractors) vie with a vastly greater number of small and medium-sized organizations. Transmission of information through such an industry is therefore difficult. Of course, there are exceptions to this pattern, most notably in the cases of the nuclear and chemical process industries. Here the long-standing operation of formal safety procedures has at least attempted to capture information from failures and to learn from them.

If people can learn from what has gone before, can machines do so? Research into failures at Bristol University[10] is aiming to achieve this through the detection of 'patterns' of factors that tend to occur before failures. If these patterns can be identified from a study of previous failure, then it should be possible to examine current projects and to detect whether potentially hazardous situations are developing. It has been demonstrated (see Chapter 9) that many major disasters develop through the same clearly defined stages and that certain general factors are often present.

Information concerning failures exists in two main formats, depending on the nature and severity of the event. In the case of major accidents there will often be a detailed report prepared by a formal committee of inquiry or similar body. Other less severe failures, much more frequent than major catastrophes, may be investigated through the use of structured interviews with individuals concerned, and may again lead to published reports.

The initial analysis of these reports in a search for common sequences of events is undertaken by forming an 'event sequence diagram' (ESD) showing in graphical form the order and interrelationship of events in each failure. A typical ESD, based upon an investigation[11] of a colliery explosion, is shown in Fig. 18.5. Here we are concerned not with the details of the ESD but rather its structure and form of representation.

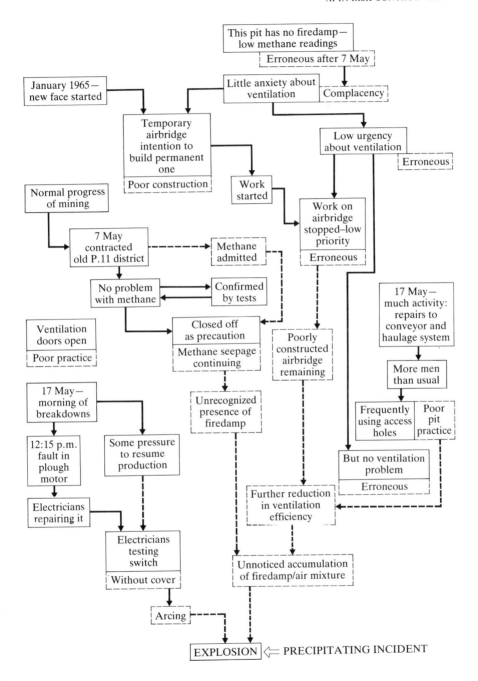

Figure 18.5 Event sequence diagram for colliery explosion. *(Source: Turner.*[11]*)*

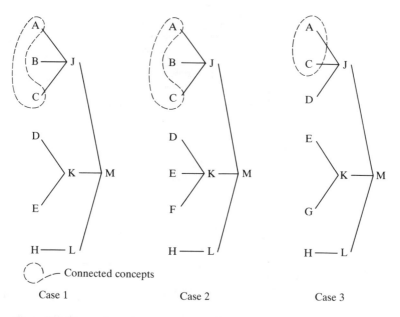

Figure 18.6 Three schematic event sequence diagrams.

The individual concepts used to describe each failure are selected from a hierarchical 'vocabulary'. At the highest, most general level are concepts related to factors such as social context, safety culture and management organization, while the lowest, most detailed level allows the representation of factors including the calculation checking procedure and a designer's work-load.

The analysis of a number of failures in this manner results in a 'library' of ESDs, which can then be compared using a clustering algorithm to find patterns. For example, Fig. 18.6 shows three ESDs in which the detailed concepts are labelled A to M, where M in each case represents 'failure' and time flows from left to right.

It is clear from Fig. 18.6 that the group of concepts [A C] is present in each case as a forerunner to J, and that H always precedes L. Inductive reasoning (see above in this chapter) might therefore suggest that, in some future case, the observation of both A and C could be evidence that J is about to occur. Similarly, the occurrence of H at some stage in a project might act as a warning that L may follow. A measure of belief in J occurring can be calculated from the evidence for each of A and C.

The use of a knowledge base in the form of ESDs may reduce the risks associated with a new project by drawing attention to similar patterns in the incubation of previous failures.

18.6 THE FUTURE

We have seen in this chapter how the use of AI can assist with complex tasks such as the interpretation of instrument signals and learning from failures. These developments have both been made possible through advances in AI over the past decade, in areas such as logic programming, the representation of uncertainty, pattern recognition and machine learning.

How will work in AI contribute to risk control in the future? We can only speculate based upon previous performance and the nature of problems in engineering. The past decade has seen an enormous increase in the speed and availability (through reducing cost) of computers, and the ease with which numerical problems can be tackled. Engineering, however, is concerned with much more than numerical calculations—it is to do with information. We might therefore expect to see an increasing emphasis on the use of computers for the collection, transmission and interpretation of information related to engineering problems. This may include greater use of telemetry to transmit data from remote sites to a central monitoring station. Many organizations are installing computer networks to enable people to share information.

If we wish to control risk through the use of AI, then we must understand and be able to represent and transform not only numbers but also the complex social and psychological issues discussed in earlier chapters. The improved processing of information in the form of natural language, parallel processing of related strands of information, and a broader understanding of the nature and representation of uncertainty are all expected to be features of future developments.

AI has an important growing role as one of the tools available to engineers for the management and control of risk.

REFERENCES

1. Boden, M. A.: *Artificial Intelligence and Natural Man*, 2nd ed, MIT Press, London, 1987.
2. Yazdani, M. (ed.): *Artificial Intelligence: Principles and Applications*. Chapman and Hall, London, 1986.
3. Feigenbaum, E. A., P. McCorduck, and H. P. Nii: *The Rise of the Expert Company*, Macmillan, London, 1988.
4. KPMG Peak Marwick McLintock/Construction Industry Computing Association: *Building on IT*, KPMG/CICA, London, 1987.
5. Lansdown, J.: *Expert Systems: Their Impact on the Construction Industry*, report to RIBA Conference Fund, Author/RIBA Conference Fund, London, 1982.
6. Topping, B. H. V., and B. Kumar: The Application of Artificial Intelligence Techniques to Civil and Structural Engineering—A Bibliography, in *The Application of Artificial Intelligence Techniques to Civil and Structural Engineering*, B. H. V. Topping (ed.), Proc. CIVIL-COMP '89 Fourth Int. Conf. Civil and Structural Eng. Comp., Civil-Comp. Press, London, 1989.

7. Finn, G. A., and K. F. Reinschmidt: Expert Systems in an Engineering Construction Firm, in *Expert Systems in Civil Engineering*, C. N. Kostem and M. L. Maher (eds), ASCE, New York, 1986.
8. Levitt, R. E.: HOWSAFE: A Microcomputer-Based Expert System to Evaluate the Safety of a Construction Firm, in *Expert Systems in Civil Engineering*, C. N. Kostem and M. L. Maher (eds), ASCE, New York, 1986.
9. Comerford, J. B., J. H. Martin, J. P. Davis, and D. I. Blockley: On Aids to Interpretation in Monitoring Civil Engineering Systems, *Proc. Conf. Expert Systems in Civil Engineering*, International Association for Bridge and Structural Engineering, Bergamo, Italy, October, IABSE/AIPC/IVBH, Milan, 1989.
10. Stone, J. R., D. I. Blockley, and B. W. Pilsworth: Towards Machine Learning from Case Histories, *Civ. Engng Systems*, vol. 6, no 3, pp. 129–135, 1989.
11. Turner, B. A.: *Man-made Disasters*, Wykeham, London, 1978.

NINETEEN

A CRITIQUE OF RELIABILITY THEORY

D. G. ELMS and C. J. TURKSTRA

19.1 INTRODUCTION

After more than 50 years of development, reliability theory contains a rich body of techniques and approaches and considerable depth of understanding. It is widely used in practice. Its range of applications is well illustrated in other chapters of this book. It does, however, have limitations serious enough to pose major problems to the unwary user. The limitations are constraints on usage within which engineers have to operate—or ignore them at their peril. Where the limitations are properly taken into account, reliability theory and risk analysis are powerful decision tools. Where they are neglected, and it is all too easy to do so, reliability theory can become not only useless but even worse, thoroughly misleading. It is rather like navigating a boat between dangerous rocks. Where the hazards are seen and the helmsman is cautious there is no problem, but lack of concentration or of knowledge of the threats can lead to a wreck. This chapter identifies a number of limitations of reliability theory and tries to show how they may be overcome. It then looks at possible future developments.

Early developments in reliability theory were necessarily simplistic, leaving holes to be filled by others as the discipline grew in age and sophistication. Indeed, it seems inevitable in the growth of any body of theory that it looks enticingly simple at its first inception. Nevertheless, when attempts are made to apply it in practical situations, complexities appear that were not initially obvious, and the attractiveness of the first idea begins to be lost in detail and a mass of empirical additions. In structural engineering, for example, plastic design followed this path, and now, though it is an important technique, its initial simplicity has been submerged. Similarly, the initial clarity of the fault tree approach is lost in large and opaque models.

There are two main reasons for the growth of complexity. Firstly, such a progress is inherent in the nature of engineering models, both conceptual and quantitative, and their relationship to reality. Their genesis is at a simple and holistic level, their mature practical application must be at a sufficient level of detail, and the process of moving from one to the other is a process of growth and development of theory as gaps are filled and understanding increases. Nevertheless, progress is seldom uniform, and during the maturation period gaps will be left for various reasons, often stemming from irrational causes such as the reigning world view of engineers (see Chapter 1). Some gaps and problem areas may never be dealt with as they are inherent in the whole approach underlying the theory. Secondly, the research process, particularly in universities, leads naturally to an elaboration of detail as a subject is thoroughly explored.

For both reasons, reliability theory has often become confusingly detailed as it has developed. Many problems have been dealt with, but some remain; these, being hard, are often the most important of all.

The historical development of risk analysis was discussed briefly in Chapter 2. There were two main threads in reliability theory, running through the areas of structures and systems, respectively, with what often seemed to be little cross-fertilization between them. In the structural field, the main emphasis was on code development, while work in the systems field grew from its initial developments in electronics and aerospace to have a major place in nuclear, chemical, offshore and more recently environmental engineering.

Some of the first applications of probabilistic ideas to structural engineering codes were introduced into Western Europe in the 1940s by a committee chaired by Torroja. In its approach, design values of physically measurable parameters were defined statistically (usually as conservative fractiles) while other design values as well as load and resistance factors were chosen by judgement. The approach was called 'semi-probabilism'. The concept was used in the USSR and adopted by ISO and many European countries as the basis of the design of more rational design codes. Even if the term 'semi-probabilism' was not used, the approach was widely applied throughout the world in civil engineering structural design.

Early analytical work in the structural area was based on the formal definition of a simple limit state and the calculation of failure probabilities by means of probability theory—essentially convolution theory. First efforts had limited application for three reasons: the small calculated risks in the range of interest were highly sensitive to distribution assumptions which could not be verified experimentally; the mathematical formulations did not consider many of the complex factors such as workmanship on which the true risks depend; and there was the practical problem that practising professionals had difficulty admitting that their designs had a finite risk.

In terms of practical structural applications, major theoretical advances occurred in the late 1960s in association with the work of an ASCE committee. Three basic ideas were put forward:

1. The problem of the sensitivity of risk calculations to distribution functions could be avoided by using a 'safety index' whose value could be computed from means and variances alone.
2. The effects of variables for which there was very little data (for instance, the effects of workmanship) or which were judgement factors (such as the effects of simplifications in structural analysis) could be introduced by means of subjective or Bayesian variables whose means and variances could be estimated by judgement.
3. Using a particular set of load and resistance models, the level of safety in existing design procedures could be estimated. New procedures yielding more uniform safety levels could then be established using the same reliability models. Such 'calibration' procedures were immediately successful with the profession, leading to the steel code work by Galambos.

The first safety indices were introduced by Cornell and by Rosenblueth and Esteva. They illustrate the trend of development discussed above, in that they and their associated concepts were initially appealingly simple. They were important early steps in development, but there were serious limitations. The most serious problems were that they were restricted to two variables, load and resistance, and that they assumed the underlying distributions were normal or lognormal whereas probability of failure was in reality highly dependent on the distributions.

A more fundamental difficulty was pointed out in the early 1970s by Ditlevsen who showed that the simple safety indices were not invariant under elementary algebraic transformations of variables. Work by Veneziano, Ditlevsen and Hasofer and Lind to correct these problems led to the first-order second-moment methods now in widespread use. (It must be said that much of this work had been foreshadowed by Freudenthal 20 years earlier.)

Though these methods for obtaining structural reliability suffer from many conceptual and analytic difficulties, as discussed below, they have been remarkably successful and widely accepted. The primary reason for their success is rooted in the history of safety concepts. Traditionally, safety was measured by one-dimensional safety factors expressed, usually, in terms of 'maximum' loads and 'minimum' capacity which could be neither defined nor measured. In the new theory, safety is measured by one-dimensional reliability (or safety) indices that involve two measurable parameters: means and variances. In other words, safety indices look like safety factors. One can even calculate them without mentioning or understanding probability theory. For these reasons practising engineers with an aversion to probability theory could accept and work with them.

Work on the development of first-order second-moment methods was mainly directed at code writing, which tended to analyse only very simple structural components in the code calibration process. For the reliability analysis of individual structures, which were inevitably complex, other problems arose. One was the question of multiple failure modes. This was tackled by the development of simplifying bounding theorems by Cornell, Vanmarcke, Ditlevsen and others. The availability of greater computing power and more sophisticated variance reduction algorithms such as importance sampling meant that Monte Carlo approaches became more feasible. However, complete structures are complex systems, and a bridge had to be made between structural reliability techniques and the other main thread of theory development, that of systems reliability.

Here again initially simple ideas led to greater complexity as the discipline matured. Early problems were concerned with the performance of networks of independent components whose individual reliability was known. In most cases the reliability of the whole could be found by splitting the network into series and parallel groupings. Dealing with redundancy was difficult, however, and if system failure depended on, say, failure of m out of n elements, the combinatorial mathematics rapidly became intractable. The first system reliability formalizations in the electronics industry such as the path tracing and event space techniques appeared simple. However, they encountered formidable practical difficulties if applied to systems of any complexity, as they required care in formulation and ran into computational problems. A further formalization stemming from the aerospace industry (see Chapter 2) was a major step forward with the development of the fault and event tree approaches. Additional refinements to deal with non-independent events, consequence analysis, repairability and so on brought these techniques to their present widely used forms. Nevertheless, serious problems remain.

The following discussion reviews limitations of reliability theory, grouping the problems involved into four categories. The first deals with basic modelling problems and discusses fundamental conceptual and theoretical issues. Secondly, a number of practical and risk-specific questions are dealt with. The next section considers difficulties of communication as an issue in its own right and discusses the problems of relating results to those who might see and use them. A final section reviews problems specifically relevant to design codes.

19.2 LIMITATIONS ON RELIABILITY ANALYSIS

Fundamental Limitations

The importance of models We never relate directly to the real world, but do so, rather, through sets of models. Even at the primitive level of sensory perception, we sample and filter the raw sensory data and match it with patterns and mental constructs before it reaches consciousness. We see a table, not a set of photons. Our models can be of many types: personal or objective, primitive or elaborate, conceptual or formal and quantitative; but models there must be, for there is no other way in which we can consciously relate to reality. Chapter 1 discusses such concepts in more detail. It is particularly important for engineers to understand the central role of the model, as any engineering activity will be based firmly on a number of interrelated models. Some of the more fundamental limitations of reliability theory stem from basic modelling issues, and in particular from four fundamental ideas: purpose, completeness, foundations and consistency.

Purpose The purpose or objective of a model guides its formation. A model must have a purpose, some reason for its being. The purpose may be to relate in some way to existing reality, in which case the model may be in some sense a mapping of a part of reality. Some models, though, could be in the imagination, relating to things that might not yet have occurred or might never be possible in reality. As models are constructs of the mind, there is no limit to their variety or extent. However, to be of use in engineering matters, they have to be chosen and developed carefully, and, in this, a clear purpose or objective is crucial. The purpose, in the end, drives the model, and it follows that an ambiguous or confused purpose will not lead to a satisfactory result. There are several reasons why it can be particularly difficult to specify precise objectives in formulating risk models.

One reason is that risk is always concerned with the present estimate of what might happen in the future. There could, ultimately, be an infinite number of possible scenarios of future events for a situation of reasonable complexity. Risk must therefore necessarily deal with open world models (see Chapter 1). Although for quantitative purposes an engineer must deal with the situation as a closed-world model in which all the information is available, nevertheless because reality is an open-world system the purpose of a risk model is inherently difficult to formulate.

A second difficulty in specifying a purpose arises because we do not yet understand human value systems fully enough with regard to acceptance of risk. Human values are an essential element of risk analysis in most practical cases. Social impacts are common. In many cases we have to accept that many people often with very different value systems are likely to be involved. This can become a major source of confusion in the clear specification of objectives.

A related difficulty arises that risk analyses often apply to proposed engineering works with an ecological impact. Ecosystems are complex, often with ill-defined boundaries. The associated human value systems are emotive and unpredictable. Here again it is not easy in a complex and ill-defined situation to specify objectives clearly and hence make precise model definitions.

Completeness The previous subsection referred to the open and closed world models first discussed in Chapter 1. The distinction between the two refers to whether the information available within them is complete or whether some is unknown. However, whenever a quantitative predictive model is used, a fundamental requirement for its formation is that it should be complete at the appropriate level of detail; that is insofar as it is trying to model a part of the real world, the model should model the whole of that part of the real world, according to the model's purpose. It should not leave out any important part that might be expected to have a substantial effect on the required result. Note that bringing 'the required result' into the statement has two implications. Firstly, the requirement of completeness applies to the level of detail appropriate to the results wanted. If rough answers are all that are required, then too detailed a model is not justified. Secondly, a model that might be complete for one purpose might be incomplete for another, such as when a crude model might suffice for comparative results but a more sophisticated model would be needed for, say, an absolute prediction of risk.

Another way to look at it is that many models can be thought of as systems made up of a number of related subsystems. The complete set of subsystems should be present at a given level.

In the case of reliability analysis, a fundamental violation of the completeness requirement frequently occurs because human factors are omitted.[1] Yet human factors such as errors in construction, management or design cannot be taken into account directly in reliability theoretic calculations for two important reasons. The first is that it is not possible to model human actions in the same way as technical matters. The behaviour of an engineering structure, for instance, can be modelled using fundamental principles of equilibrium and compatibility and so on, deduced from basic theory and laboratory tests. No such strong body of theory exists for human behaviour. Human actions remain fundamentally unpredictable except in a broad sense. Psychometric studies on one individual are not readily transferrable to another, and behaviour is too easily influenced by factors outside the realm of any possible model. The previous night's activities could affect the likelihood of sleeping on the job, or an angry confrontation might affect concentration. The second reason is that, even if suitable models of human behaviour were available, the very nature of the information would be different from that available for technical analysis. Much of it would be fuzzy rather than crisp, and a good deal would be anecdotal.

In structural reliability theory, omission of human factors has been a particular and well-recognized problem. Various attempts have been made to bring together human and technical matters using fuzzy set and other approaches. However, the real difficulty is that the two are not equal contributors to failure. Rather, human factors are more important causes of failure than technical considerations by an order of magnitude or so. This raises a serious question as to whether it is sensible to carry out complex technical analyses in structural risk at all. Fortunately, there is a reasonable answer, at least for work leading to code development: it involves a somewhat different view of the relationship of design codes to design. The point will be discussed in the later section devoted to code matters. The dominance of human factors does, however, underline the importance of good risk management practices.

With regard to general quantitative risk analyses, human factors can, and should, be taken into account, but only with great care as to how the results are developed and used. The first writer, for instance, brought human factors into rail transport safety studies in two ways: as part of broad (and rough) studies based on incident statistics and for more detailed comparative studies. For the latter, industrial psychologists were able to provide comparative but not absolute estimates of, say, propensity to sleep in different situations. The necessary absolute figure was obtained more roughly by back calculation.

Besides the contribution of individual human failure to risk, there is a sense in which the organization as a whole can be a source of failure (see Chapter 9). In any complex system, whether technical, human or both, unexpected system failures are bound to occur and are indeed the normal cause of most disasters.[2] Here again the effect is important and often dominant: normal reliability theory cannot take it into account and must rely on incomplete models.

Foundations The models used by reliability theory are constrained by their underlying assumptions. This is a limitation of any model, and indeed it is better to think of models as being founded on sets of assumptions rather than being limited by them. Though the limitations are real, where they are overt they can often be chosen at will to suit a particular situation. The greatest difficulty occurs where the underlying assumptions are tacit, for then they can be overlooked.

One restriction underlies most of what we do: it is that, as yet, the philosophy of technology is at a rudimentary level. As discussed in Chapter 1, we do not have a very clear idea of what engineering is about. For many, this will not seem to matter in practical day-to-day terms, but yet it leads to a lack of clarity in thinking that is pervasive. Specifically, ideas are not yet fully worked out as to the nature of model building and its relation to reality, and therefore criteria for good modelling practice are not readily available. This leads to such fallacies as the frequently held idea that a poor (or incomplete) model is better than none. Sometimes this is true, but often it is not. However, at the philosophical level, ideas as to the nature of probability and risk are now reasonably clear (Chapters 1, 2 and 7).

Limitations due to the world views of engineers and others involved are too individualistic to be reviewed here. They are important, real and often covert, and so are genuine limitations for both individuals and groups. For the most part they will vary from person to person. To give two examples, though, one would be simple causality—the assumption that every effect has an immediate cause. The emphasis is on immediacy and simplicity. Many engineers think in such terms, and indeed the assumption is often reasonable. However, very often in the risk area complex system effects govern and counter-intuitive phenomena are important. The other example is the view that stationarity holds, that is, that most things do not change with time. However, many things do, from building requirements to social criteria, sea levels and weather patterns. Other world view examples are given in Chapter 1.

Finally, reliability theory itself has underlying assumptions, which can be limitations. The most obvious is that crisp set theory and two-valued logic apply. This immediately puts a constraint on the way in which a problem can be formulated. When setting up a fault tree analysis, for instance, great care must be taken with definitions in order to set up the problem correctly in the first place, that is in precise set theory terms. In some ways the language needed is not that of everyday engineering usage. Binary logic requires that what is being dealt with should be specified as true or false. It has been argued elsewhere that engineering is goal oriented rather than truth oriented: searching for truth is the aim of science, but engineering has the very different objective of trying to get something done. The distinction is reflected in the language of engineering, as opposed to that of science. Engineers tend to use words such as 'appropriate' or 'adequate' rather than 'true', and value-related words such as 'better' or 'best'. Thus the formulation of a risk problem in a logical framework requires a use of language that is different from and more tightly disciplined than that of normal engineering usage. The point is simple, but has been a major source of problems in practice.

In structural engineering, a related limitation in thinking has been the continued use of binary limit states. In practice, the idea of failure is far from clear-cut, and a structure will pass through a number of progressive states of degradation as it deteriorates. It is obvious that serviceability limit states must be somewhat arbitrarily defined. How much deflection or movement, for instance, should be taken as a limit state? However, the definition of structural failure is normally equally arbitrary. The restriction of thinking to a binary limit state framework has hindered both the development and application of reliability theory in the structural field.

Consistency Consistency is one of the major requirements for a good system model. It means, roughly, that all parts of a model should be roughly the same in size, type and quality. Thus if, in the whole of a model, some parts were dealt with in fine detail while others were treated in a simplistic and cursory manner, then the model would be ill-balanced and internally inconsistent. The end use and input information are both taken to be parts of the overall model. It is a limit on the justifiable complexity of a model, as it implies that no part should be much more complex than the least complex element. It relates to the 'principle of consistent crudeness' used elsewhere as a methodological tool or guide in model development.[3] The point being made is that the quality of the results produced by a quantitative model are governed by the lowest quality aspect of data or model, and not by the average quality. Thus, where it is simply not possible to get other than crude data for one part of a model, or where part of an analysis can only be handled in crude terms, a more sophisticated approach for the rest of the model cannot be justified.

The concept is salutary, for it would seem that unjustifiable complexity abounds in the area of reliability theory. However, it must be said that the *effect* of crude data can be improved in some circumstances by taking a range of believable values for it. This is especially useful if the intent of a risk analysis is to learn about a particular situation. Also, where the results are to be used in a comparative rather than an absolute way, the range of the model is in effect reduced to cut out the undesired part. The requirements for consistency can then be relaxed.

There are other limitations on the justifiable complexity of models, most of which relate to commercial considerations. This is certainly true of code use where engineers stand to lose much but gain little in using an unduly complex code, and would therefore tend to reject it in practice. More generally, the marginal return on increased complexity for most model types would be bound at some stage to drop off to a level at which further work would not be justified, though research impetus often carries detail beyond its natural cut-off level.

A final point is that a practical limitation on reliability theory arises when model complexity becomes high. The greater the complexity, the more liable is the model to run into errors—not so much of correctness but of the kinds of problem discussed here, of completeness, consistency and balance. These are all covert rather than obvious limitations. The models will still give results. The danger is, rather, that the unwary user will give greater weight to the results than can possibly be justified.

Practical and Reliability-Specific Problems

As well as the general issues discussed above, reliability theory has a number of specific and practical problems, some of which are serious limitations on its applicability. The following list is by no means exhaustive.

The system failure problem Many failures in practice have occurred due to highly unlikely combinations of circumstances coming together. In a complex system, this is a very frequent cause of failure because, though each combination might have only an infinitesimal chance of occurrence, the number of such combinations could be exceedingly high; and even though the probability of an event is very low, it could occur. Fault tree and other formal analysis techniques cannot readily deal with such problems. One answer in practice is to design a system in discrete subsystems as far as possible with minimum interactions between them, so reducing the number of complex failure combinations. Another is to accept that failures might occur and concentrate on levels of defence against the consequences. In practice, though, neither approach is always easy to apply.

The zero–infinity problem Formal risk techniques find it difficult to deal with the so-called zero–infinity problem, where an event has an extremely low probability of occurrence but where the consequences of the event are very severe—a major nuclear incident, for instance. The result of multiplying zero by infinity, or in other words, of trying to estimate the risk for such a situation, is indeterminate. All the numbers involved cease to be meaningful. Very low probability values are not easily understood and are suspect; it is difficult if not impossible to put a value on the cost of a major catastrophe and any product of the two to give a risk figure is not seen as believable by either professionals or the public.

Dependency is difficult to deal with Association between the probabilities of occurrence of different events must be taken into account. Fault tree formulations, in particular, assume independence between events. Often this is not true in practice, for instance where individual failure events are triggered by a common cause. In a structure, for instance, an earthquake would simultaneously subject many elements to a high load or many components in a river system could be tested by the same flood or weather system. In many instances dependency can be avoided by the use of conditional probabilities, but this approach cannot deal with all dependency difficulties. A particular problem arises when reliability theory has to be used, as is often the case, in situations where much of the data is sparse or poor. If independence can be assured, surprisingly useful results can be obtained from sparse data by looking at the body of data as a whole in the context of the analysis rather than as a string of independent pieces of information. However, it is very difficult to get satisfactory information on correlation if the fundamental data quality is poor.

System and time effects are not easily handled Where the system to be analysed is complex and there is a high degree of interdependence in its parts, reliability theory rapidly finds it is impossible to deal with the intricacy in a formal manner without resorting to major approximations. Combinatorial system problems, for example where failure of the whole relates to the failure of m

out of n components, soon become intractable. Likewise, if the system varies with time, again the theory cannot easily deal with it other than by using often gross approximations. An important example of an intractable problem is the behaviour of structures in earthquakes. Most simplifying assumptions, such as that the system is stationary and linear allowing the use of random vibration theory, are inadequate for realistic risk modelling.

Incorporation of judgement variables is difficult Most risk analyses in practice require some variables to be quantified by judgement rather than by observed statistics. There is as yet no agreed procedure for incorporating judgement variables into otherwise objectively based reliability theory. This is a serious matter because judgement variables, as mentioned earlier, can often be dominant contributors to risk.

There is also a danger that if statistical and subjectively derived data are mixed, as they could be using a Bayesian approach, then the result could be interpreted, wrongly, in a statistical way.

Limit states are hard to define Failure criteria, or more generally limit states, are often hard to define. Where a limit state is not obvious on physical grounds some other definition must be made. It need not be purely arbitrary. For instance, seismic failure of a reinforced concrete multistorey frame building has been defined as occurring when the interstorey drift angle of any storey exceeds $3/100$. This definition is based on observed laboratory behaviour of reinforced concrete members and on an assumption that for a well-designed building failure can only occur due to excessive lateral displacement. However, though the reasons for the choice of criterion in this case can be well argued, it is still a very indirect way of defining collapse.

Performance functions are hard to formulate A performance function is a function of the basic variables of a model which is equal to zero at the corresponding limit state. Negative values imply failure. The performance function is expressed in terms of a measure of the performance of the system. For example, the appropriate performance measure for the fire safety performance of part of a facility might be fire resistance, expressed as the time taken for fire to penetrate a barrier. Performance measures are sometimes hard to define. Further, the failure or limit state criterion must then be expressed in terms of the performance measure. This again may not be straightforward, depending on the complexity of the model.

Distributions and parameters are difficult to obtain To enable probabilities of failure to be calculated, probabilistic data are required for a system's basic variables. The data would normally be expressed as the parameters of a probability distribution. In many cases it is not easy to determine the appropriate distribution and its parameters. Statistics alone are unlikely to indicate the correct distribution, so unless there is some physical reason why a particular variable should be chosen (such as the choice of an extreme value distribution for, say, floods) the choice must be somewhat arbitrary. Unfortunately, risk analysis using the variable will often be sensitive to the choice of distribution as the limit state exceedance probability will depend on the extreme tail of the distribution. The distribution parameters are also often difficult to determine as the exceedance events are few. The problem is compounded when the available data are poor and sparse. It is not just a question of collecting more statistics. In many cases of natural hazards, for example, data have to be accumulated over years. It cannot be hurried, for example with regard to earthquake frequencies, and so if it has not been collected it will simply be unavailable for use, even in principle, until far into the future. It may also, once collected, be no longer appropriate if the nature of the system and its environment have changed.

Computational problems might limit the applicability of theory Sometimes, although reliability theory may have been worked out satisfactorily in principle, computational problems limit its applicability in practice. For example, the calculation of probabilities of failure by numerical integration can become intractable in a hyperspace involving several variables, and the first-order second-moment method can become numerically unstable for more than very simple formulations. The problems can usually be overcome with care; but this is just the point: complex problems in reliability analysis must be treated warily.

Human factors are difficult to deal with Human error and other human factors are usually major if not dominant contributors to risk. A number of formal techniques exist for quantifying human factors.[4] However, these give results that are in general less reliable than those for technical matters.

Practical applications need simplicity Various practical reasons to do with design and applications require processes that are not too complex and time-consuming. This relates to issues of purpose and consistency discussed above, but it also concerns the practical constraints of time and resources which limit the scope of a project. Such limitations could be called 'simplicity imperatives'. Application rules should be simple. In practice the simplicity imperatives render many arguments about assumptions irrelevant.

Risk-balancing approaches have not been well developed Two fundamental problems in risk management are, firstly, to obtain the greatest reliability for a given cost or, secondly, to obtain a given reliability for the lowest cost. Apart from a relatively primitive early formulation[5] little seems to have been done on this problem.

Problems of the Social Process

People often find it difficult to relate to the results and the processes of risk analysis. This applies to both lay people and, often, to other professionals who have to use the results. In part this is to do with language, with the terms and measures used to describe risk. However, the pervasive nature of the difficulty also raises basic questions as to whether risk analysis techniques deal adequately with the real problems of risk and decision making in a social context. Communication is often seen as a peripheral issue. However, such a view is mistaken as communication is fundamental to all human activity and is central in both social and technical areas. We cannot act in common without communication, and neither can we act individually as communication is both an essential part of thinking and the necessary link with the outside world. The communication difficulties that seem to be inherent in risk problems must therefore be taken seriously in any overview of reliability theory. We now look at some of the issues.

Human value systems are not well understood The value systems used by people in decision-making processes are bafflingly difficult to understand. A major reason for this is that decisions are never made in a closed world system. The input to any decision is indeterminate. Besides the well-defined issues assumed by decision theory, many personal and emotional matters affect people's attitudes. Individual experiences are brought in at both a conscious and an unconscious level. Greater weight is given to immediate or recent experience. Then there is the matter of style: whereas one person might analyse a problem in detail, another would prefer to act from a total 'feeling' of the situation, in the Jungian sense. World view, mentioned earlier, has a crucial effect on personal value systems. Beyond individual value systems there are also the consensus values of a societal group, held and developed for a myriad reasons.

The problem would not, perhaps, be as serious if there were only one decision maker. In most political systems, though, weight must ultimately be given to the views of interested parties, even though reluctantly, and if sufficient public feeling is generated by, say, pressure groups, the course of an engineering project could be changed or even stopped.

Various strategies are available. One would be to aim for secrecy and ensure that only one decision maker is involved. This might be tempting but is too risky to be sensible, quite apart from its dubious ethic. Another would be to be open with information, and seek to educate, an approach needing great care in translating technical matters into an appropriate form. A common variation would be to try not only to educate but to persuade–to preach, even. There is an obvious ethical constraint here. Yet another strategy would involve all interested parties at an early stage. There are many possible approaches. The point is that all take a significant investment of time and resources. Nevertheless, because the ultimate success of a project hangs on the issue, an investment in communication is not only advisable but is vitally necessary.

However, we are moving away from the main and immediate point of the discussion, which is that human value systems are not well understood. Next we must move on to look at the more specific problem of how to communicate risk.

Risk is difficult to communicate It is hardly surprising that risk is difficult to communicate in a given situation as risk is itself a difficult and sophisticated concept. This was touched on in Chapter 2, which discussed different types and meanings of risk. Assuming, though, that a meaning has been settled, then there is the matter of communicating an *understanding* of the risk levels involved. This is more than simply communicating numbers: the hearer has to internalize the information, that is to relate it to already-understood experience. The trouble is that a hearer may simply not *have* any personal experience relating to very remote risks and would have to resort to imagination. Yet some imaginary events, such as the likelihood of being struck by a meteorite, are so remote that they barely make sense. Lists of comparative events such as the risks of death due to driving a car, working as a miner or drinking coffee are sometimes used in trying to communicate risk, but they are not always acceptable or seen as relevant. More work needs to be done on the problem.

It is hard to define acceptable risk The intention of a defined level of 'acceptable risk' is that it should be used as a standard that engineering projects should meet. Design codes, for instance, are frequently calibrated to meet or exceed target values of reliability index. However, the whole idea of agreeing on an acceptable level of risk for major projects is a difficult and emotive area which has not yet been settled (Chapter 7). The lack of an agreed standard puts a serious limitation on the use of reliability theory.

People have difficulty in understanding small probabilities Most people find it difficult to understand very low probabilities and relate them to their experience. While they might be happy to think in terms of, say, a one in ten chance of something happening, the difference between 10^{-6} and 10^{-8} is meaningless. This has been found to be particularly true in establishing personal utility values for extreme events. The difficulty of establishing meaning shows up in inconsistencies of choice at low probability levels.

Calculated probabilities are misleading Normally, probabilities of failure calculated using reliability theory should never be compared directly with statistical probabilities obtained from observations of actual failures. The two quantities have very different meanings. Calculated probabilities are always obtained from limited models that do not take into account all possible contributions to failure, and so represent an often not very good lower bound on failure probability. Brown, for example, points out that typical calculated probabilities of failure for structures are of the order of 10^{-6} while observed failures seem to be between 1 in 100 and 1 in 1000.[6]

This is not to say, of course, that calculated probabilities of failure have no use. To do so would imply that reliability theory itself would be of little value. Calculated failure probabilities have two main uses. The first is in comparative analysis. In fact, most risk analyses are in some sense comparative, so the question really concerns the breadth of the system within which the comparison is being made and whether the necessary requirement of completeness, discussed above, is maintained. What is meant by comparative analysis, therefore, is situations in which similarly obtained figures are compared, perhaps using variations within the same analysis. A legitimate example of comparative analysis could be a project comparing the probabilities of train accidents if there were either one or two personnel in the locomotive cab. Here the aim should be strictly limited to comparing the safety implied by the two situations, and there should be no question of using the results in any absolute sense.

The second use of calculated failure probabilities is in trying to estimate the likelihood of rare failure events where no statistics are available and, one hopes, never would be. Major nuclear incidents are one example, offshore platform failures another. The computer results are useful and an essential part of design and assessment. The point is, though, that the figures obtained are lower bounds and not full estimates, so that in the process of risk communication, discussed above, they should not be compared directly with observed probabilities.

The legal system does not always relate well to risk analysis There is little to be said here other than to observe that in some ways there seems to be a fundamental mismatch between the requirements of the legal system and the use of risk analysis methods. There are many grounds on which the products of reliability theory can be questioned in court, and not all seem either just or rational. Some grounds revolve around fundamental philosophical or semantic questions such as the meaning of 'safe'; others are to do with precedent rather than logic and yet others might be concerned with the qualifications of the persons involved. The legal world view is different from that of the engineer. This may or may not be a bad thing. The point is, though, that the difference exists and that in practice it is important enough to put a practical constraint on the usefulness of reliability theory and risk analysis techniques.

Concerning Design Codes

The indirect use of reliability theory in ensuring structural safety through the intermediary of design codes is sufficiently important to justify separate comment, not least because of the major economic consequences of design code changes.

It is important to distinguish between performance-based and prescriptive codes. Performance-based codes set standards of performance, and it is up to the designer to decide how these are achieved. A structural code, for instance, might simply require that structures should achieve a reliability index level of 2.5 for all loadings other than earthquake. Prescriptive codes, on the other hand, give specific requirements for which the rationale is not always obvious. For example, a fire code might limit the size of fire compartments or require that all doors in a certain type of building should have a three-hour fire-resistance rating. In practice, most codes contain a mixture of performance and prescriptive requirements, though with a heavy weighting in the direction of prescription.

Codes are inherently limiting Prescriptive codes in particular limit the flexibility of designers, and thus can inhibit the use of innovative methods, designs and materials. Most codes allow the possibility of any design provided the designer can demonstrate its equivalence to code requirements. However, in practice it is difficult to establish code equivalence to the satisfaction of the governing authority because of the limited time and, often, analytic capability of local body staff. Performance-based codes would be less limiting to industry, but as they require more design effort they are generally less acceptable where the design and construction functions are separate, as is mostly the case in the English-speaking world.

Codes have a deficient philosophical foundation The whole idea of a design code is complex. It provides an interface between technical and social requirements. It deals with risk, itself a complex concept, in an indirect and, particularly for prescriptive codes, sometimes obscure way. It has to allow for human variability as well as quantifiable technical matters. Should the code be a minimum standard or a norm? There are moral issues, political issues and practical issues of implementation, and there are underlying matters such as the meaning of 'a structure is safe' or the relative weighting of commercial and safety requirements. It is hardly surprising, therefore, that some codes seem confused in both aims and provisions. Codes have grown enormously in sophistication since Hammurabi's primitive rules in ancient Babylon, but their complexity has not been matched by corresponding developments in underlying philosophy and understanding.

Code-implied safety varies Design codes group structures into categories. For practical reasons the number of categories cannot be too great. Therefore a wide variety of possible structures is often covered by one category. This in turn means that the calculated safety level of structures within a category can vary considerably. Some must be too strong or others insufficiently safe. The situation is neither optimal nor satisfactory, but is a necessary consequence of the use of codes.

Minimum standards may be taken as the norm There is an apocryphal story of a railway bridge known to vibrate in resonance if a train crossed it at 30 mi/h. The engineering response was to post a notice restricting train speeds to 30 mi/h. Though the story does not entirely apply, it is used here to make the point that many designers regard code compliance as both a necessary *and* a sufficient condition for good design. In fact, a code is a necessary but *not* a sufficient condition. Code compliance does not ensure good design, though without it the design would be inadequate. No doubt, in the failure of the Hyatt Regency walkways most if not all code provisions were covered correctly in the design, but it was a relatively minor detail outside the main code provisions that caused the disaster. The appropriate attitude to the role of a code should be that the code provisions look after the calculable and conventional matters contributing to safety. Code compliance means these can be taken out of consideration. The designer's main role should then be to concentrate on those things *not* dealt with by the code, such as overall system behaviour and also the human factors emphasized so much in other parts of this book as being major contributors to failure. Pigeon, Blockley and Turner[7] give a good illustration of the point in describing a roof collapse. Such an attitude to design is in contrast to the more conventional approach where design is code focused and seen primarily as a matter of fulfilling code requirements.

19.3 POTENTIAL AND FUTURE DEVELOPMENTS

Few could have imagined the transformation that has taken place in the field of engineering risk analysis in the past 20 years. The uncertainty under which engineering decisions are made can now be seen clearly and dealt with explicitly.

However, similar progress cannot be expected in the next generation largely because of requirements for simplicity, because of political constraints on codified procedures and because of some of the more fundamental limitations discussed above. It is fair to say that, except for certain areas of high technology, the field of reliability analysis is mature. Many new applications remain but the fundamental methodologies are generally sufficient for their purpose.

This is not to say there may not be scope for significant improvements in practice. Perhaps the most promising trend of current activity is an increased interest in human factors and organizational constraints. It is now widely recognized that these factors play a dominant role in safety levels but until recently they have been beyond the influence of research and comparative evaluation. Approaches founded in the social sciences, including formal auditing of organizational structures to establish their potential for human error, can be expected to increase both the safety and performance of engineered works significantly.

Looking further into the future, risk assessment can be expected to move beyond its present emphasis on failure, whether expressed in terms of top events in fault tree analyses or limit states in structural applications. As mentioned previously, few real situations involve a binary transition from acceptable conditions to totally unacceptable conditions—the space of system response is much more complex. The concept of failure is a useful fiction through which a precise and deterministic appearance can be superimposed on an imprecise and highly uncertain reality.

In some cases a promising replacement for the limit states concept and failure probabilities would be the use of estimated damage over a system's lifetime. This requires a measure of relative damage mapped on to system states together with a measure of system state probabilities. Total expected damage provides a very realistic basis for comparing alternative designs, although the measure of damage may have to be a vector of attributes. However, it cannot be used in isolation as it does not address the design requirement of providing a defined minimum level of safety.

Design codes represent a problem in some areas. They may protect society from some abuses but they can also trivialize design. There is room for fundamental improvement in code formation and use. The development of a deeper understanding of the issues involved is therefore to be hoped for, with the emergence of a sensible body of philosophical analysis of the relevant issues.

With the power, speed and low cost of modern computers, simulations and iterative non-linear analysis are now practical. It is therefore more feasible to take system and time effects into account. In general, more satisfactory models are to be expected, with a better integration of all effects into a total analysis.

A further development using the availability of cheap computer power will be the increased appearance of intelligent knowledge-based systems (IKBS) in the areas of design and risk assessment. Appraisal of the organizational and human factor issues will be more easily carried out using IKBS techniques, and risk management will be more easily systematized. Indeed, a better integration of design into a risk management context is to be expected, both at an organizational level and at the level of a society as a whole, as perhaps represented by local authorities and monitoring agencies.

Such systematizations may, however, produce new dangers. At present, one of the most important reasons for carrying out risk assessments is that they lead to deeper insight into the systems being assessed. They are, in effect, crucial mechanisms for learning about complex engineering projects. There is a danger that increased systematization and reliance on perhaps opaque computer packages will downgrade this most important role of risk analysis.

The past 30 years has been a golden age for reliability analysis and its techniques. It is now clear, however, that significant innovation in the future must go beyond technique. It will require fundamental revisions to both underlying ideas and engineering practice. What is needed is a deep integration of risk ideas and methods not only into design and management but even, perhaps, within the community as a whole, for it is there, ultimately, that decisions on major risks must lie.

REFERENCES

1. Turkstra, C. J.: Human and Organizational Aspects, theme paper, *Proc. IABSE Symp.*, Tokyo, pp. 97–106, 1986.
2. Turner, B. A.: *Man-Made Disasters*, Wykeham Press, London, 1978.
3. Elms, D. G.: The Principle of Consistent Crudeness, *Proc. Workshop on Civil Engineering Applications of Fuzzy Sets*, Purdue University, p. 35, 1985.
4. Reason, J.: *Human Error*, Cambridge University Press, New York, 1990.
5. Elms, D. G.: Risk Balancing for Code Formulation and Design, *Proc. Third Int. Conf. on the Application of Statistics and Probability in Soil and Structural Engineering*, Sydney, Australia, pp. 701–713, 1979.
6. Brown, C. B.: A Fuzzy Safety Measure, *Proc. ASCE*, vol. 105, no. EM5, pp. 855–872, October 1979.
7. Pidgeon, N. F., D. I. Blockley, and B. A. Turner: Design Practice and Snow Loading—Lessons from a Roof Collapse, *The Structural Engineer*, vol. 64A, no. 3, pp. 67–71, 1986.

CHAPTER
TWENTY

CONCLUDING REFLECTIONS

D. I. BLOCKLEY

20.1 INTRODUCTION

At the start of the book we posed a number of questions such as 'How safe is safe enough?', 'What are safety factors?', 'Are engineering failures really failures of engineers?', 'Is design to manage trouble as important as design to prevent trouble?'. The many contributors to the book have shed light on the answers to these and many other related questions. Each contributor has discussed the issues, in the light of his knowledge and experience, of dealing with large-scale facilities in various industries. Many of the examples used are drawn from structural engineering, with its consequent emphasis on the use of codes of practice. However, the examples in this book are really vehicles for articulating ideas about engineering safety. It is the clear identification of some of the issues in engineering safety for all large-scale facilities that is one of the central objectives of the book.

The purpose of this final chapter is to review the discussion and to provide some concluding thoughts. The strategy will be, firstly, to review the technical aspects of safety, the role of safety factors and limit state design and the relationship with reliability and risk analysis; secondly, to reexamine the difficulty of defining acceptable levels of safety; thirdly, to highlight the human and organizational factors in engineering safety. Finally, a new activity to be called hazard engineering will be proposed.

20.2 THE TECHNICAL PARADIGM

So what are safety factors? What are they intended to cover? It is clear from a number of earlier chapters that safety factors are incomplete—whether they be the traditional in-built factors of allowable stress design or the more modern partial factors of limit state design. They are partial measures of some specific aspect of technical concern. That aspect of technical concern is represented by a theoretical model, the domain of applicability of which may or may not be clearly identified and the parameters of which may be known only imprecisely. The model will have a degree of uncertainty associated with its use in solving a particular problem and this, together with the uncertainty in the parameter values, has to be covered by the safety factor. It is known that the use of simple factors can produce inconsistent results. It was inevitable therefore that more rational ways of dealing with safety should be sought (see Chapter 2).

The basis for a more rational treatment of safety factors has been the development of a sophisticated theory of reliability based on probabilistic risk assessment. Elms, Ellingwood and Melchers (Chapter 2, 5 and 6) have described the basic concepts of that approach. Elms and Turkstra (Chapter 19) have provided a comprehensive critique of the theory under the four headings of basic modelling, systems effects, social processes and codes. From that discussion it is clear that a measure such as a probability of failure is also incomplete for the same reason that a simple safety factor is incomplete. It is a partial measure of some technical aspect of an artefact since it can only refer to that part of the world which is modelled.

Brown[1] was the first to point out the order of magnitude difference between the statistics concerned with failure rates of real structures and the calculated probabilities of failure, a difference that could only be explained by the fact that the calculated probabilities refer only to one small part of the actual reasons for structural failure.

The theory of probabilistic reliability analysis as applied to single elements has reached a sophisticated level of development with FORM, SORM and the numerical methods such as importance sampling in the Monte Carlo method (see Chapters 5 and 6). However, the treatment of whole systems of elements connected together to form complex artefacts or systems has some way to go. Important characteristics of good designs such as connectivity and robustness have, as yet, received scant attention. One of the principle problems for probabilistic analysis is the difficulty of estimating the dependency between random variables.

In general, any system may exhibit behaviours that seem more than can be explained by considering an aggregation of the components of the system. There is a possibility of such a large number of unforeseeable combinations of factors within any reasonably complex system that the possibility of occurrence of unforeseen combinations is high. This point will be amplified later when discussing systems thinking and practice.

Indeed, as Fanelli pointed out (Chapter 10), if the system is non-linear, as most real systems undoubtedly are, then the effects of small errors in the values of the parameters can produce dramatic variations in the behaviour of a deterministic system through time. The results of the new theories of non-linear dynamics and chaos will have fundamental impacts on the technical treatment of engineering safety.[2]

Thus there are fundamental reasons why all of these technical measures of engineering safety are incomplete and therefore of limited applicability. The central issue is not so much the nature of the measure itself; rather it is the clarity of the definition of the domain of applicability of the theoretical model. The usefulness of the measures is that they enable rational judgements to be made by experienced engineers who appreciate the limitations of applicability. Unfortunately engineers have often not, in the past, articulated sufficiently these limitations nor identified their own skills which are required to deal with them. They have allowed themselves to appear to promise a certainty to clients, laymen and to the general public that cannot always be delivered since the problems with which they are dealing are often not at all easy. The quality of the decision making required to handle these problems and to engineer safe artefacts goes largely unrecognized. It is widely believed, by lay people, that technically certain solutions are available and that if anything does go wrong it must be because the engineers are negligent or incompetent. It is perhaps partly as a consequence that society in general vastly undervalues the skill and expertise of the engineer.

More often than not the neglect of the partial nature of the technical view has no practical consequence. However, in dealing with technology, where the consequences of failure are beyond many people's ability to comprehend (for example a major nuclear incident), then the points may be crucial to the survival of the human race. For example, it may be argued that the undisciplined use of the term probability of failure, where the numbers appear to have a statistical basis, is highly dangerous. There is a strong need for a properly developed philosophy of engineering which would provide a forum for the development of these ideas.

20.3 WORLD VIEW AGAIN

So is PRA a mature discipline? Elms and Turkstra (Chapter 19) argue that few could have imagined the transformation that has taken place in the field of engineering risk analysis in the past 20 years. They state that the uncertainty under which engineering decisions are made can now be seen clearly and dealt with explicitly and so the field is mature.

An alternative view is that a discipline cannot possibly be mature if the problems referred to in the last section remain. The answer really depends on your world view—it depends on your perspective. The theory, as developed within a certain technical view of engineering safety, is sophisticated and mature. In other words, if we interpret the words 'engineering safety' as two nouns describing a technical discipline of which PRA is a part, then the theory is indeed mature.

However, if 'engineering' is interpreted as the present participle then 'engineering safety' refers to the way safety is managed, controlled or engineered. This wider view of a total consideration of safety still requires considerable development. As pointed out in Chapter 1, the world view of the systems problem solver is a crucial ingredient in the way in which problems are identified and consequently solved. Elms (Chapter 2) pointed this out with respect to risk assessment when he discussed risk as involving the changes of an undesirable event, the consequences of the event and the context of the event. It is the world view that defines the context.

Perhaps we can therefore conclude that risk assessment is coming out of adolescence. It is becoming self-consciously aware of its limitations and as soon as it has come to terms with those limitations then it will be truly mature.

20.4 CODES OF PRACTICE

The role of codes of practice and the detailed guidance within them varies between different industries and disciplines. In much of engineering design practice, where fairly detailed guidance on safety is given in the codes, it is assumed that the provisions of the codes handle technical risk. Risk assessment, as a separate exercise, is usually reserved for only very large or prestigious projects.

The move, world-wide, in the writing of structural engineering codes of practice, has been from allowable stress design to limit state design. The reason has been to try to achieve a more rational basis for the choice of safety factors. Galambos has discussed (Chapter 3) how this has attempted to remove some of the inconsistencies. Attempts have been made to 'calibrate' codes so that consistent levels of safety are achieved.

The continued use of a particular code of practice to deal with all of the technical aspects of risk involves making one of two assumptions. Firstly, it assumes that the other potential safety hazards are independant of code provisions (which is extremely difficult to judge) or, secondly, that the conditions, under which the code is applied, do not change significantly in the long run. In the past the use of codes and procedures for the design and construction of large-scale facilities has provided acceptable levels of safety as judged by experience. In modern times of rapid change it is unclear whether conclusions based on this experience continue to apply. They certainly do not seem unreasonable for relatively simple technical problems. However, even then a case history for a simple factory building has shown[3] that failure can result from unintended interactions between the technical aspects and human and organizational factors.

It is clear that the application of codes to new technologies must be used with careful consideration of the other factors. The assumptions underlying the drafting of all codes of practice ought to be spelt out very clearly. It may well be necessary to include the formal consideration of safety and the provisions of codes in the procedures of quality assurance. Matousek in Chapter 4 (Sec. 4.5) has outlined the structure of a 'safety plan' which includes the specification of 'safety goals', which necessarily must include any regulatory or legal requirements.

20.5 LIMIT STATE DESIGN

In Chapter 1 (Sec. 1.2), a number of criticisms of the use of limit state design and partial factors in codes of practice were identified. Most of them have been answered in other chapters of the book. In summary, while limit state design does involve slightly more complicated calculations than those for allowable stress design, the degree of extra complication is small, unless PRA is explicitly used, and the potential benefits large. Limit state design certainly does not preclude the use of judgement by engineering designers: in fact, the intention is to make the exercise of judgement easier by providing a logical framework of ideas. It is true that with the introduction of limit state design many codes have become long and complicated. However, it is rarely the actual adoption of limit state design that has caused this lengthening; rather it is due to a natural tendency to try to incorporate the benefits of the large increases in available engineering knowledge. Another criticism was that since uncertainty is diverse and varies from site to site then limit state design is inappropriate. This is dealt with by the recognition that judgement has to be used on technical measures of safety which are acknowledged to be incomplete. The remaining criticism mentioned in Chapter 1 was that of whether limit state design depends on the use of statistics. This is a central difficulty in many of the confusions that surround this topic and we will therefore amplify on it a little more.

One of the first requirements in addressing this issue is to be clear about the difference between the theories of statistics and probability. Elms (Chapter 2) has discussed the different interpretations of probability theory. All interpretations are attempts at dealing with uncertainty; the differences stem from the quality and quantity of available data. If one has a plentiful supply of good data then probability can be interpreted as a measure of frequency and that is the province of statistical theory. If, however, one is attempting to deal with a problem where the data are sparse then one can interpret probability subjectively as a measure of belief or judgement, in the so-called Bayesian sense. However, the results of Bayesian calculations cannot then be interpreted statistically as frequencies of occurrence; they are measures of opinion and judgement. Clearly the results of probabilistic calculations based on large quantities of good data are more dependable than those based on subjective judgement and should always be preferred. However, in practical engineering problems the data are usually sparse and so Bayesian probability does allow for more rational assessment and use of the data and hence improved decision making. More advanced treatments of uncertainty, which allow for vague or fuzzy definitions and possible inconsistencies, have been suggested.[4] Let us return to our discussion of the relationship between statistics and limit state design. Galambos has outlined the theory in Chapter 3 (see Fig. 3.2) and has compared allowable stress design to limit state design with the basic variables, of demand (Q) and capacity (R), as random variables without, quite correctly, requiring any particular interpretation of probability theory.

In fact in the implementation of the first generation of limit state codes in the United Kingdom, the recommended values for the nominal, or characteristic, values Q_n, R_n and for partial factor values were not chosen by the use of statistical methods—they were chosen subjectively by a committee. In principle, as discussed above, that was acceptable except that it did result in certain inconsistencies and confusions. For example, the values of imposed loads for UK floor loadings were the same for allowable stress design and for limit state design, although one was supposed to be a working load and the other a characteristic value of load. The design of the second generation of codes has tried to remove inconsistencies and to make the whole process more rational, principally by the use of calibration procedures as described by Galambos.

One of the central advantages of the limit state design approach is not in any way associated with a probabilistic interpretation. The introduction of the concept of a limit failure surface in an n-dimensional hypervolume is a powerful model both conceptually for developing an understanding of technical risk and computationally for PRA (see Chapter 6). The axes of this volume are the parameters that describe an artefact and the limit state surfaces are the limits, based on the various theoretical models, of the ways in which the artefact can behave without exceeding the allowable levels. The design point on the limit state surface is a concept not present in allowable stress design and is a concept of some significance. If the axes of the hypervolume are defined as random variables then probability theory can be used for structural reliability calculations as described by Ellingwood and Melchers in Chapters 5 and 6.

Elms and Turkstra surmise (Chapter 19) that in the future of structural reliability theory the concept of accumulated damage may become more important than that of a limit state surface. In terms of design, qualities such as robustness, which is related to the connectivity and hence the reliability of a system, will need to be examined and developed considerably. It is important to try to bring these ideas together and that the whole safety problem be seen as a process requiring management. This is a theme to which we will return later in the chapter.

20.6 ACCEPTABLE RISK

How safe is safe enough? Insofar as the present rates of failure are acceptable and that the current state of the art of engineering design is sufficient, then this question need be of no concern. We have discussed above how codes of practice set tacit technical risk criteria and Pidgeon in Chapter 8 also points out the role of codes as institutionalized means of setting acceptable risk levels.

However, as Reid (Chapter 7) has argued, the problem of defining acceptable levels of risk is a matter of great concern to designers of unusual structures and to regulatory authorities, particularly those concerned with the development of codes of practice. He points out that the regulatory authorities would dearly like to have simple dependable methods of risk assessment with clearly defined risk acceptance criteria. Similarly engineers would like to have available simple dependable methods so that 'correct' decisions can be made. However, the determination of appropriate risk acceptance criteria depends fundamentally and inescapably on value judgements which cannot be standardized or quantified. In many practical problems there needs to be a subtle balance drawn between risk and benefit which will involve many or all of the factors listed in Table 7.1 of Chapter 7.

There cannot be one simple answer to the question 'How safe is safe enough?' for all circumstances and situations. The answer depends on value judgements which transcend analysis. Acceptable risks are the products of acceptable processes of risk management and regulation, and acceptable risks cannot be determined independently of the processes of risk assessment. Douglas and Wildavsky[5] have argued that public perception of risk and its acceptable levels are collective constructs, a bit like language and a bit like aesthetic judgement. Their central thesis was that the selection of dangers and the choice of social organization run hand in hand. Knowledge is not a solid thing, bounded or mapped out; rather they preferred the idea of knowledge as the changing product of social activity: 'It is like a many sided conversation in which being ultimately right or wrong is not at issue. What matters is that the conversation continues with new definitions and solutions and terms made deep enough to hold the meanings being tried'.

The way in which a problem is conceived and framed depends on the 'world view' of the problem solver, as indicated above and in Chapter 1. The way in which a problem is conceived by others affected or involved in the process will depend on their, possibly quite different, world views also. The decision process has to recognize and deal with these differing perceptions. There is clearly therefore a human psychological element to risk.

Pidgeon points out in Chapter 8 the importance of the psychology of risk to engineering safety. He also asserts that the question of what constitutes acceptable risk is a complex issue involving not just technical assessments but ultimately the values that society puts upon such things as progress, the distribution of the costs and benefits from a technology and the consequences of breakdowns in safety. The perceptions people have of risk and how they communicate risk concerns are complex topics in themselves. For example, Pidgeon discusses the effects of the way questions are framed on the replies given. However, he reports that individuals in Western societies do tend to rank the chances of dying from particular hazards very much in line with available statistical estimates. Where systematic discrepancies do occur it is in dealing with extreme values; that is people tend to overestimate the chances of dying from very low probability events and underestimate those of high probability events. Another fairly robust conclusion from psychological research on risk is that people will happily take on risky activities if they feel that they have a degree of personal control over the situation.

People's judgements of hazardous activities are sensitive not only to statistical frequency and personal controllability but also to factors such as the familiarity of the activity, its catastrophic potential and its anxiety potential. Pidgeon reports that experts, such as professional engineers, are less influenced by these qualitative factors but even they do not always agree on appropriate estimates. Nuclear power occupies a rather unique position with regard to these factors since it is seen by many as scoring badly on all counts. As an illustration of the differing value systems held by differing 'actors' in the nuclear risk debate he quotes the work of Eiser and Van der Pligt (Ref. 11 in Chapter 8) who surveyed groups of pronuclear and antinuclear individuals. The work serves to illustrate the important fact that the beliefs underlying risk perceptions cannot be divorced from the more general world views that individuals hold in their daily lives. It also implies that individuals with judgements that differ from expert assessments are not of necessity irrational; rather that lay conceptions of risk are much wider and qualitatively different than is implied by the model underlying traditional risk management.

If decisions about acceptable risk are products of the risk management process then the problem of risk communication becomes important. For example, Pidgeon argues that an expert may try to allay the fears of the population local to a particular chemical plant by stating that 'a year living within a one mile radius of this chemical facility is equivalent to crossing the road once'. However, the statement may fail to have the required impact if the recipients do not perceive the two activities as being qualitatively equivalent. For example, the recipient may feel that the degree of personal control and the catastrophic potential of the two activities (i.e. crossing the road and making chemicals) are quite different.

Douglas and Wildavsky[5] have argued that the social sciences are responsible for part of the confusion about risk:

> The wrong division between the reality of the external world and the gropings of the human psyche have allocated real knowledge to the physical sciences and illusions and mistakes to the field of psychology. Causality in the external world is generally treated as radically distinct from the results of individual perception. According to this approach, risk is a straightforward consequence of the dangers inherent in the physical situation, while attitudes toward risk depend on individual personalities. ... The main questions posed by the current controversies over risk show the inappropriateness of dividing the problem between objectively calculated physical risks and subjectively biased individual perceptions. The sudden appearance of intense concern about the environment can never be explained by evidence of harm from technology. Weighing the balance between harm and help is not a purely technical question. ... Between private, subjective perception and public, physical science there lies culture, a middle area of shared beliefs and values.

20.7 THE TWO CULTURES OF ENGINEERING

It is clear therefore that we cannot talk in terms of engineering safety in technical terms only. Individuals, their organizations and groups and their cultures are all involved. Engineering involves decision making and decision always involves people and risk.

The decision process, with the need to consider the balance of risks and benefits, as Kletz points out in Chapter 15, begins at the very earliest stages of a project. For example, at the design stage decisions are made about the nature and location of the facility to be constructed and the methods and procedures to be used. It may well be possible to avoid hazards by choosing alternative less hazardous products for a chemical plant or by locating equipment or plant away from urban areas. Hazard and operability studies are often used to try to identify circumstances that might lead to accidents. These types of consideration are relevant to every stage of a project; they are all decisions by people and are hence prone to error.

Are all failures then really failures of engineers? Turner (Chapter 9) points out that committees of enquiry into large-scale disasters usually have a long list of recommendations concerning human factors. Many people have commented on the way engineers are educated and trained on these matters. In Chapter 1 a report of the UK Council for National Academic Awards was quoted as saying that the education of engineers is 'both technically narrow and narrowly technical'. This implies that too little attention is given to non-technical material and of the technical material too much attention is given to specialisms.

Traditionally engineering has been seen as a technical discipline, objective and value free. That view is no longer tenable; there are value systems underpinning everything that humans do. As technology becomes more powerful and the consequences of failure become so much greater then engineers must not fail to broaden the horizons of their discipline. The definition of acceptable levels of safety, discussed in the previous section, for risky technology is an important issue that requires an enlightened technical input to the wider debates in society concerning the environmental impact of technology.

A culture is a set of norms and beliefs about the world. The technical tradition provides the dominant culture of the education and professional training of engineers. Research and development is almost entirely applied physical science. By contrast the problems of professional activity and business depend heavily on the behaviour and organization of people.

The particular manifestation of these two cultures referred to in Chapter 1 is on the one hand the technical approach of limit state design, risk analysis and reliability theory and on the other hand the managerial approach to quality and hence to safety that is embodied in quality assurance.

20.8 THE INTELLECTUAL STATUS OF ENGINEERING

As discussed in Chapter 1, the search for truth has dominated Western intellectual thought since Plato. Indeed one philosopher, A. N. Whitehead, said that all philosophy is just a set of footnotes to Plato. The ancient Greeks set the scene when they came to the conclusion that the ultimate form of human endeavour came from concepts held in the mind and not from empirical experiences. For example, the concept of the perfect circle can be held in the mind but any attempt to draw a circle is inevitably imperfect. Western intellectual thought has been driven by a search for an elusive ultimate form of perfection held in the mind. This Platonic view has most ably been promoted in recent times by Penrose.[6] However, even accepting the more everyday definition of truth as 'correspondence to the facts' the concept of truth proves to be elusive. The question that now needs asking is: 'Is truth really of such dominant importance?'

Arguably one of the most fundamental questions of all to ask is: 'How can we attain quality of life?' Perhaps some would argue that this is not a philosophical question. Here we will maintain that insofar as it requires us to reflect on the human condition it certainly is a philosophical question and it certainly is one that should exercise all our minds. One of the first qualities of life is survival and in order to survive we must take practical decisions about problems, both short term and long term, and we must measure the effectiveness of our decisions against factors that relate to the other qualities of our lives. These other qualities will include aspects such as truth but also will include other valued characteristics such as function, form, aesthetics, environment.

Engineers are practical problem solvers. The intellectual importance of engineering is that a wide set of skills are required to solve problems that make up many aspects of our quality of life. Yet engineers have allowed themselves to be intellectually intimidated by the purists of science, mathematics and philosophy and the search for truth.

It is interesting to contrast the low academic status of engineering with the various levels of status in society accorded to engineers in different countries. Engineers in many European and other countries have a higher status in society than do their counterparts in the United Kingdom. This is largely the result of different historical development. Broadly speaking, in the United Kingdom, engineering has sprung from a craft-base tradition whereas on the Continent, largely due to the influence of Napoleon, engineering has a much more academic tradition.

In modern society engineering is crucial to the survival of the human race. This is not merely to provide the new engineering facilities that modern conditions require but also to maintain and control those that we already depend upon. The tension between the two cultures of engineering must be resolved urgently. Engineering is not just a technical discipline, it involves human beings. This is recognized in the practice of engineering but it is not recognized widely in the education of engineers and in the research and development that engineers perform. It is essential that the academic and intellectual scope of engineering is widened immediately to provide academic support to the so-called non-technical activities that all engineers find are part of their work. This is the 'social science' of engineering and the 'philosophy of engineering', both of which must be turned into active academic subjects. Although there is some indication of the development of research into these matters and into project and construction management, this research is minute in comparison with the efforts in the 'applied physics of engineering'. The amount of research into a topic such as quality assurance is small. Indeed, one could imagine many people questioning the fact that any research could indeed be performed on such a subject—so constrained are they in thinking in terms of research being only 'applied physics'. Perhaps the practical way of developing these disciplines is through the developing ideas of the 'systems approach'.

20.9 SYSTEMS THINKING AND SYSTEMS PRACTICE

'Systems' is a modish word that people often use, but what exactly does it mean? It really is itself a subject in which one can think and talk about other subjects; it is a meta-discipline whose subject matter can come from virtually any other discipline. Thus it is more an approach than a topic—a way of going about tackling a problem. Probably most people tend to think that a systems approach involves the use of a computer; this is not necessarily so although of course as a particularly powerful tool computers are often used for all types of problem solving. In simple terms a systems approach is one that takes a broad view, tries to take all aspects into account and concentrates on the interactions between different parts of the problem. So what is the difference between the scientific method and the systems method and why is it relevant to engineering? The scientific method is an approach that characterizes the world by assuming that natural phenomena are ordered, regular and not capricious. Following Descartes, it is a reductionist approach which takes a complex problem and breaks it down into component parts and tackles them separately. Systems thinking, alternatively, questions the assumption that the component parts are the same when separated out as when they are part of the whole.

It is clear that whole systems have characteristics that subsystems do not have. For example, a human being is made up of a set of subsystems (nervous system, blood circulation, skeleton, etc.) and none of them are able, on their own, to walk about, for that is a characteristic of a human being. The term 'holon' was coined by Koestler to describe the idea of something that is both a whole and a part. Thus a human is a holon in that he/she is a whole (with a set of subsystems) and a part in that a human is part of higher-order systems such as family, work and other societal groupings. For an extensive discussion of these ideas, applied to 'soft' systems, the reader is referred to Ref. 7.

Since engineers are primarily engaged in solving practical problems in order to make a living, it is probably fundamental to their nature to be more interested in techniques for direct problem solving, for getting an answer to the current problem, than in more general issues. These issues may be of general interest and perhaps of some philosophical importance, but because they are not central to the current task they are squeezed out of consideration—there seems to be no time, when running a business, to worry about them. However, many of the most successful engineers do develop an ability as systems thinkers, although many may not describe themselves in such terms. It is unlikely that this has developed from a traditional engineering education; more likely it has developed from their own natural ability plus exposure to other disciplines and talented individuals from whom they have learnt. It seems that engineers are often not systems thinkers but that their discipline demands that they should be.

Perhaps one of the fundamental reasons why engineers have not developed a systems approach in the past is that there have been no practical tools to enable them to address problems in this way. With the advent of computers, which can now manipulate alphanumeric symbols just as readily as they have always been able to manipulate numbers, comes the means to produce programs to perform inference as well as calculation. The rise of artificial intelligence has not only provided new tools (Chapter 18) but also new problems which have forced researchers to examine their assumptions about the meaning of their work as engineers. Thus there has been, in recent years, an increased interest by engineering researchers in systems approaches for AI applications and this has thrown up questions that have required some philosophical issues to be faced.

20.10 HUMAN FACTORS

The design and construction of any large-scale facility is a system that involves human beings. It is therefore a sociotechnical system, embedded in a particular culture, in which problems can occur of a human kind only (for example dishonesty) or of a technical kind only (inadequate data), but it is a system where the greatest problems may occur at the interface between social and technical difficulties. There may be interactions that have not been foreseen and were certainly unintended. Attention has to be given both to the individual human factors (the psychology) and the collective and organizational human factors (the sociology) of the system. Pidgeon has provided an analysis (Chapter 8) of the slips and lapses that individuals can make, on the one hand, and mistakes on the other. Slips and lapses are essentially failures to achieve an intended plan, whereas mistakes involve the correct execution of an inappropriate plan.

Reason[8] has provided an extensive discussion of the nature of human error. It encompasses all those occasions in which a planned sequence of mental or physical activities fails to achieve its intended outcome and when this failure cannot be attributed to the intervention of some chance agency. The role of intentionality is central to the notion of error. Intention is the specification of the required end state. Questions relevant in the identification of error are, for example, 'Were the actions directed by some prior intension?', 'Did the actions proceed as planned?', 'Did they achieve their desired end?'. Of course, one of the primary functions of our consciousness is to alert us to differences between action and intension and to the likelihood that the planned actions will not achieve the required objective. However, although consciousness is specifically tuned to picking up departures from intension, i.e. slips and lapses, mistakes can pass unnoticed for lengthy periods of time and even when detected may remain a matter of debate.

It is the slips, lapses and relatively straightforward mistakes that have lent themselves to technical analysis by engineering researchers (e.g. see Ref. 9). It is possible to measure and estimate the error rates of people in various tasks and to analyse the likelihood of major errors slipping through into a finished artefact. However, it is rare for these factors alone to be responsible for failure. Pidgeon describes two further types of error: cognitive decision errors and procedural violations. These types of error are much more bound up with the context within which people operate, that is they are related to organization. Turner in Chapter 9 has discussed human factors at a sociological, organizational and cultural level and that is a theme to which we will return later.

When things go wrong it seems that there is a natural tendency for people to look for someone to blame. As discussed in Chapter 1, society seems to expect that someone must be at fault. In Chapter 17 Furmston has described the legal position very clearly. The courts are not interested in the historical causes of an accident except insofar as it leads them to the answer to the central question of who is trying to do what to whom? In other words, the courts wish to allocate blame. Furmston concludes that the courts can therefore make only a limited contribution to safety. The way to improved safety involves developing mechanisms for learning from past disasters and incorporating them into the practice of the future as quickly and cheaply as possible.

A recent case history showed that failures can occur where it is at least arguable that no one is to blame.[3] A series of organizational and technical changes resulted in a failure and each change could individually be fully justified in terms of duty of care. The unintended consequence of the changes was that previously conservative assumptions in snow loading on roofs were invalidated by justifiable changes in the design of the strength of roof beams. The lesson from this case was that it is possible for failure to occur without someone being legally at fault. However, if the engineers had adopted a systems view of the problem (including a systematic scan for the likelihood of unintended consequences of decisions) then those unintended consequences would have been less likely to happen.

It is important to recognize that one of the reasons for the introduction of quality assurance and quality control is to reduce the possibility of human error. In terms of slips, lapses and the more obviously identifiable mistakes then this is relatively straightforward. However, there exists a more subtle and difficult type of human factor, relating to the sociology of organizations, that needs to be specifically addressed.

20.11 SAFETY CULTURE

Earlier references to the two cultures of engineering can be broadened to relate to a whole project or particular company so that one may examine the whole organizational culture. A UK CBI study[10] has found that there are real business benefits from managing risk effectively. The benefits are reduced costs, better employee relationships, morale, productivity and quality. The authors conclude that although the language of health and safety is different from the language of production and budgeting, the responsibilities for health and safety must be those of in-line management. They must not be left to specialists but must be integrated into other business responsibilities. The vital element in the success of this approach is the commitment of the chief executive. Some companies have found that performance in managing health and safety is a good indicator of a manager's general competence.

Safety culture is the set of norms and beliefs that all members of an organization share about risk, accidents and health. One answer, from a senior manager to a question asking why he thought the development of a good safety culture was important, was 'If you think safety is expensive try an accident'.

The prevention of accidents is therefore not simply a technical matter and nor is it simply dealt with by adopting a formalized procedure such as quality assurance, important though those matters are. It is a problem that forms an essential ingredient of quality management. Few companies seem to presently consider safety to be at the centre of commercial success.[11] The CBI report[10] points out the importance of a good safety culture within a company to avoid the costs of client and public liability and the market damage that can flow from a poor public image with regard to safety. A significant number of small companies involved in a major incident or other harmful incident cease trading completely as a result and even large companies are not immune to such effects. Quite apart from the immediate tragic consequences of loss of life, accidents place other costs on companies; the total costs including damage, disruption and lost contracts are rarely audited.

The important point in the development of a good safety culture is that management must give genuine and visible leadership, with full commitment to safety matters. It should be noted, however, that there is a great danger of management slipping into a way of thinking that relates more to how things ought to be than how things actually are. Management therefore needs to achieve consistency of behaviour against agreed standards and to check this performance by auditing, and it is important that these audits reflect the complex sociotechnical nature of engineering.

20.12 TURNER'S MODEL

In order to conceive the role of risk management in preventing failures it will be fruitful to summarize Turner's model presented in Chapter 9. It is based on the observation that most system failures are not caused by a single factor and that conditions for failure do not develop instantaneously. Rather, multiple causal factors accumulate, unnoticed or not fully understood over a considerable period of time, a period called the 'incubation period'.

Within the incubation period a number of types of conditions can be found, in retrospect. Firstly, events may be unnoticed or misunderstood because of wrong assumptions about their significance: those dealing with them may have an unduly rigid outlook, brushing aside complaints and warnings, or they may be misled or distracted by nearby events. Secondly, dangerous preconditions may be unnoticed because of the difficulties of handling information in complex situations: poor communications, ambiguous orders and the difficulty of detecting important signals in a mass of surrounding noise may be all-important here. Thirdly, there may be uncertainty about how to deal with formal violations of safety regulations that are thought to be outdated or discredited because of technical advance. Fourthly, when things do start to go wrong, the outcomes are typically worse because people tend to minimize danger as it emerges, or to believe that the failure will not happen.

The incubation period, in which interlinking sets of such events build up, is brought to a conclusion either by taking preventative action to remove one or more of the dangerous preconditions that have been noticed or by a trigger event after which harmful energy is released. The previously hidden factors are then brought to light in a dramatic and destructive way, which provides an opportunity for a review and a reason for a reassessment of the reasons for failure. There can then be an adjustment of precautions to attempt to avoid a recurrence of similar incidents in the future.

20.13 THE BALLOON MODEL

Imagine the development of an accident (failure, disaster) as analogous to the inflation of a balloon. The start of the process is when air is first blown into the balloon when the first preconditions for the accident are established. Consider the pressure of the air as analogous to the 'proneness to failure' of the project. As the balloon grows in size, so does the 'proneness to failure' of the project. Events accumulate to increase the predisposition to failure. The size of the balloon can be reduced by lowering the pressure and letting the air out, and this parallels the effects of management decisions that remove some predisposing events and thus reduce the proneness to failure. If the pressure of such events build up until the balloon is very stretched then only a small trigger event, such as a pin or lighted match, is needed to release the energy pent up in the system. The trigger is often confused with the cause of the accident. The trigger is not the most important factor—the overstretched balloon represents an accident waiting to happen. In accident prevention, it is thus important to recognize the preconditions—to recognize the development of the pressures in the balloon. The symptoms that characterize the incubation of an accident need to be identified and checked.

20.14 HAZARD ENGINEERING

There is therefore a need to define a discipline that is particularly concerned with the development and practice of safety and hazard management. The words safety, hazard and risk have many different interpretations and are used in many different contexts. There is a need for a discipline that would unify all the disparate ideas and techniques in various hazard and safety audits and risk and reliability assessments across the various sectors of the engineering industry.

Safety has been defined as freedom from unacceptable risks/personal harm, or the elimination of danger where danger represents the balance between the chance for an accident and the consequences of it. Alternatively a hazard has been defined as 'a set of conditions in the operation of a product or system with the potential for initiating an accident sequence'. This latter definition is appropriate for the Turner model of accident incubation and the balloon model of accident management. Thus a general term is hazard engineering.

What is hazard engineering and what would a hazard engineer do? Clearly all engineers have to deal with hazards. Nature is a cunning adversary and everything is subject to its forces. It is part of the job of an engineer to design and build artefacts that are able to resist the forces of nature and satisfy the needs of the client in terms of quality, cost function, etc. Blockley, Turner and Pidgeon[12] have suggested that hazard engineering should be an extension of general engineering practice where specialist skills are used to identify and to control hazardous projects. Hazard engineering should, it is argued, be concerned with the identification and management of exceptional circumstances where hazards exist and which need to be controlled by the use of specialist skills. The identification would be carried out through a hazard audit. The control would be exercised by hazard management. Both of these activities could be included as part of a quality assurance safety plan as outlined by Matousek in Chapter 4.

For many projects where the problems are relatively straightforward, the hazards may be managed, in the usual way, without the use of specially trained engineers. For more complex projects the appointment of hazard engineers, either in-house or as separate consultants, depending on the nature of the work, would need to be considered as part of the contractual arrangements.

The appointed engineers would exercise their specialist skills to carry out enquiries into all of the potential hazards likely to be faced during the conception, design, construction and use of the artefact. Rational judgements about the incorporation of these demands into the finished artefact would follow. In practice no designer, and especially no individual designer in commercial practice, can hope to assess all such demands from scratch. Reliance has to be placed upon the application of proven, tried and tested techniques, including rules of thumb, upon references to codes of practice and to the best recognized practice in the field. In many cases the reliance on such tools of guidance and the pressure to design to a justifiable and defensible position, in the face of liability legislation and other demands, means that a certain lack of perspective can be incorporated into designs.

This can result in some potential failure scenarios not being included; they are unintended unwanted consequences that may or may not occur.

How then can a specialist hazard engineer address the issues? It is clear that engineers cannot know what they do not know if they do not know that they do not know (see Chapter 1). Taken collectively for all engineers this defines that there is a limit to knowledge and to any model of design. It is imperative that this limit is recognized by society at large, by clients and by lawyers. Similarly engineers cannot consider designing for eventualities which are not expected. The central issue is not that engineering designers can ensure by prediction that a design will be safe but that by obtaining suitable feedback about performance of the whole sociotechnical system that the process is managed safely.

Hazard engineering has therefore been defined as being concerned with ensuring the appropriate resolution of conflicting requirements placed upon the design, construction and use of the artefact by a range of uncertainties about its likely future operation identified by a hazard audit.[12]

The detailed factors to be considered in a hazard audit will not be discussed here. Existing techniques such as hazop and hazan (Chapter 15) will need to be placed in a more general systems approach. It is important to recognize that the audit will need to bridge the gap between the two cultures of engineering, the technical and the human. Accordingly audits must be constructed with great care and sensitivity if they are to identify conditions that may contribute to accidents and failures. There will not be one type of audit for every situation but many different but compatible audits which would be suitable for differing types of projects. For relatively simple projects, for example, a simple check-list may suffice. For large and complex projects a long and detailed examination will probably be needed at regular intervals. Techniques of artificial intelligence, as outlined in Chapter 18, may be used in the future for these detailed audits so that comparisons may be made with accumulated experiences from case histories. The time intervals between audits will need to be considered carefully so that a reasonable balance between the costs of an audit and the need to detect problems is drawn. It is also important that contractual arrangements are clearly made.

There is one final word of warning required concerning risk management. Douglas and Wildavsky[5] have pointed out that anticipation to secure safety can create a false sense of security. The design of a system in which it is thought that all potential errors have been allowed for can lead to a disregard for coping with breakdowns. Probably the classic example is that of the *Titanic*, where the new ability to control most kinds of leaks led to the understocking of lifeboats, the abandonment of safety drills and disregard of reasonable caution in navigation. Without continuous experience in dealing with a variety of problems, organisms are likely to adapt to a steady state. When dramatic change does occur then these organisms are likely to perish. Resilience is the capacity to use change to better cope with the unknown; it is a characteristic that stems from the ability to call upon a variety of alternative ways to solve problems and it is a characteristic that all organizations that cope with risk must have. Hazard management must not result in organizations that are not resilient; in fact the management system needs to be designed so that resilience is enhanced.

As Douglas and Wildavsky conclude, obviously we care about the quality of life and the safety of future generations. We need to leave them with resources of knowledge, skills, organizations and institutions and perhaps most of all mutual trust, so that they may exercise their discretion. Since we do not know what risks that they will incur, our responsibility is to create resilience in the institutions that we hand on.

20.15 CONCLUSION

The purpose of the book has been to present an overview of engineering safety for engineers who are not specialists in safety but who are concerned with the planning, design, construction and maintenance of large facilities such as bridges, buildings, dams, chemical plant, power stations and marine structures. Thus there has been no attempt to describe detailed procedures or techniques. The thesis has been that there are presently two paradigms for the discussion and treatment of safety, the technical and the managerial. These two views have been typified by the technical approaches of limit state design, risk and reliability analysis and the managerial approach of quality assurance and the social science of human factors analysis, all of which are embedded in an organizational culture. The need that has been addressed by this book is to bring them together into a common approach that bridges the gap. The model of incubating disaster first presented by Turner in 1978 has been used in this final chapter to develop the concept of hazard engineering, which it has been suggested should consist of hazard auditing and hazard management. The single most important factor that has emerged in the control of hazard is the responsibility of management to develop a good corporate safety culture. This requires a commitment from top management which it has been suggested will lead not only to cost savings but also to increased quality, worker satisfaction and other significant benefits. As Turner writes in Chapter 9, there seem to be four general characteristics of a good safety culture: the establishment of a caring organizational response to the consequences of actions and policies; a commitment to this response at all levels, especially the most senior; provision of feedback from incidents; and the establishment of generally endorsed and comprehensive rules and norms for handling safety problems. A resilient, high-reliability organization seems to be characterized by the ability to create and to maintain open learning systems, a system where accidents are regarded as opportunities for learning rather than as occasions for attributing blame.

How many organizations measure up to those requirements?

REFERENCES

1. Brown, C. B.: A Fuzzy Safety Measure, *Proc. ASCE*, vol. 105, no. EM5, pp. 855–872, 1979.
2. Thompson, J. M. T., and H. B. Stewart: *Nonlinear Dynamics and Chaos*, Wiley, Chichester, 1986.
3. Pidgeon, N. F., D. I. Blockley and B. A. Turner: Design Practice and Snow Loading: Lessons from a Roof Collapse, *The Structural Engineer*, vol. 64A, no. 3, pp. 67–71, 1986.
4. Cui, W. C., and D. I. Blockley: Interval Probability Theory for Evidential Support, *Int. J. Intelligent Systems*, vol. 5, no. 2, pp. 183–192, June 1990.
5. Douglas, M., and A. Wildavsky: *Risk and Culture*, University of California Press, London, 1982.
6. Penrose, R.: *The Emperor's New Mind*, Vintage, London, 1989.
7. Checkland, P.: *Systems Thinking, Systems Practice*, Wiley, Chichester, 1981.
8. Reason, J.: *Human Error*, Cambridge University Press, London, 1990.
9. Novak, A.: Modeling Human Error in Structural Design and Construction, *Construct. Div. ASCE, Proc. NSF Workshop*, Ann Arbor, June 1986.
10. CBI: *Developing a Safety Culture*, CBI, London, 1990.
11. Fido, A. T., and D. O. Wood: *Safety Management Systems*, Further Education Unit, London, 1989.
12. Blockley, D. I., N. F. Pidgeon and B. A. Turner: Hazard Engineering, unpublished.

INDEX